Companion Booklet

Prayer and Spirituality

Module Consultant
Edith Prendergast, RSC

Echoes of Faith Plus Program Directors

Edmund F. Gordon, MA
National Conference for Catechetical Leadership

Jo Rotunno, MA
RCL Benziger

Educational Consultant
Judith Deckers, MEd

Contributors
Rev. Louis J. Cameli, STD
Thomas H. Groome, PhD
Rev. Robert J. Hater, PhD
Most Reverend Robert F. Morneau, DD

**A Project of the
National Conference for Catechetical Leadership
Produced by RCL Benziger**

November 16th 2014

Islam
Day after
Day I stand
Before You.
assurance → Gratitude

Special Thanks

We wish to extend special thanks to Bishop Robert F. Morneau for his contributions to the original *Prayer and Spirituality* module and to the following individuals who appear in the bonus interviews for this module.

Rev. Louis J. Cameli, PhD

Rev. Ronald Rolheiser, PhD, STD

---

* Spirituality is the the experience

* Religion is the vehicle

* Begining of a human being

Adoration:
God is looking at me.
I am looking at God.

Nihil Obstat
Rev. Msgr. Robert Coerver
Censor Librorum

Imprimatur
† Most Reverend Kevin J. Farrell, DD, Bishop of Dallas

February 6, 2008

The Nihil Obstat and Imprimatur are official declarations that the material reviewed is free of doctrinal or moral error. No implication is contained therein that those granting the Nihil Obstat and Imprimatur agree with the contents, opinions, or statements expressed.

Send all inquiries to:
RCL Benziger
200 East Bethany Drive
Allen, TX 75002-3804

Toll Free   877-275-4725
Fax   800-688-8356

Visit us at   www.RCLBenziger.com
              www.EchoesofFaith.com
              www.FaithFirst.com
              www.WholeCommunityCatechesis.com

Printed in the United States of America

20593   0-7829-1155-2

1 2 3 4 5 6 7 8 • 13 12 11 10 09 08

ACKNOWLEDGMENTS

Excerpts from English translation of the *Catechism of the Catholic Church* for the United States of America Copyright © 1994, United States Catholic Conference, Inc.—Libreria Editrice Vaticana. English translation of the: *Catechism of the Catholic Church Modifications from the Editio Typica* Copyright © 1997, United States Catholic Conference, Inc.—Libreria Editrice Vaticana. Used with permission.

Scripture quotations from *New Revised Standard Version Bible: Catholic Edition,* copyright © 1989, 1993 Division of Christian Education of the National Council of the Churches of Christ in the United States of America. Used by permission. All rights reserved.

Excerpts from *General Directory for Catechesis*, copyright © 1997, United States Conference of Catholic Bishops—Libreria Editrice Vaticana. All rights reserved. No part of this work may be reproduced or transmitted in any form without the permission in writing from the copyright holder.

Excerpts from *National Directory for Catechesis*, copyright © 2005, United States Conference of Catholic Bishops, Washington, DC. Used with permission. All rights reserved. No part of this work may be reproduced or transmitted in any form without the permission in writing from the copyright holder.

Excerpt from *The Book of Her Life* in *The Collected Works of St. Teresa of Avila,* translated by K. Kavanaugh, ODC and O. Rodriquez, OCD (Washington DC: Institute of Carmelite Studies, copyright © 1976).

Excerpt from *The Cloister Walk* by Kathleen Norris. Copyright © 1996. New York: Riverhead Books.

Excerpt from *Gracias! A Latin American Journal* by Henri Nouwen. San Francisco: Harper & Row, copyright © 1996.

Excerpt from *The Inner Voice of Love* by Henri Nouwen. New York: Doubleday Image books, Copyright © 1999.

Excerpt from *Touching the Holy* by Robert Wicks. Notre Dame, Ind: Ave Maria Press, 1992.

Contents

Welcome to *Echoes of Faith Plus!*

The *General Directory for Catechesis (GDC)* tells us, "The Lord Jesus invites men and women, in a special way, to follow him, teacher and formator of disciples. This personal call of Jesus Christ and its relationship to him are the true moving forces of catechetical activity" (*GDC* 231). This call needs a response from you in order to flourish. As you begin your ministry as a catechist, you will need to deepen your knowledge of the faith and of the Gospel. You will need to develop techniques and skills for presenting the faith and adapting it to your group of adults, children, or youth. Catechesis is always about communicating the faith!

Echoes of Faith Plus has been developed by the National Conference for Catechetical Leadership (NCCL) to provide you with the basic tools to begin your ministry as a catechist. It is being used in more than one hundred dioceses in the United States and Canada and has proven to be an effective process to set you on the way to have a wonderful experience as a catechist.

We have designed this program for use in varied settings. If you are working alone on a module, it is important that you link up with someone, e.g., your local DRE, catechist trainer, or parish priest. Since catechesis always involves communication, it is important that you have someone with whom to discuss your new learning, to ask questions, and to try out new ideas!

Catechesis is an activity of the whole Church. As a catechist you join a worldwide network of catechists who support each other in prayer. The Church is depending on you to bring "tidings of great joy" to the classrooms, religious education centers, homes, and wherever catechesis takes place.

May the Holy Spirit guide you, energize you, and sustain you!

Lee Nagel
NCCL Executive Director

Edmund F. Gordon
NCCL Project Director

A Project of the National Conference for Catechetical Leadership Produced by RCL Benziger

How to Use
Echoes of Faith Plus

Echoes of Faith Plus is a basic-level, video-assisted resource for the formation, training, and enrichment of catechists in parish and Catholic school settings. *Echoes* was sponsored and developed by the National Conference for Catechetical Leadership (NCCL) and produced by RCL Benziger.

The *Echoes* project is divided into three series of modules. Each series relates to one of the three aspects of catechist formation explained in the *General Directory for Catechesis*—being, knowing, and *savoir-faire*. (See *GDC* 238.)

The Catechist: (being)	Three modules on the vocation and roles of the catechist, plus first steps for getting started in the ministry
Methodology: (*savoir-faire*)	Four modules for different grade levels of children and youth One module for facilitators of adult faith formation One overview module on human and faith development
Theology: (knowing)	Four modules treating the four pillars of the *Catechism of the Catholic Church,* plus a fifth module introducing Sacred Scripture. (Note: These modules can also be used for general adult faith formation.)

The main components of each module are:

- **A DVD.** The DVD is comprised of a four–segment video process related to the module content plus two related expert interviews.
- **A Companion Booklet.** The booklet anchors the *Echoes* process. Each booklet begins with an article for spiritual formation and a prayer. The booklet then provides a four–segment process of reflection, discussion, faith sharing, and prayer as the participant moves back and forth between the DVD and print material. Each segment includes a follow-up enrichment article. The back of the booklet offers related articles and resources. These resources and two bonus interviews on the DVD could provide material for additional sessions.
- **A CD-ROM.** The CD-ROM features compressed files that offer a way to review the basic video content of the four segments on a computer. However, it does not include the interviews found on the DVD. The CD-ROM is included at no charge with each companion booklet.

The length of time required to complete each module varies with the length of the DVD and how it is used. This module should take approximately four hours to process. The key to success with *Echoes of Faith Plus* is your willingness to engage in the complete process. Ideally, your reflection process will take place in a group setting that models the kind of Christian community you wish to establish in your own catechesis. If you must process the module alone, share your insights later in a group setting or with a friend in ministry.

Catechists do not merely instruct their students about Christ; they lead them to him.

National Directory for Catechesis (NDC) 55E

Visit http://www. EchoesofFaith.com for additional resources to enrich your catechetical ministry.

Personal Prayer:
The Prayer of the Heart

by Reverend Louis J. Cameli, STD

For many years, I taught spirituality in the major seminary in Chicago. A curious phenomenon occasionally occurs with my former students, now ordained priests. A group in their parish will ask one of them to do a talk or workshop on prayer. In a panic, they call me and ask, "What can I do? Can you come out here and do a talk?" I respond, "But you studied this. Besides, you preach every Sunday to your people. You have the resources, most especially your own experience of prayer. I'll help you organize your thoughts."

This strange sort of panic may not be so strange after all. I would guess that most of us are insecure about our prayer lives. With regard to prayer, we feel that we could always be doing better, doing more, have more regular times set aside for it. Our insecurities can easily be exacerbated when we are asked to teach someone else how to pray. And yet, whether as parents, catechists, or other committed Catholics, we may be called upon to help others learn how to pray. It is, of course, much more than teaching formulas for prayer, although the memorized vocal prayers of our tradition are essential. It has to do with personal prayer, prayer of the heart, encountering God in a dialogue that is heart to heart. All this can present a challenge to us.

Three aspects of effective prayer are familiarity with God, persistence and confidence.

I would suggest taking a look at Saint Luke's Gospel. This evangelist highlights the importance of prayer with special emphasis. Read, for example, Luke 11:1–13. It begins: "He was praying in a certain place, and after he had finished, one of his disciples said to him, 'Lord, teach us to pray, as John taught his disciples.'" Jesus goes on to teach them the Lord's Prayer. He then speaks of a friend knocking on another friend's door at midnight looking for bread for a late-arriving guest. Jesus encourages his disciples to ask, search, and knock. He tells them that if they with their sins know how to give what is good to their children, "how much more will the heavenly Father give the Holy Spirit to those who ask him?"

Reflection

There are probably many elements of your experience of prayer in Jesus' teaching, although you may not always be conscious of them. They are essential elements that you would want to share in any teaching on prayer. The first element is a sense of familiarity with God, literally a sense of family or of belonging to God's household. It is only on the basis of that familiarity that we can and ought to address God "Abba, Father" and be bold, as a child is bold, in bringing our needs, feelings, and aspirations to him.

Another important element of prayer both in the Gospel and in our lives is persistence. We are to keep knocking. Ideally, we "pray without ceasing" (1 Thessalonians 5:17). We do not stop, because we feel that we have not had a hearing. We stay the course when it comes to prayer.

A third element is assurance. We pray with complete confidence that our prayer will be answered, that we are in communion with the living God, that the greatest petitions containing every good thing—thy kingdom come, thy will be done—will surely be answered.

To know prayer this way and to know it in our own experience will give us confidence to share this great blessing with others.

• • • For Reflection • • •

- Do you feel the familiarity with God that is described in this article? Why do you feel the way you do?
- In what ways do you feel that God has truly heard your prayer and responded to you?

Louis J. Cameli is a priest of the Archdiocese of Chicago and pastor of Divine Savior Parish in Norridge, Illinois. He completed his theological studies at the Gregorian University in Rome and obtained a doctorate in theology with a specialization in spirituality. He is the former director of ongoing formation of priests in the Archdiocese of Chicago and director of the Cardinal Stritch Retreat House, Mundelein, Illinois. In February, 2002, he received the Pope John XXIII Award from the National Organization for the Continuing Education of Roman Catholic Clergy (NOCERCC) for his contributions to the continuing education and ongoing formation of priests. He has authored numerous books on spirituality and also served as a writer and theological consultant for RCL Benziger's *Faith First* and *Faith First Legacy Edition* K-8 curriculum.

The Magnificat
Mary's Song of Praise

My soul magnifies the Lord,

and my spirit rejoices in God my Savior,

for he has looked with favor

on the lowliness of his servant.

Surely, from now on all generations

will call me blessed;

for the Mighty One has done

great things for me,

and holy is his name.

His mercy is for those who fear him

from generation to generation.

He has shown strength with his arm;

he has scattered the proud

in the thoughts of their hearts.

He has brought down the powerful from their thrones,

and lifted up the lowly;

he has filled the hungry with good things,

and sent the rich away empty.

He has helped his servant Israel,

in remembrance of his mercy,

according to the promise he made

to our ancestors,

to Abraham and to his descendants forever.

Luke 1:46–55

Overview: Prayer and Spirituality Module

This module explores our relationship with the living God that we call prayer. It places prayer within the context of our spirituality, the name we give to the entire life lived in response to God's call. Prayer and spirituality are our wholehearted "yes" to the mystery of God seeking us. We express this mystery in our creeds, celebrate it in our liturgy, and live it out as we attempt to follow the way of Jesus.

You will engage in a process of faith reflection using three components: a DVD, this companion booklet, and a CD-ROM. See page 5 for an explanation of how these components complement one another. You began the process on pages 6 and 7 with a reflection on personal prayer. On the next page you will engage in a reflection on your experience of prayer up to the present time.

The first segment of the module is a reflection on the meaning of Christian prayer. It is followed by three additional segments, each of which is divided into two parts. Here is an overview of the module topics:

1. **What Is Prayer?**
2. **How Do We Pray?**
   Part 1: Ways of Prayer
   Part 2: Growing in the Spiritual Life
3. **The Prayerful Life**
   Part 1: Christian Spirituality
   Part 2: Reflections on the Spiritual Life
4. **The Our Father**
   Part 1: A Summary of the Gospel
   Part 2: The Seven Petitions

You will find a booklet process for each segment to help you reflect on the DVD content and choose ways to apply what you have learned to your life. Here is the structure you will find:

1. **Introduction:** The goal and objectives for each session, plus an opening reflection question.
2. **Looking Ahead—Presentation** A video overview for each of the two parts of the segment, plus a space to write comments and questions.
3. **Looking Back—Reflection:** For each part, three questions to check comprehension and invite dialogue.
4. **Looking Beyond—Application:** An activity that invites you to imagine a way that you could apply what you have learned to a community experience of prayer.

Following each segment are two features: an enrichment article and space for journaling about prayer.

This module is only a brief introduction to the Christian life of prayer. As you continue to read, study, reflect, and attend classes and workshops, you will grow in knowledge and insight. Formation requires the mutual support of the community. Try to participate in this module process in a group setting. If you must work independently, find at least one other person with whom you can share your reflections.

Edith Prendergast, a Religious Sister of Charity and native of Ireland, has been involved in religious education and spiritual formation in the United States for over thirty years. She has served as Director of the Office of Religious Education for the Archdiocese of Los Angeles, a parish director of religious education, a high school teacher, and a youth minister. She served as a collaborator on *The Challenge of Adolescent Catechesis: Maturing in Faith* developed by the National Federation for Catholic Youth Ministry. Sr. Edith has been involved in retreat work and spiritual direction, and offers workshops nationally in the areas of spirituality and spiritual formation. Sister Edith holds a doctorate degree in Ministry from Claremont School of Theology, a master's degree in Theology from Boston College, and a certificate in Spiritual Formation from St. Louis University, St. Louis, Missouri.

Before You Begin

Underneath each of the ages listed below, write a sentence or two describing prayer as you experienced it at that time in your life.

- **Seven years old**

  I knew God was always watching me. I talked to him about whatever was on my mind. asked for help. Said songs. So on —

- **Thirteen years old**

  Asked for help alot. in thought + in writing.

- **Twenty-one years old**

  Same as above

- **Today**

Let me hear what God the LORD will speak, for he will speak peace to his people, to his faithful, to those who turn to him in their hearts.

Psalm 85:8

What Is Prayer?

Prayer is listening and responding to God. It is listening with an openness to hear God's word calling to us. Sometimes God seems to speak loudly and clearly through the words of Scripture or the events of our lives. At other times God's word comes to us in a gentle breeze or a still silent voice, as the prophet Elijah experienced (1 Kings 19:9–13). We are called to listen at all times for the voice of God. This listening involves an openness of heart, a risking to be ourselves, a yielding, and a willingness to be changed.

We come to prayer just as we are, with our hopes, fears, joys, and doubts. God speaks and invites us to respond with a "Yes" to God's offer of love. Our response involves a willingness to spend time with God, pondering the words of Scripture, discerning God's message to us, and opening up our lives to God's transforming power. Mary, following the example of her Son, models for us how we should pray.

> The life of prayer is the habit of being in the presence of the thrice-holy God and in communion with him.
> *Catechism of the Catholic Church (CCC) 2565*

Goal

To appreciate the rhythm of prayer as listening and responding to God's call

Learning Objectives

- To identify examples of God's presence in creation
- To describe why Mary is our model of prayer
- To explain the importance of praying throughout the day

Exercise

Take a few moments to reflect on the following. Then discuss it with another person or with your group.

Think of a time when you listened to God in prayer, and when you felt God listened to you. Describe your experience.

Looking Ahead

This segment suggests a response to the general question, "What is prayer?" Below you will find an outline of the principal content of the DVD that accompanies this segment. You may wish to refer to this outline as you watch the DVD. Below the outline, there is space for you to jot down comments and questions that occur to you during and after the viewing.

Video Outline

- A reflection on the many ways that God's voice speaks to us through our human experiences
- A description of the Angelus as a way of marking time throughout the day with prayer
- An explanation of Mary as our model of prayer
- Observations about the relationship of all prayer to the community of faith

Comments and Questions

Use the space below to list comments, questions, feelings, or ideas that occur to you as you view the video.

> we say "yes" – our life changes = prayer
>
> not an escape from life = but a commitment
>
> Prayer arises out of Gods Call / faith
>
> Mary's Fiat "Let it be" our model
>
> God speaks through creation
>
> Prayer always has a community aspect.

The angelus human need responds for prayer

↓

Pause at beginning middle + End of day

The church calls us to pause + respond

Watch Segment 1 of the DVD or CD-ROM now.

Looking Back

Reflect silently on one or more of the questions below and then jot down your response(s). Then share your thoughts with another person or with a group.

1. God speaks to us through all of creation. In what ways do you create opportunities in your life to hear the voice of God speaking to you?

2. Like Mary, our prayer must begin, "Let it be . . ." What situation in your own life is calling you to speak those words right now?

3. The Church teaches us that our personal prayer is always joined with the prayer of the community. Describe some times in your life when you have been strengthened by that knowledge.

Remember . . .

God speaks to us through all of creation.

•

Prayer is listening and responding to God's call.

•

The Angelus recalls the moment when Mary accepted God's call to be the mother of the Savior.

•

Mary is our model of prayer.

•

All prayer has a community aspect because of our Baptism.

Looking Beyond

You have learned that, because of your Baptism, all personal prayer is joined to the community of faith. In the activity below you will have an opportunity to apply what you have learned to the needs of the community.

PRAYING WITH OTHERS

If you wished to encourage others to have a meaningful experience of community prayer, what three suggestions could you give them that could make their time of prayer more fruitful?

What Did I Learn?

In this space summarize the most important insights you gained in this segment.

What Will I Change?

In this space write one thing you will do differently as a catechist because of what you learned in this segment.

FOR CATECHISTS AND PARENTS

Children have many distractions, but also have a wonderful capacity for prayer. Offer them regular opportunities to spend time in silent prayer.

The Heart of Prayer

by Jo Rotunno

Saint John Damascene called prayer "a raising of the mind and heart to God." Saint Thérèse of Lisieux called prayer "a surge of the heart." The *Catechism of the Catholic Church* affirms that the wellspring of prayer lies in the human heart, that seat of the soul or "hidden center" where only the Spirit of God can go. (*CCC* 2563)

Sacred Scripture shows us that the origins of human prayer arise in history after the entry of sin into the world. From this moment, God desires to restore us to friendship. In the Hebrew Scriptures we learn the qualities of a prayerful life. From Abel we learn that prayer is walking with God. From Abraham and Sarah we discover attentiveness of heart and conformity to God's will. From Jacob we learn that prayer can be a "wrestling" with God, but that perseverance has its rewards. In Moses we find a deep intimacy with God and see the power of intercession as Moses brings the needs of the people before God. From Samuel we learn the importance of listening for God, whose Word often comes as a whisper rather than an earthquake. From David we learn both how to praise and how to repent. From the prophets we learn of righteousness, and the power to proclaim the truth that is born of intimacy with God.

In the Psalms we find an entire school of prayer, so much so that some have said that all study of the Scriptures should begin with the Psalms. These masterpieces of prayer both nourish and speak the prayer of a community of faith. While the Psalms arose in a particular time and place, they have become universal expressions of praise and thanksgiving, of lamentation and repentance. In the Psalms, the Word of God becomes our word—our prayer (*CCC* 2587).

Jesus is the perfect model of prayer. Jesus, though Son of God, was human like us. He took his first steps in prayer as we do, learning from his family and his religious tradition. Jesus found God in his human heart, where he discovered his deep intimacy, with his Father. He shows us the way to that intimacy, which is available to all of us who are willing to make the journey.

Jesus found God in his human heart.

Jo Rotunno serves as Director of Marketing and Electronic Media for RCL Benziger and is the project director for *Echoes of Faith Plus.* She has worked in Catholic schools, parish, and diocesan programs for more than thirty-five years. Her special interests are catechist and adult faith formation. Jo holds an MA in religious studies from Mount St. Mary's College in Los Angeles. She speaks on catechetical topics throughout the United States.

When did Jesus pray? He prayed before all the decisive moments in his ministry, most memorably before his Passion. He prayed before the great moments in the ministry of his disciples. He spent an entire night alone in prayer before the call of the Twelve. The night he was betrayed he told Peter he had prayed that Peter's faith would be strong, that this man to whom he must entrust so much would not be tempted.

Where and how did Jesus pray? Jesus often prayed in solitude, sometimes apart from others, often at night. All of his words and works were empowered by these times of silent prayer. One of the great public prayers of Jesus occurs at the raising of Lazarus (John 11:41–42). Here Jesus teaches us that all prayer begins in thanksgiving. He acknowledges that in all cases "the Giver is more precious than the gift" (*CCC* 2604 [see Matthew 16:21, 33]). In all decisive situations, Jesus submits his own will to his Father's will.

Jesus taught his disciples how to pray. He reminded them of the constant conversion of heart that bringing the reign of God would require. He encouraged them to strive for great things in their prayer—to be bold. In the Lord's Prayer, he summarized for them his entire message, so much so that his disciples incorporated it into their worship from the very beginning. He cautioned them to be watchful in prayer, to be patient and humble as he had been. He told them to always pray in his name, in the power of the Spirit which remains with us.

At the end of his earthly life, it was Jesus' prayer, spoken from the depths of his heart, that was heard by God and effected salvation for us all. He stayed faithful to the attitude of prayer he learned first from his mother: "Let it be with me according to your word" (Luke 1:38).

For Reflection

What insights have you gained from this article about the importance of prayer in the Christian life?

Prayer Journal

During the next week, find at least one time when you can spend fifteen minutes alone in silent, prayerful thanksgiving. Afterward, describe your experience in this space and conclude with words of prayer and thanksgiving for God who created you.

Prayer Journal

How Do We Pray?

Prayer arises from the center of our being and gives expression to all our human experiences. We praise and give thanks, knowing that all our blessings are gifts from God. We give thanks in good times and in bad, because in faith we know that God is with us on our journey. Because God has blessed us, we also bless the One who is the giver of all good things. Prayer is not always easy. Distractions, discouragement, and even laziness can stand in our way. But God is patient and is present to us even when we fail to listen. We know we stand in need. This awareness of our poverty is gift as well, for it acknowledges our dependence on God as we ask for healing and forgiveness for ourselves and for others.

At the heart of prayer is the Eucharist, where we join the community of the Church in listening and responding to God' Word. We listen to God's Word in the Scriptures. We bless and give thanks; we praise God's glory. We ask the Spirit to intercede for us. We offer all that we are and all that we do to God, joined with the Paschal mystery of God's own Son. The Eucharist nourishes us and challenges us to make our entire lives a prayer of blessing.

Goal
To gain a deeper understanding of the importance of prayer and of why we pray

Learning Objectives
- To identify some of the traditional kinds of prayer
- To examine some distractions to prayer
- To appreciate the Eucharist as the prayer of the Church community

Exercise
Take a few moments to reflect on the following questions. Then discuss them with another person or with your group.

Think of a time when you felt God did not respond to your needs. How did you feel? What did you learn about yourself and about God through that experience?

Prayer

Loving God, you bless us with the gift of your presence. Help us be open to all that you wish to tell us, and give us the grace to respond with love. Give us the gift of your Spirit to help us overcome all distractions to hearing your voice clearly. We ask this in the name of your Son, who teaches us how to place you first in our lives. Amen.

Looking Ahead

Part 1: Ways of Prayer

The first part of this segment explores various kinds of prayer. Below you will find an outline of the principal content of the DVD that accompanies part 1 of this segment. You may wish to refer to this outline as you watch the DVD. Below the outline, there is space for you to jot down comments and questions that occur to you during and after the viewing.

Video Outline

- A description in words and images of the ways that God is present within and around us
- An overview of the principal forms of prayer in the Christian tradition: blessing and adoration, praise, thanksgiving, petition, and intercession
- A reminder that God always speaks first in the dialogue of prayer
- A definition of the three principal expressions of prayer: vocal prayer, meditation, and contemplation

Comments and Questions

Use the space below to list comments, questions, feelings, or ideas that occur to you as you view the video.

Canon = Rule = most sacred + normative

Ethiopian orthodox Church = the most books

46 old 26 new testament

[36 gospels] only 4 made it

passages of scripture must be interpreted in context.

Watch Segment 2, Part 1 of the DVD or CD-ROM now.

FORMS OF CHRISTIAN PRAYER

- Blessing and adoration
- Praise
- Thanksgiving
- Petition
- Intercession

Looking Back

Part 1: Ways of Prayer

Reflect silently on one or more of the questions below and then jot down your response(s). Then share your thoughts with another person or with a group.

1. Reflecting on your own life of prayer, recall a time when you prayed each of the following kinds of prayer.

   Blessing and Adoration

   Praise

   Thanksgiving

   Petition

   Intercession

2. Imagine a typical day in your life. What is going on in your life at each of the following times? Write those activities on the diagram below, and describe what your prayer at those times of day might be.

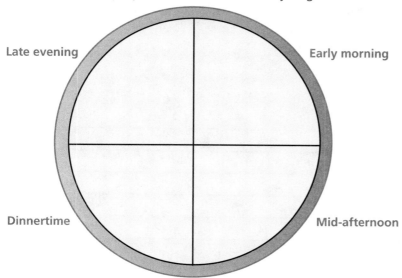

Late evening

Early morning

Dinnertime

Mid-afternoon

3. There are three forms of prayer mentioned on the video: vocal prayer, meditation, and contemplation. Which of these forms have you practiced? Describe your experience of them.

Remember . . .

Glimpses of God's grace are all around us.

•

God always speaks first in prayer.

•

The three main expressions of prayer are vocal prayer, meditation, and contemplation.

Looking Ahead

Part 2: Growing in the Spiritual Life

The second part of segment 2 explores the requirements needed to grow in the spiritual life. Below you will find an outline of the principal content of the DVD that accompanies this part. You may wish to refer to this outline as you watch the DVD. Below the outline, there is space for you to jot down comments and questions that occur to you during and after the viewing.

Video Outline

- A description of three requirements needed to grow in the spiritual life: work, effort, and attention
- An explanation of the transformative results of a focused prayer life
- An overview of some obstacles to prayer
- Some suggestions for growing in the life of prayer
- A reminder of the faithfulness of God

Comments and Questions

Use the space below to list comments, questions, feelings, or ideas that occur to you as you view the video.

> Through prayer we become aware of the life of God within us and it is this God within us who allows us to recognize the God among us.
>
> **Henri J. M. Nouwen**

Watch Segment 2, Part 2 of the DVD or CD-ROM now.

Looking Back

Part 2: Growing in the Spiritual Life

Reflect silently on one or more of the questions below and then jot down your response(s). Then share your thoughts with another person or with a group.

1. Name three obstacles you have encountered in your prayer life. What can you do to overcome these obstacles?

2. On the video, Sr. Rosa Maria distinguished between knowing God and knowing about God. How do you understand the difference?

3. Many people create a space for prayer. Describe in words or images the objects, music, and arrangement of space that would enhance your prayer.

Remember . . .

Prayer is a dialogue with God leading to intimacy and transformation.

•

Prayer requires discipline.

•

Lack of concentration, laziness, and discouragement can impede our prayer.

•

Reading Sacred Scripture assists the life of prayer.

•

God is always faithful.

Looking Beyond

This segment has helped you gain a deeper understanding of prayer and learn ways to grow in the spiritual life. The exercise below will help you apply what you have learned.

Vocal prayer is an essential element of the Christian life.

CCC 2701

PRAYING WITH OTHERS

Think of some descriptive names for God that would be appropriate when you are

- filled with joy.
- troubled and confused.
- in need of forgiveness.

Use these names for God and combine them with a prayer response of your choosing to create a litany. Pray this litany with your family or with another group of believers.

FOR CATECHISTS AND PARENTS

When we ourselves are tired or discouraged, it is easy to skip opportunities for prayer with children in our care. This is a good time to teach children that God is willing to hear our laments as well as our joys.

What Did I Learn?

In this space summarize the most important insights you gained in this segment.

What Will I Change?

In this space write one thing you will do differently as a catechist because of what you learned in this segment.

Contemplation: Looking at God with Love

by Sr. Edith Prendergast, RSC

Jesus' teaching on prayer in Luke's Gospel begins in the story of Jesus' visit to the two sisters, Martha and Mary (Luke 10:38–42). When Martha complains that Mary is not doing her share of serving, Jesus responds that Mary "has chosen the better part." Mary is sitting at Jesus' feet, gazing at him and listening with love. That is contemplation.

In contemplation the initiative always begins with God, who seeks to be an "insider" in our lives. Through contemplation we are brought into the heart of God, who speaks and invites us to respond. Christian contemplation is an interpersonal relationship with God, present to us here and now in Jesus Christ.

Saint Ignatius of Loyola, in his *Spiritual Exercises,* gives us a way to look at Jesus in the various "mysteries," or events, of his life. Ignatius invites us to read a Scripture passage; imagine the scene; to use our senses to see, hear, taste, smell, and touch the experience being recounted; and to place ourselves in the scene and open our hearts to respond in love, awe, wonder, and gratitude.

Centering prayer is another way of entering into the mystery of God. Repeating a mantra, such as the name of Jesus or a phrase such as "Be still and know that I am God," allows us to center on the person whose name we say, in whom our heart finds rest and solace.

Contemplation calls us to "waste time" with God. Its form can be as simple as reciting the words of a psalm slowly, or taking a mindfulness walk where we tune in to the rhythm of our breathing and become aware of God's presence with us.

Solitude and silence are central to the development of a contemplative stance. The desert fathers and mothers moved away from the busy-ness of the city to commune with God in the starkness and emptiness of the desert. Most of us are not called to this radical lifestyle, but we are called to be contemplatives in action, which means to find God in all situations, relationships, and experiences of life. To do so, we must intentionally choose to build quiet

In contemplation we discover our utter dependence on God

Contemplation is a "gaze" of faith, fixed on Jesus.
CCC 2715

> **Contemplative prayer in my opinion is nothing else than a close sharing between friends; it means taking time frequently to be alone with him who we know loves us.**
> **Saint Teresa of Avila**

times into our day. Our cars can become hermitages or places of refuge as we travel along the highway. Even our kitchens or offices can become places of contemplation for a few minutes during the day. A person on the street, the sight of a baby, a loving glance—all can provide moments of contemplation.

In contemplation, we discover our utter dependence on God. Julian of Norwich, the fourteenth century mystic, was overwhelmed by God's love for us. In one of her revelations she saw a hazelnut lying in her hand and realized that it was God's faithful love that prevented it, and indeed, everything else, from falling into nothingness.

In contemplative prayer, not only is God revealed to us, but we are revealed to ourselves. Knowing God's wondrous love for us makes us aware of our goodness, but also of our need for change and renewal. Such love demands receptivity, openness, and a belief that God is with us on the journey, both challenging and comforting us. We believe that as we stand before our God, we are transformed into God's likeness. From this place of transformation, we go forth to be bearers of good tidings, to image God to others, and to empower them to find God everywhere in life.

● ● ● *For Reflection* ● ● ●

What is one practical thing you could do to make more room in your life for a more contemplative style of prayer?

Prayer Journal

What is your mood right now? Place yourself in God's presence and talk with God right now about your feelings. Choose the words of praise, thanksgiving, petition, or lament that best describe your life situation. Then sit in silence for awhile. After a period of time, record what thoughts come to you and offer them to God. You may wish to record your thoughts and your prayer in this way several times during the week.

Prayer Journal

The Prayerful Life

For the Christian, the spiritual life is the response of the whole person to God, body and soul. It involves our thoughts, our feelings, and our actions. Jesus was not a disembodied spirit; he was the incarnate Son of God. His entire life and being were a response to God's love, and so must our lives be. Christian spirituality could be compared to the three legs of a milking stool. It is first and foremost a relationship with God, nurtured by prayer. Second, it is a relationship with others, characterized by a life of service and ministry. Third, it is a relationship within ourselves, characterized by an asceticism, or discipline, that leads to life and freedom. These three—prayer, service, and asceticism—lay the foundations for the spiritual life.

Prayer reveals God to us and also reveals us to ourselves. In prayer we discover the places in our lives in need of conversion and healing. We are sometimes like cluttered houses with no room for God, held captive by people, things, and our need to accumulate. Through asceticism, we learn what we must let go of and what discipline we must practice in order to respond to God's voice. From this stance we can go forth to be a word of God, to do the truth in love, to put on the mind of Jesus, and to live for one another.

Goal

To gain a better understanding of some key aspects of the Christian spiritual life

Learning Objectives

- To explain why prayer, service, and asceticism are three central aspects of the spiritual life
- To identify ways in which the spiritual life is both a personal and communal response to God's love
- To understand more clearly the path of your own spiritual life

Exercise

Take a few moments to reflect on the following question. Then discuss it with another person or with your group.

What practices do you have that are related to your prayer life?

Prayer

One God, you are a communion of three divine Persons united as one God. Guide us so that our own individual lives of prayer can be united as one in praise of you. Help us to accept our call to bring others into the loving relationship with you that we experience through your grace. We ask this in the name of Jesus, who is our model of prayer. Amen.

Looking Ahead

Part 1: Christian Spirituality

The first part of this segment is an introduction to Christian spirituality. Below you will find an outline of the principal content of the DVD that accompanies part 1 of this segment. You may wish to refer to this outline as you watch the DVD. Below the outline, there is space for you to jot down comments and questions that occur to you during and after the viewing.

Video Outline

- An explanation of why our personal prayer life has a communal dimension
- A description of the connection between prayer and life
- An overview of three aspects of healthy Christian spirituality: prayer, service, and asceticism

Comments and Questions

Use the space below to list comments, questions, feelings, or ideas that occur to you as you view the video.

We pray as we live because we live as we pray.
CCC 2725

Watch Segment 3, Part 1 of the DVD or CD-ROM now.

Looking Back

Part 1: Christian Spirituality

Reflect silently on one or more of the questions below and then jot down your response(s). Then share your thoughts with another person or with a group.

1. Consider the three aspects of the spiritual life: prayer, service, and asceticism. Which one of these three "legs" of your spiritual life is most in need of attention? Describe an action you can take to strengthen your spiritual life.

2. Read the quotation from the *Catechism of the Catholic Church* on the preceding page. In what ways have you seen this statement about the connections between life and prayer validated by your own experience?

3. The spiritual life is both a personal and communal response to God. Complete the following statements.

   The faith community strengthens me by

   I strengthen the faith community by

Remember . . .

We are all connected in prayer through our Baptism

•

Three key aspects of Christian spirituality are prayer, service, and asceticism.

•

We have a responsibility to return to the community the gifts we have been given.

•

Politics raises moral questions that must be answered for the common good.

Looking Ahead

Part 2: Reflections on the Spiritual Life

The second part of this segment is a reflection on the spiritual life. Below you will find an outline of the principal content of the DVD that accompanies this part. You may wish to refer to this outline as you watch the DVD. Below the outline, there is space for you to jot down comments and questions that occur to you during and after the viewing.

Video Outline

- A reiteration of the fact that our relationship with God has a communal as well as a personal dimension.
- Reflections of a former governor about faith and life including the following topics:

    The gift of being able to pray in times of crisis

    The call to nurture the life of God that lies in the hearts of their children

    The debt to the community that all are called to repay

    The importance of spiritual discipline in deepening our relationship with God

    The moral dimensions of a life in politics

Comments and Questions

Use the space below to list comments, questions, feelings, or ideas that occur to you as you view the video.

> **Gratitude is the attitude which enables us to receive the hidden gifts of those we want to serve and to make these gifts visible to the community as a source of celebration.**
>
> **Henri J. M. Nouwen**

Watch Segment 3, Part 2 of the DVD or CD-ROM now.

Prayer and Spirituality

Looking Back

Part 2: Reflections on the Spiritual Life

Reflect silently on one or more of the questions below and then jot down your response(s). Then share your thoughts with another person or with a group.

1. In the video former Governor Gilligan shared several "pages" from his own spiritual journal. If you were to think of your own life of faith as a journal, how would some chapters be titled and what story would they tell? Think of three examples and describe them in this space.

2. Describe a time when you have been faced with a crisis. What role did prayer play in your life at that time?

3. Imagine yourself interviewing someone you consider to be a person of prayer. What questions would you ask them about their spiritual life?

Remember . . .

Our relation-ship with God has both communal and personal dimensions.

•

We have an obligation to give back to the community the gifts we have been given.

•

Spiritual disciplines deepen our relationship with God.

Looking Beyond

You learned that you have a responsibility to deepen your life of prayer using whatever disciplines are helpful to you. In the activity below you will have the opportunity to reflect on the use of symbolic objects as prompts that can bring you to deeper prayer.

PRAYING WITH OTHERS

Choose a symbolic object that has meaning for you and that you could use as a focus for prayer. Discuss with your group how each of you could incorporate your objects into a communal experience of prayer. Summarize the results of your discussion here.

  (P)

FOR CATECHISTS AND PARENTS

Help children understand that sacramentals and other symbolic objects can deepen their prayer lives. Describe for them objects that have significance for you and invite them to gather objects of their own that can help them to pray.

What Did I Learn?

In this space summarize the most important insights you gained in this segment.

What Will I Change?

In this space write one thing you will do differently as a catechist because of what you learned in this segment.

A Thankful Heart

by Rev. Robert J. Hater

A thankful heart lies at the center of the Christian life. I was fortunate to learn this lesson when I was only five years old—on Thanksgiving Day.

All day long we looked forward to the wonderful Thanksgiving meal that Mom was preparing. Shortly before we were to sit down at table, the front doorbell rang. My four-year-old sister, Mary Ann, and I ran to answer it. A boy about eleven and a girl about ten stood there. The girl held a baby, covered with a shawl. The boy said, "We are poor and have no money for food this Thanksgiving. Will you give us money so we can buy food?"

Mary Ann and I called our mother. Mom answered, "We don't have much money, but we would like you to share what we have. We invite you to join us for our Thanksgiving." The children seemed surprised, and the boy said they could not stay. Mom replied, "Then let us prepare meals for you to take along with you."

While the children waited in the hall, Mom, Mary Ann, and I went into the kitchen and packed the meals. I felt good as we gathered turkey, dressing, cranberries, potatoes, beans, a piece of cake, and soda pop. Mom prepared a bottle of milk for the baby. Mary Ann and I were joyful when we gave the food to the children. They took it and left.

Since it was a beautiful day, my sister and I went onto the front porch to watch the children leave. They went down the steps and walked up the street toward the intersection. When they arrived there, the girl suddenly threw the baby to the boy. We screamed, "They're hurting the baby, they're hurting the baby!" Hurrying inside, we told Mom and Dad.

All of us returned immediately to the porch. As we got there, the girl, now holding the baby, tucked it under her arm. As she did, the boy, who carried the food, laughed in the strangest way. Then he took the Thanksgiving meals we had so lovingly prepared and threw them down the sewer. They continued laughing as they disappeared around the corner.

My sister and I cried, "They hurt the baby and threw away our food!" As

Reverend Robert J. Hater is an internationally known lecturer and writer and has served as professor of religious studies at the University of Dayton, Ohio. Father Hater was the religious education director for the Archdiocese of Cincinnati from 1973 to 1979 and initiated the Lay Pastoral Ministry Program for the Archdiocese. He received the 1994 Catechetical Award from the National Conference of Catechetical Leadership. Father Hater holds a doctorate in Philosophy from St. John's University, Jamaica, New York.

we cried, Mom and Dad embraced us. Mom said, "Bob and Mary Ann, it's okay. We are going to have a wonderful Thanksgiving." We continued to cry, "But they hurt the baby and threw away our food!"

Mom said, "The children tricked us. That wasn't a baby; it was a doll. They didn't want food; they wanted money. Nevertheless, you are going to learn a very important lesson today." When we quieted down, Mom spoke words that made an indelible impression on us. She said, "We gave the children a wonderful gift today, sharing a big part of our Thanksgiving meal with them. This was a wonderful gift, even though they did not accept

The important thing is to give with a thankful heart.

it. The important thing is that we gave with a thankful heart."

Mom continued, "God did that long ago, when he gave us the greatest gift—his own Son. Just as the children rejected our gift today some people rejected Jesus too. Some continue to reject him today by lying, cheating, or hurting one another. But God keeps on giving, and Jesus is the greatest gift we could receive. Let's remember God's gift and all our gifts today as we go in and have a wonderful Thanksgiving meal together."

This attitude of thankfulness is our fundamental perspective as Christians. It is our first prayer, the acknowledgment of our total dependency on God, and our acceptance of the great love which God desires to share with us.

● ● ● *For Reflection* ● ● ●

What great gifts is God offering you in your life? How do you express your thanks for these gifts?

Prayer Journal

Prayer always flows from our experience. If we express what we are truly feeling, our prayer might be one of praise, petition, thanksgiving, or lament. Which prayer are you most likely to pray today? Write it here.

Prayer Journal

The Our Father

Coming into the presence of the Hallowed One is an awesome and wondrous thing. In prayer we approach God, gathering up all that we are and acknowledging in humility who God is. Such is the gift of praying the Our Father. The seven petitions of the Our Father reveal the heart of the Gospel (see *CCC* 2761). We begin by blessing the name of God. We pray for truth, charity, freedom, and justice that mark the coming of God's kingdom. We pray that God's will be done, and that the gift of God's nourishment will empower us physically and spiritually to continue God's work. We pray to be forgiven as we too forgive, and to be freed from all the temptation that separates us from God. We conclude by asking deliverance from evil, especially that of selfishness.

The Our Father beckons us into the mystery of God. It calls us to believe in the now, to experience God with us, and to reach out in hope for the final coming of the reign of God through Christ's return.

Goal
To explore the richness of the Our Father as expressing the heart of the Gospel

Learning Objectives
- To be able to explain why the Our Father is the most perfect of Christian prayers
- To describe the seven petitions of the Our Father
- To reflect on the ways the Our Father expresses your own relationship with God

Exercise
Take a few moments to reflect on the following questions. Then discuss them with another person or with your group.

How and when did you learn to pray the Our Father? In what ways do you include praying the Our Father in your life of prayer?

Prayer

Our Father, who art in heaven, hallowed be thy name; thy kingdom come; thy will be done on earth as it is in heaven. Give us this day our daily bread; and forgive us our trespasses as we forgive those who trespass against us; and lead us not into temptation, but deliver us from evil. Amen.

Looking Ahead

Part 1: A Summary of the Gospel

The first part of this segment is an introduction to the Our Father as the foundation of all Christian prayer. Below you will find an outline of the principal content of the DVD that accompanies this part. You may wish to refer to this outline as you watch the DVD. Below the outline, there is space for you to jot down comments and questions that occur to you during and after the viewing.

Video Outline

- Introduction
- A definition of the Our Father as the foundation of all Christian prayer
- A summary of the seven petitions of the Our Father
- An illustration of the petitions as they are lived in daily life

Comments and Questions

Use the space below to list comments, questions, feelings, or ideas that occur to you as you view the video.

Watch Segment 4, Part 1 of the DVD or CD-ROM now.

Looking Back

Part 1: A Summary of the Gospel

Reflect silently on one or more of the questions below and then jot down your response(s). Then share your thoughts with another person or with a group.

1. Describe a time when it was easy for you to follow God's will and a time when it was difficult.

2. Justice is a central aspect of the reign of God. What do you feel called to do in your own life to bring about justice?

   In your home?

   In your workplace?

   In your neighborhood?

Remember . . .

The Our Father is the foundation of all Christian Prayer.

•

The seven petitions are a summary of the whole Gospel.

•

The Our Father is an important part of the worship of the Christian community.

•

The Our Father expresses the attitudes we bring to the Eucharist.

Looking Ahead

Part 2: The Seven Petitions

The second part of this segment reflects on the seven petitions of the Our Father. Below you will find an outline of the principal content of the DVD that accompanies this part. You may wish to refer to this outline as you watch the DVD. Below the outline, there is space for you to jot down comments and questions that occur to you during and after the viewing.

Video Outline

This section includes an interview with a theologian who explains the meaning and significance of each of the seven petitions of the Our Father.

Comments and Questions

Use the space below to list comments, questions, feelings, or ideas that occur to you as you view the video.

Watch Segment 4, Part 2 of the DVD or CD-ROM now.

Looking Back

Part 2: The Seven Petitions

Reflect silently on one or more of the questions below and then jot down your response(s). Then share your thoughts with another person or with a group.

1. Which is more difficult: to forgive someone or to ask someone for forgiveness? Explain your answer.

2. The Our Father is a prayer of faith. What are some ways you are living the faith you profess by this prayer?

3. Illustrate your understanding of one of the petitions of the Our Father using words or images.

THE SEVEN PETITIONS OF THE OUR FATHER

•

Hallowed be thy name . . .

•

Thy kingdom come. . . .

•

Thy will be done on earth as it is in heaven.

•

Give us this day our daily bread . . .

•

Forgive us our trespasses as we forgive those who trespass against us. . . .

•

Lead us not into temptation . . .

•

Deliver us from evil.

Looking Beyond

In this segment you have seen the centrality of the Our Father in the spiritual tradition of Christianity. In the activity below you will have the opportunity to apply what you have learned to a concrete experience of Christian prayer.

Simple and faithful trust, humble and joyous assurance are the proper dispositions for one who prays the Our Father.
CCC 2797

FOR CATECHISTS AND PARENTS

Ask various members of your group or your family to write or draw their understanding of one of the seven petitions of the Our Father. Use their responses as part of a community or family prayer. Discuss the experience afterwards.

PRAYING WITH OTHERS

Recall the most recent time that you prayed the Our Father with a group. Reflect on or discuss with a partner ways that this experience of prayer could have been enriched for all those present.

What Did I Learn?

In this space summarize the most important insights you gained in this segment.

What Will I Change?

In this space write one thing you will do differently as a catechist because of what you learned in this segment.

Reflections on the Our Father

by Bishop Robert F. Morneau

Saint Paul urges us to "pray unceasingly." We can do no better in following his advice than by praying from the heart the fundamental Christian prayer—the Our Father. When the disciples asked Jesus how to pray, he taught them—and now us—a prayer that contains seven elements, each holding a petition. Each is a map pointing the way on a part of our spiritual journey.

1. Hallowed be thy name. God is the one who has given us life and, like a human father and mother, we owe our existence to God and to our parents. Jesus teaches us that God is our Father, which makes us all sisters and brothers with one another. Our creator God dwells in heaven but is also here on earth among us in Jesus and the gift of the Holy Spirit. Recognizing God's name as Father, as a Brother in Jesus, as a Friend in the Holy Spirit, we honor, or hallow, God's many names: Father, Son, Spirit, Creator, Redeemer, Sanctifier, Water, Fire, Wind.

Jesus, teach us to know your Father and your Spirit. Give us the gift of reverence to speak your name with love and respect. Help us to long for heaven and the gift of eternity as well as to treasure our lives here on earth. Jesus, teach us how to pray.

2. Thy kingdom come. Saint Paul reminds us that the kingdom of God is not one of eating and drinking. Rather, it is a kingdom of peace, love, and joy (Romans 14:17). God's kingdom comes when God rules and guides our hearts and our history. Too often we can choose to stand under the banner of another kingdom: the kingdom of greed, violence, pride, sloth. God's kingdom is one of peace, and it involves four qualities: truth, charity, freedom, and justice.

Jesus, empower us through your Spirit to be kingdom people. May we speak the truth and not live in the land of falsity and illusion; may we be a loving and caring community and not yield to apathy and indifference; may we gain freedom from our addictions and sin by means of discipline and grace; and may we do the works of justice by respecting and promoting the rights of all. Jesus, teach us how to pray.

Bishop Robert F. Morneau was ordained auxiliary bishop of Green Bay, Wisconsin, on February 22, 1979. He has served as Diocesan Director for Religious in Green Bay and as an instructor of philosophy at Silver Lake College in Manitowoc, Wisconsin. He has also taught at the Summer Theological Institute of St. Norbert's Abbey in De Pere, Wisconsin. Bishop Morneau's writings appear frequently in such periodicals as *Contemplative Review, Review for Religious, Sisters Today, Spiritual Life,* and *Pastoral Life Magazine.* He is very popular as a retreat director and lecturer throughout the United States. Bishop Morneau is the author of a book entitled *Reconciliation* that is part of the series Christian Spirituality for Adults series published by Orbis Books.

3. Thy will be done on earth, as it is in heaven. The prophet Micah tells us basically what God wants from us: that we act with justice, that we love with tenderness, that we walk humbly in faith with our God (Micah 6:8). That's all! One of the great struggles on our Christian journey is that tension between doing our own will ("I did it my way!") or doing God's will. When the front wheels on our car are not aligned, the car begins to shake, rattle, and roll. When our wheels are aligned—when God's wheel and our wheel are going in the same direction—both cars and souls experience peace.

Each petition is a map for a part of our spiritual journey.

Jesus, guide us in your way—the way of justice, compassion, and forgiveness. Help us know God's will in the daily events of our lives. May your Spirit enlighten us to see what you ask of us, and may that same Spirit give us the courage and strength to do your will. Jesus, teach us how to pray.

4. Give us this day our daily bread. We hunger for life at every level: physical, psychological, and spiritual. We need our daily cereal and milk, we need to belong and experience love, we need union with God. Our God not only creates but also sustains us. We acknowledge in this petition God's providential caring. God will give us what we need: food, love, belonging, wisdom, peace.

Jesus, we know our poverty and dependence upon you and your Father. Satisfy our longings of body and soul with your grace, especially with the gift of the bread of life, the Eucharist. May we always be grateful for all you give us. Jesus, teach us how to pray.

5. . . . and forgive us our trespasses, as we forgive those who trespass against us. The Our Father is a dangerous prayer. We ask God to forgive us just as we forgive others. We all sin and stand in need of God's mercy. If we refuse to forgive those who hurt us, something happens in our hearts that prevents us from experiencing God's abundant mercy.

Jesus, through your death on the cross you conquered sin and death. As you forgave those who injured you, help us forgive one another. Only the strength of your Spirit and the gift of your compassion can enable us to be a forgiving community. Jesus, teach us how to pray.

6. . . . and lead us not into temptation . . . As we journey as a pilgrim people back toward God there are temptations along the way that entice us away from God. We fail to put first things first or, worse, we choose some idol instead of the living and true God. God has given us certain means that can help us get to heaven: pleasure, power, possessions, prestige, people. But if these means become ends, we have yielded to temptation and endanger our salvation.

Jesus, may we never become confused in making your gifts more important than you, the Giver. When temptations come our way, give us the strength to turn always to you. If we fail, may we rise quickly in your mercy and resolve to be your faithful servants. Jesus, teach us how to pray.

7. . . . but deliver us from evil. Jesus came to set us free, to win us deliverance from evil, darkness, and death. Every day we confront good and evil; every day we need the gifts of the Spirit to be delivered from sin. None of us is immune from doing great evil. Only through constant prayer, fasting, and generosity can we stay on the path Jesus has marked out for us.

Jesus, you are our redeemer and savior. Draw us close to you so that we might put on your mind and heart and thereby be delivered from evil. Free us all, body and soul, from sin's alienating darkness. Jesus, teach us how to pray.

For Reflection

What insights did you gain from this article that will allow you to pray the Our Father with more feeling and attention?

Let It Be Done Unto Me

The Angelus reveals Mary's willingness to submit herself to God's will, just as her Son taught us to do in the Our Father. Traditionally, the Angelus was prayed three times a day as a reminder of God's presence. Pray this prayer at least once a day for a week and then write in the space below the prayer the difference praying it made in your spiritual life.

The Angelus

Reader: The angel spoke God's message to Mary,

All: and she conceived of the Holy Spirit.

All: Hail, Mary . . .

Reader: "I am the lowly servant of the Lord:

All: Let it be done to me according to your word."

All: Hail, Mary . . .

Reader: And the Word became flesh

All: and lived among us.

All: Hail, Mary . . .

Reader: Pray for us, holy Mother of God,

All: that we may become worthy of the promises of Christ.

Reader: Let us pray.
Lord, fill our hearts with your grace: once, through the message of an angel you revealed to us the Incarnation of your Son; now, through his suffering and death lead us to the glory of his Resurrection.
We ask this through Christ our Lord.

All: Amen.

Prayer:
The Way of Love
by Tom Groome

The old *Baltimore Catechism* (1885) definition of prayer as "raising the mind and heart to God" was a fine definition for prayer reflects our extraordinary human potential to be in personal relationship and communication with God. Before we explore some prayer practices, let us recognize the amazing faith convictions that make possible the Christian call to prayer. These foundations will suggest that prayer is well understood as the "talk of love," though it is often done in silence.

1. God is unconditionally in love with each and every one of us. We Christians believe that both toward us and within Godself, God is a Triune Loving Relationship. This is why God is forever reaching out toward communion, longing to draw us ever more deeply into loving relationship, desiring that we realize all the more how much God loves us. Thus, the initiative is from God. However, as we respond to God's loving outreach, we are assured that we are welcome and that our prayers are heard.

No wonder Jesus could say with such confidence, "Ask and you will receive; seek and you will find; knock and the door will be opened to you"

(Luke 11:9). Of course, we may not get the response that we were hoping for, but our prayers will always be heard nonetheless, and with unconditional love. Prayer, therefore, is the talk of love in that we believe in God's love enough to communicate with confidence.

2. God is actively present within human history,
God is bringing about the reign of peace and justice, love and freedom, holiness and fullness of life. God knows and calls each of us "by name" (Isaiah 45:4), both personally and as a community, to enter into a covenant, or partnership—to live as God's own people. The infinite God calls us to collaborate as partners toward God's hopes for all creation, and further, gives us the grace we need to do God's will "on earth as in heaven" (Matthew 6:10). However, God respects our freedom. God prompts and empowers us, yet never forces our loving response. Our prayer helps us discern and choose God's will.

Our covenant response calls us to ever greater holiness of life. The Bible reveals this holiness as a right and

God longs to call us ever more deeply into loving relationship.

Thomas H. Groome is Professor of Theology and Religious Education at Boston College. his most recent book is *What Makes us Catholic* (Harper).

loving relationship with the Triune God, oneself, others, and creation. Jesus taught such loving relationships in the Great Commandment, uniting love of God with love of neighbor as oneself. Not only did Jesus teach such a "way, truth, and life" (John 14:6), but he modeled and made it possible through his life, death, and Resurrection. So to grow into the holiness of love is our defining human vocation—the very best way to flourish as persons.

We need our prayerful exchange with God precisely to discern what God's love is "doing" in our lives, how best to respond in love and to ask for the grace needed. The time-honored sentiments of prayer in Christian tradition are *worship* and *thanksgiving, petition* and *repentance.* All four presume that we are constantly looking at and reflecting prayerfully on our daily lives—ever raising our minds and hearts to God about what is going on and responding as disciples of Jesus. How else will we recognize why and for what to give *praise* and *thanks* to God, why and for what to *petition* and *repent?*

Maintaining such an intentional and reflective attitude throughout the day is, I suspect, what makes the rare few into great mystics. Meanwhile, most of us—mystics in the making—need good daily practices of prayer, moments we consciously set aside to raise our minds, hearts, and lives to God.

Prayer Practices
Morning Prayer and Perspective.
No time is more appropriate for prayer

than our first waking moments. If done with consciousness and intentionality, our morning prayer can lend a loving "spin" to everything that follows throughout the day. Some people may favor a traditional formula said while consciously thinking about the day ahead. However, it can be even more effective to have our own personally-crafted morning prayer that puts in place some of the perspectives we wish to have permeate the day ahead.

This "foundation" prayer might include such sentiments as thanking God for the gift of a new day and a good night's sleep; recognizing anew and embracing God's love, with the intent to respond throughout the day; committing ourselves to live as disciples of Jesus with his kind of radical love; raising up before God the concerns and worries, hopes and dreams for the day ahead, placing all in God's loving hands; and asking for God's love to be at work this day in all our actions.

Night Prayer and Examen. Evening is an ideal time for a reflective prayer-moment. A person may favor a traditional formula (I remember fondly the "Now I lay me down to sleep" of my childhood.) Another very effective night practice is an "examination of conscience," going back over the day to recognize the times and moments when we did or did not respond to the promptings of God's grace—God's love at work. Such prayerful discernment can have four moments:

• Quiet down and get comfortable.

- Thank God for the gift of the day gone by.
- Review the day slowly, with God as partner, recognizing the movements of God's Spirit and how well or poorly you responded.
- End with a prayer of repentance as needed, and always of faith, hope, and love. Done deliberately, the Lord's Prayer expresses all those sentiments.

Giving Thanks at Meal Time. This traditional practice is well named as "grace" for it calls us to recognize and give thanks to God for the food we receive—a very concrete gift of God's love. Again, some may favor a traditional formula. However, it can be more effective for a family to develop its own grace as a tradition, reciting it together by heart. Craft such a shared prayer to help family members recognize the many loving gifts of God to their lives, and to renew their commitment to care for those who are less fortunate. Both are demanded by our covenant.

Daily Praying of a Scripture Passage. The Second Vatican Council (1962–65) called Catholics to re-center the Bible at the core of our faith. This requires that we study the Scriptures and come to know their spiritual wisdom. However, it also calls us to pray them, in the sense of reflecting and talking to God about them and discerning what they might mean for our lives. This can be done alone, of course, but the discernment is heightened by doing it in conversation and community.

Whether alone or with others, select a particular text. First, place yourself in the presence of God and become aware of God's love for you. Next, look over your own life, its present cares and concerns, hopes and joys. If in a group, share these in conversation. Now bring your life with you as you read and listen intently to the text. Recognize whatever might be a "word of God" for your life at this time. Now, imagine how to bring this "word of God" back to life again, and discern the decisions it invites. Such a dynamic of "bringing life to Scripture and Scripture to life" can be a powerful experience of discernment.

There are many more rich prayer practices in Christian tradition. The key is to choose a few that appeal to you and then to practice them regularly. As you move ever more deeply into awareness and embrace of God's love for you.

Recognition of God's goodness and practical love for the poor are demanded by our covenant.

● ● ● **For Reflection** ● ● ●

- What difference has it made for you to know that you are loved unconditionally by God?
- What is your daily practice of the prayerful life? What new practice would you like to develop?

Resource Bibliography

Church Documents

Abbot, Walter M., SJ, gen. ed. *The Documents of Vatican II.* New York: Herder and Herder, 1966.

Benedict XVI. *Deus Caritas Est (God Is Love).* Vatican City: Libreria Editrice Vaticana, 2006.

———. *Spe Salvi (On Christian Hope.)* Vatican City: Libreria Editrice Vaticana. Washington, DC: USCCB, 2008.

Catechism of the Catholic Church, Second Edition. Libreria Editrice Vaticana. Washington, DC: United States Catholic Conference, 2000.

Compendium: Catechism of the Catholic Church. Washington, DC: United States Conference of Catholic Bishops, 2005.

Compendium of the Social Doctrine of the Church. Vatican City: Libreria Editrice Vaticana, 2004.

Congregation for the Clergy. *General Directory for Catechesis.* Vatican City: Libreria Editrice Vaticana, 1997.

Connell, Martin, ed. *The Catechetical Documents: A Parish Resource.* Chicago: Liturgy Training Publications, 1996.

International Commission on English in the Liturgy. *Book of Blessings: Study Edition.* Collegeville, MN: The Liturgical Press, 1989.

National Directory for Catechesis. Washington, DC: United States Conference of Catholic Bishops, 2005.

United States Catholic Catechism for Adults. Washington, DC: United States Conference of Catholic Bishops, 2006.

Theological Resources

Barry, William A., S.J. *God's Passionate Desire: And Our Response.* Notre Dame, Ind.: Ave Maria, Press, 1993.

———. *Who Do You Say I Am?* Notre Dame, Ind.: Ave Maria Press, 1996.

Cistercian Studies: No. 59. *Sayings of the Desert Fathers.* Kalamazoo, Minn.: Cistercian Publications.

Huebsch, Bill. *Vatican II in Plain English.* Three volumes. Allen, Tex.: Thomas More, 1997.

Keating, Thomas. *The Heart of the World: A Spiritual Catechism.* New York: Crossroad Publishing, 1984.

Leech, Kenneth. *Experiencing God: Theology as Spirituality.* New York: Harper & Row, 1985.

McBride, Alfred, O.P. *Essentials of the Faith: A Guide to the Catechism of the Catholic Church.* Huntington, Ind.: Our Sunday Visitor, Inc., 1994.

Merton, Thomas. *Life and Holiness.* Garden City, N.Y.: Doubleday, 1962.

———. *Thoughts in Solitude.* New York: Noonday Press, 1956.

———. *What Is Contemplation?* Springfield, Ill.: Templegate Publishers, 1978.

Mourneau, Robert F. *Ashes to Easter: Lenten Meditations.* New York: Crossroad Publishing, 1996.

———. *A Retreat with Jessica Powers: Loving a Passionate God.* Cincinnati: St. Anthony Messenger Press, 1995.

Nhat Hanh, Thich. *The Long Road Turns to Joy: A Guide to Walking Meditation.* Copyright 1996 by Thick Nhat Hanh.

Norris, Kathleen. *The Cloister Walk.* New York: Riverhead Books, 1996.

———. *Amazing Grace: A Vocabulary of Faith.* New York: Riverhead Books, 1999.

Nouwen, Henri J.M. *Gracias! A Latin American Journal.* San Francisco: Harper & Row, 1983.

———. *The Inner Voice of Love: A Journey Through Anguish to Freedom.* New York: Doubleday,

Rolheiser, Ronald, OMI. *The Holy Longing.* New York: Doubleday, 1999.

———. *The Restless Heart.* New York, Doubleday, 2004.

Rupp, Joyce. *Prayer.* MaryKnoll, New York: Orbis Books, 2007,

Whitehead, Evelyn Eaton and James D. Whitehead. *Christian Life Patterns.* New York: Crossroad Publishing, 1992.

Wicks, Robert. *Touching the Holy.* Notre Dame, Ind.: Ave Maria Press, 1992.

———. *Crossing the Desert: Learning to Let Go, See Clearly, and Live Simply.* Notre Dame, IN: Sorin Books, 2007.

———. *Snow Falling on Snow: Themes form the Spiritual Landscape of Robert J. Wicks.* Mahwah, NJ: Paulist Press, 2001.

Videos

The Mystery of Faith: An Introduction to Catholicism. A ten-part video series featuring Fr. Michael Himes. Fisher Productions, Box 727, Jefferson Valley, New York 10535.

The Faithful Revolution: Vatican II. Allen, Texas: RCL Enterprises, Vatican II Productions, 1997.

Computer Resources

Catechism of the Catholic Church for Personal Computers. United States Catholic Conference, 1994. Available on disk and CD/ROM in English, Spanish, French.

Echoes of Faith ® *Plus*

Certificate of Completion

_____

Name

has successfully completed the process
for the Prayer and Spirituality module
in the Echoes of Faith Plus program.

This certificate of completion is given at

_____

Parish

_____

Diocese

_____

Signature

_____

Date

Feedback Form

We hope that you have benefited from your use of this *Prayer and Spirituality* module. Please take time to fill in your comments to the questions below. They will help the *Echoes of Faith Plus* team in planning additional resources to assist you in your ministry. If possible, discuss your responses with your program director before you mail it.

Thank you,

The *Echoes of Faith Plus* Team

1. What are the three most important insights or suggestions that you carry away with you as you complete this learning module *Prayer and Spirituality?*

   _____

   _____

   _____

   _____

2. List up to five issues or questions that you would still like to discuss with your program director.

   _____

   _____

   _____

   _____

   _____

3. In a sentence or two describe how this learning module was helpful to you in your service as a catechist.

   _____

   _____

   _____

   _____

   _____

Tear out this sheet, fold and tape it closed, and return it to us. There is a business reply mechanism on the back of this page. Or you may fill out this survey online at www.EchoesofFaith.com. Thank you.

BUSINESS REPLY MAIL

FIRST-CLASS MAIL   **PERMIT NO 100**   **ALLEN TX**

POSTAGE WILL BE PAID BY ADDRESSEE

ATTN PUBLISHER
ECHOES OF FAITH® PLUS PROJECT
RCL BENZIGER
PO BOX 7000
ALLEN TX 75013-9972

-- *Fold* --

THE TOOTH ROBBERS
A PRO-FLUORIDATION HANDBOOK

THE TOOTH ROBBERS
A PRO-FLUORIDATION HANDBOOK

Edited by
STEPHEN BARRETT, M.D.
Chairman, Board of Directors
Lehigh Valley Committee
Against Health Fraud, Inc.
&
SHELDON ROVIN, D.D.S., M.S.
Professor and Chairman
Department of Dental Care Systems
University of Pennsylvania
School of Dental Medicine

GEORGE F. STICKLEY COMPANY
210 W. Washington Square
Philadelphia

The Tooth Robbers is a special publication of the Lehigh Valley Committee Against Health Fraud, Inc., an independent organization which was formed in 1969 to combat deception in the field of health. The purposes of the Committee are:

  1) To investigate false, deceptive or exaggerated health claims.
  2) To conduct a vigorous campaign of public education.
  3) To assist appropriate government and consumer-oriented agencies.
  4) To bring problems to the attention of lawmakers.

The Lehigh Valley Committee Against Health Fraud is a member organization of the Consumer Federation of America. Since 1970, the Committee has been chartered under the laws of the Commonwealth of Pennsylvania as a not-for-profit corporation. Inquiries about Committee activities may be addressed to P. O. Box 1602, Allentown, Pa. 18105.

Manufactured in the United States and published by the George F. Stickley Company, Philadelphia, Pa.

CONTENTS

INTRODUCTION

This book was written to protect teeth. It will help you understand the politics of fluoridation. More important, it can help you bring fluoridation's benefits to the citizens of your community.

ABOUT THE CONTRIBUTORS

Stephen Barrett, M.D., a practicing psychiatrist, is the nation's most vigorous opponent of health fraud and quackery. Since 1970, he has been Chairman, Board of Directors, of the Lehigh Valley Committee Against Health Fraud, Inc., a member organization of Consumer Federation of America. An expert in medical communications, he serves as medical consultant to WFMZ-TV, Allentown, Pennsylvania. He is editor of *The Health Robbers—How To Protect Your Money And Your Life* and co-author of the college textbook *Consumer Health—A Guide to Intelligent Decisions*. He has been a member of the Committee on Quackery of the Pennsylvania Medical Society and the Committee on Health Fraud of the Pennsylvania Health Council. He is a scientific advisor to the American Council on Science and Health and a scientific consultant to the Committee for Scientific Investigation of Claims of the Paranormal. In 1972, he introduced the resolution passed by the American Medical Association's House of Delegates to re-endorse fluoridation and increase its priority in AMA educational programs. In 1975, the Lehigh Valley Dental Society gave him the Dr. Francis J. Trembley Outstanding Citizen Award for "decisive contributions dedicated to the betterment of oral medicine."

Sheldon Rovin, D.D.S., M.S., is Professor and Chairman, Department of Dental Care Systems and Associate Director of the Leonard Davis Institute of Health Economics at the University of Pennsylvania. A board certified oral pathologist, he is a former chairman of the Dental Division of the American Association for Cancer Education. In 1973, while serving as Dean of the University of Washington School of Dentistry, he helped lead the successful fluoridation referendum campaign in Seattle, Washington. For this effort, he was given the 1974 American Dental Association Preventive Dentistry Public Service Award. In 1976, he helped lead the statewide campaign to defeat an antifluoridation referendum which would have banned fluoridation in the state of Washington. He is the author of *Oral Cancer: Diagnosis and Detection, The Programmed Textbook of Oral Pathology* and more than 70 articles published in dental and medical journals. He is consultant to the United States Public Health Service Center for Disease Control, the National Center for Health Services Research, and the Veterans Administration Department of Medicine and Surgery. He is also a member of the Editorial Board of the *Journal of Dental Education*.

———

Mary Bernhardt is a freelance journalist who specializes in dental topics. From 1968 to 1976, she was Secretary of the American Dental Association's Council on Dental Health.

Joel M. Boriskin, D.D.S, who practices general dentistry in Oakland, California, is Chief of the Dental Health Bureau, Alameda County Health Care Services Agency. He is also a consultant in the area of fluoridation programs to the California Dental Association, the California State Department of Health, the American Dental Association and the U.S. Public Health Service Center for Disease Control. In 1974 and 1980, he led referendum campaigns which brought and retained fluoridation to the large two-county area served by the East Bay Municipal Utility District. Since 1975, he has also participated actively in four other referendum campaigns in California, three of which were successful.

Consumers Union is a nonprofit corporation established in 1936 to provide consumers with information and counsel on consumer goods and services. It publishes the monthly magazine *Consumer Reports* and produces a wide variety of other educational materials.

Peter K. Domoto, D.D.S., M.P.H., is Associate Professor and Chairman of Pedodontics at the University of Washington School of Dentistry. His major areas of interest are prevention, behavioral science and dental care for underserved populations. He was co-chairman of the successful referendum campaign in 1973 to retain fluoridation in Seattle, Washington.

Robert C. Faine, D.D.S., M.P.H., a Diplomate of the American Board of Dental Public Health, is Deputy Chief, Dental Disease Prevention Activity, United States Public Health Service Center for Disease Control. As a USPHS Regional Dental Program Director in Seattle, Washington, from 1970 to 1977, he was involved in several fluoridation campaigns in the Pacific Northwest. In 1978, he received the USPHS Commendation Medal.

Norma A. Kaplis, D.D.S., is Assistant Professor of Dental Care Systems at the University of Pennsylvania. She has been a Clinical Fellow in Ecological Dentistry at the Harvard School of Dental Medicine and worked as a dentist and health educator at the Martha Eliot Neighborhood Health Center in Jamaica Plain, Massachusetts.

Cora S. Leukhart, who entered the Public Health Service in 1966, recently retired as Public Health Advisor, Dental Disease Prevention Activity, where her major responsibilities included consultation, training and technical assistance concerning fluoridation.

James A. Lincoln, LL.B., now retired, served from 1960 to 1977 as Judge of the Wayne County Probate Court, Juvenile Division, in Michigan. During that period he chaired or served on dozens of committees which sponsored new programs or legislation. In 1971-2, he was President of the National Council of Juvenile Court Judges. He is the author of *Anatomy of A Riot*. From 1954 to 1960, he served as a City Councilman in the City of Detroit. His superbly written analysis of the fluoridation controversy—written in 1956—generated widespread public interest and influenced many other legislators to vote for fluoridation.

Alan M. Slutsky, D.M.D., M.B.A., is an instructor in the Department of Dental Care Systems at the University of Pennsylvania.

Benjamin M. Spock, M.D., is the author of 10 books, including *Baby and Child Care*—the book on childrearing which has sold 28 million copies since its initial publication in 1946. Trained in both pediatrics and psychiatry, he practiced pediatrics in New York City from 1933 to 1947 except for two years in the Navy. Subsequently he joined the staff of the Mayo Clinic in Rochester, Minnesota, organized a teaching program in child development at the University of Pittsburgh, and served for 12 years as Professor of Child Development at Western Reserve University in Cleveland before retiring in 1967. During the early 1960's, he joined the National Committee for a Sane Nuclear Policy and became its chairman.

Bob Sprague, a freelance writer and newspaperman for 10 years, is Assistant Sunday Editor of the *Times-Herald Record* in Middletown, New York. Raised in a fluoridated community, he got his first cavity at the age of 32.

FOREWORD
How I Feel About Fluoridation

Benjamin Spock, M.D.

You might guess that I would be opposed to fluoridation of the water supply (to prevent tooth decay) on several counts. I've been against pollution of the diet of children and adults with extra sugar and salt, and with additives and preservatives. I've always disagreed with those health professionals who assumed, without solid proof, that they knew more than Nature—when, for example, some physicians used to prescribe tonsillectomy on a wholesale basis or tried to change growth patterns of normally short or tall children by means of growth hormones. I'm also against imposing regulations on people in an arbitrary and undemocratic manner.

The fact is that I started out as somewhat skeptical and cautious about fluoridation in the 1940's and early 1950's. But then I became a firm believer as proof was assembled by scientists in the 1950's and afterwards that fluoridation of a water supply will reduce the production of tooth cavities (our most prevalent disease) by 60 per cent; and, just as important, that no disease or defect is caused by this procedure. What particularly allayed my early doubts about adding a chemical to public water supplies was learning that fluoride has always occurred *naturally* in water supplies—in concentrations from several parts per million in some regions of the southwest to a mere twentieth of a part per million in the northeast. Obviously, it is a natural, though varying, ingredient of water. Because of this, any long-term bad effect could be—and was—searched for in those people who had drunk water with a moderate or high concentration all their lives.

In the late 1950's and the early 1960's I was chairman of a national committee to educate the public and public officials about the value and safety of fluoridation. As such I received hundreds of letters, some politely explaining that I was mistaken, others abusing me as intentionally evil. (One was an indignant letter from one of my sisters, a vigorous environmentalist and organic farmer.) But I've also received favorable mail, and awards from two national dental associations, so it wasn't all painful. My book *Baby and Child Care* has advocated fluoridation since the 1950's.

The many endorsements of fluoridation by professional organizations are certainly impressive. After careful review of all scientific evidence, including claims of opponents, fluoridation has been recommended as safe and effective by the American Dental Association, the American Medical Association, the American Public Health Association, the American Academy of Pediatrics, the National Institute of Dental Research (an arm of the U.S. Department of Health, Education and Welfare), the Royal Society of Physicians in Great Britain, and the World Health Organization. In fact, no major health organization or recognized scientific body has ever differed with these conclusions.

The story of how fluoridation's value was discovered is not only fascinating, but should also be reassuring to some doubters since it reveals that the early researchers had no bias, no axe to grind. They were simply looking for answers to certain dental problems. Dr. Frederick S. McKay, a practicing dentist in Colorado with an extraordinary curiosity and dedication to human betterment, spent the first 30 years of this century tracking down the cause of a certain type of tooth stain which has always been prevalent in Colorado and several southwestern states. He first found, strangely enough, that this staining occurred in people whose teeth had a high resistance to decay. He finally discovered, in 1931, that the staining and resistance to decay were both due to the high concentration of fluoride which occurred naturally in that region.

Then Dr. H. Trendley Dean and a team from the U.S. Public Health Service spent 10 years evaluating the dental health of 7,000 children in 4 southwestern states with moderate to high concentrations of naturally occurring fluoride to find what concentration gave the best protection without staining. They found it to be one part fluoride in a million parts of water.

A crucial test was begun in 1945 in Newburgh, New York, to see whether deliberate addition of fluoride to a water supply which had very little natural fluoride would provide the same benefit. Over a 10-year period, the children of Newburgh developed nearly 60 per cent fewer cavities than the children of the comparable city of Kingston, where the water was not fluoridated. Since then, thousands of studies of the effectiveness and safety of fluoridation have been made with consistent results.

The natural occurrence of moderate to high concentrations of fluoride in certain regions has made it possible for scientists to search without delay for possible bad effects by carefully comparing rates for such diseases as cancer, heart disease, birth defects and allergies in regions with high, medium and low concentrations of fluoride. All studies have agreed: the only adverse effect is staining of the teeth when the fluoride concentration is several times as high as that recommended for artificial fluoridation.

You've probably heard the accusations against fluoridation—that it is a poison; that it may cause cancer, heart disease, birth defects, allergies and other diseases; that its use in a public water supply is an invasion of people's constitutional rights unless they consent. Other, wilder, claims are that it is a *communist* plot to weaken our country (even though the Soviet Union uses fluoridation), or that it is simply a money-making scheme of the aluminum companies who produce the fluoride as a by-product. All adverse claims and accusations which had the slightest plausibility have been scrupulously investigated by scientists and government officials and have been found to be baseless. But nothing seems to keep the more determined opponents from repeating old accusations and making new ones.

In this book you will learn about the major opponents of fluoridation, what motivates them, and what methods they use. You will learn much more about the importance of fluoridation. (For example, that during World War II, 10 per cent of all the young men examined for armed service were rejected because they didn't have 12 usable teeth left out of the normal complement of 32!) You will learn the essential—and difficult—ingredients of a pro-fluoridation campaign. You will find practical educational and political materials.

So this book is for community leaders, journalists, city officials, legislators, health professionals, students and other citizens concerned with improving dental health in this country.

Ben Spock

June, 1980

PART ONE

TOOTH ROBBERS AND HOW TO SPOT THEM

THE POISONMONGERS

More than 20,000 scientific studies attest to fluoridation's safety and effectiveness in preventing tooth decay. Don't let the poisonmongers scare you.

MARY BERNHARDT
Former Secretary, Council on Dental Health
American Dental Association
&
BOB SPRAGUE
Assistant Sunday Editor
Times-Herald Record
Middletown, New York

On May 27, 1975, 213,573 people in Los Angeles exercised their democratic privilege—*and voted against healthier teeth!* Since 1973, more than 270 Nebraska communities have done the same. In cities from coast to coast, citizens have voted to deprive themselves, their children, and their neighbors' children of the proven health benefits of fluoridation.

Of course, none of these negative voters meant to inflict cavities upon anyone. They were confused—influenced by alarmists who claim that adding fluoride to a city's water supply will "poison" people.

These alarmists are the "poisonmongers." Antagonistic to scientific research, they are commonly known as "antis" (short for "an-tifluoridationists"). Leaders of the 35-year struggle for fluoridation are frustrated by their tactics. Newspaper editors are commonly taken in by their publicity stunts. And legislators are often overwhelmed by their various and sometimes shrill arguments.

G. Herbert Seberg, D.D.S., knows the antis well. Past-President of the Nebraska Dental Association, he has been fighting to fluoridate Nebraska since 1950. In 1973, Dr. Seberg received two awards for his work in gaining passage of a bill which ordered statewide fluoridation by January 1, 1975.

Promoting the bill, the Nebraska Dental Association led a five-month campaign which had the editorial support of most of

1

2

the state's newspapers. Opposing the bill was the Nebraska Pure Air and Water Committee. Though loosely organized, its members distributed scare pamphlets, wrote letters to newspaper editors and paid for misleading advertisements.

Though the fluoridation bill passed, Dr. Seberg and his allies could not stem the dogged opposition of a few senators who attached an "escape clause" to it. Fifteen percent of a town's voters could petition for a referendum which would decide the fate of fluoridation in their community. By 1975, although 69 percent of Nebraska's one and one-half million people were drinking fluoridated water, more than 300 of its communities put the issue to a vote. Most of these were small, conservative prairie towns. Fewer than ten percent of these communities voted to fluoridate.

Los Angeles was the largest city ever to vote on this issue. Because of this, its referendum defeat was a great disappointment to fluoridation proponents. In September 1974, the Los Angeles City Council had voted 10-5 to fluoridate. But a few weeks later, pressure from frightened constituents persuaded the Council to allow the public to vote. After the referendum was defeated, 213,573 to 166,549, councilmen voted unanimously to rescind the fluoridation ordinance. Labeling the referendum defeat "a victory of strident scare tactics over medical evidence," a *Los Angeles Times* editorial criticized City Council for "retreating from its best judgment."

To date, more than 2,000 American communities have decided the matter of fluoridation at the voting booth. In thousands of other communities, the decision to fluoridate was made by city councils. In recent years, most voters have been rejecting fluoridation. Though this trend is discouraging, public health leaders are not suprised by it. As far back as 1951, Dr. Frank A. Bull, Director of Dental Education for the Wisconsin State Board of Health, summed up the problem quite well. Speaking at the Fourth Annual Conference of State Dental Directors, Dr. Bull said:

"I don't believe that you can win approval of any public health program where there is organized opposition. I mean clever, well thought-up opposition. I think it is possible to beat almost anything."

In the years since this statement was made,

antifluoridationists have developed clever political tactics which can play on the fears of ordinary citizens. Increasingly, these tactics have been employed to bring about referendums—to defeat fluoridation. The sad fact is that people can easily be frightened by things which they do not understand and can easily be confused by contradictory arguments.

Fluoridation's Credentials

There should be no mystery about what fluoridation is. Fluoride is a mineral which occurs naturally in most water supplies. Fluoridation is the adjustment of the natural fluoride concentration to about one part of fluoride to one million parts of water. More than 20,000 scientific studies attest to fluoridation's safety and effectiveness in preventing tooth decay.

The history of fluoridation in the U.S. underlines its unique standing as a public health measure copied from a natural phenomenon. In the early 1900's, Dr. Frederick S. McKay began an almost 30-year search for the cause of the staining of teeth which was prevalent in Colorado where he practiced dentistry. Traveling to trace this condition, he found it common in other states, including Texas where it was known as "Texas teeth." In 1928, he announced that these teeth, although stained, showed "a singular absence of decay." He concluded that both the staining and the decay resistance were caused by something in the water. In 1931, the "something" was identified as fluoride.

The Public Health Service then took over to determine precisely what amount of fluoride in the water would prevent decay without causing staining. Years of "shoeleather epidemiology" by Dr. H. Trendley Dean traced the dental status of 7,000 children drinking naturally fluoridated water in 21 cities in four states. In 1943, he reported that the ideal amount of fluoride was one part per million parts of water. This concentration was demonstrated to result in healthy, attractive teeth which had one-third as many cavities as might otherwise be expected—and no staining. Dean, later known as the "father of fluoridation," thus paved the way for public health application of this natural phenomenon.

The next step was to determine whether water engineering could copy nature's amazing dental health benefit. At several test sites, the fluoride concentration of the public water supply was adjusted to one part per million.

One such test was conducted in the neighboring cities of Newburgh and Kingston, New York. First, the children in both cities were examined by dentists and physicians. Then fluoride was added to Newburgh's water supply. After ten years, the children of Newburgh had 58% fewer decayed teeth than those of unfluoridated Kingston. The greatest benefits were obtained by children who had drunk the fluoridated water since birth. Other studies showed that teeth made stronger by fluoride during childhood will remain permanently resistant to decay.

As the evidence for fluoridation piled up, thousands of communities acted to obtain its benefits. By 1975, more than 105 million Americans were drinking fluoridated water. But 70 million other Americans were receiving public water supplies which were not fluoridated—thanks largely to the efforts of poisonmongers.

Opposition to Fluoridation

Since it began, fluoridation has encountered opposition from scattered groups and individuals. Many of them have been associated with the health food industry—which aligns fluoridation with its general propaganda that our food supply is being "poisoned." Chiropractors have opposed fluoridation as an interference with "free choice of health care." Christian Scientists have regarded it as "forced medication" and the John Birch Society has seen it as a "Communist plot."

By the early 1950's, individuals and local groups began exchanging ideas and experiences with each other. A few physicians and dentists became very vigorous in opposing fluoridation and began traveling around the U.S. to appear at court hearings and public meetings. One of them, George Waldbott, M.D., started the *National Fluoridation News*, a four-page newspaper now edited by Mrs. Ethel Fabian of Gravette, Arkansas.

Several national groups have been formed for the sole purpose of fighting fluoridation, but it appears that none of these has achieved sufficient funding to have much impact outside of the communities of their leaders. However, several well-funded national multi-issue organizations have managed to disseminate large amounts of scare propaganda throughout the country. Among them are Rodale Press, the John Birch Society and the National Health Federation.

The early efforts of the antifluoridationists were assisted by the caution and conservatism of many physicians, dentists and other scientists who felt that not enough research had been done for them to take a positive stand. As time went on and data piled up, however, the overwhelming majority of health scientists concluded that fluoridation is safe and effective.

But while scientists were refining and publishing their experiments, the antis were refining and publishing their battle plans. In the mid-1960's, the National Health Federation published *An Action Guide...On How to Fight Fluoridation in Your Area*. Available for 25¢, this four-page leaflet details the strategy which can be used in any community where fluoridation is being considered.

"Neutralizing" Politicians

Once fluoridation proponents are known to be active, the leaflet says, antis should immediately send a letter to each member of governing bodies. The letter should emphasize "the most recent evidence" that fluoridation is "harmful." Most important, it should urge the officials to "remain absolutely neutral" by putting the matter to public vote. "When this is done," the leaflet states, "whatever political figures may be concerned are relieved of any and all responsibility in the matter."

This opening blast is designed to neutralize politicians. It aims to arouse doubt about the safety of fluoridation. It also offers an easy excuse for delaying favorable action—while the antis begin their hatchet job on public opinion.

How Poisonmongers Work

The antis' basic technique is *the big lie*. Made infamous by Hitler, it is simple to use, yet surprisingly effective. It consists of claiming that fluoridation causes cancer, heart disease, kidney disease and other serious ailments which people fear. The fact that there is no supporting evidence for such claims does not matter. The trick is to keep repeating them—because if something is said often enough, people tend to think there must be some truth to it.

A variation of the big lie is the *laundry list*. List enough "evils," and even if proponents can reply to some of them, they will never be able to cover the entire list. This technique is most effective in debates or letters to the editor.

A key factor in any anti campaign is the use of printed matter. Because of this, antis are very anxious to have their views printed in any publications. Scientific journals will rarely print them, but most local newspapers are sympathetic toward the expression of minority viewpoints regardless of whether they are supported by facts. A few editors even welcome the controversy the antis generate—on the theory that it will increase readership.

The aim of anti "documents" is to create the illusion of scientific controversy. Often they quote statements which are *out of date* or *out of context*. Quotes from obscure or hard-to-locate journals are particularly effective. Another favored tactic is to *misquote* a pro-fluoridation scientist, knowing that even if the scientist himself protests, his reply will not reach all of the people who saw the original misquote.

Half-truths are commonly used. For example, saying that fluoride is a rat poison ignores the fact that poison is a matter of dose. Large amounts of many substances—even pure water—can poison people. But the trace amount of fluoride contained in fluoridated water will not harm anyone.

"Experts" are commonly quoted. It is possible to find someone with scientific credentials who is against just about anything. Most "experts" who speak out against fluoridation, however, are not experts on the subject. There are, of course, a few dentists and physicians who oppose fluoridation. However, many of them oppose it on the basis of government action rather than on safety. Curiously, when anti experts change their minds in favor of fluoridation, they sometimes find that the antis keep on quoting their earlier positions.

Innuendo is a technique that has broad appeal because it can be used in a seemingly unemotional pitch. Some antis admit that fluoridation has been found safe "so far," but claim that its long-range effects have "not yet" been fully explored. *The waiting game* is a related gambit in which antis suggest that waiting a bit longer will help to resolve "doubt" about fluoridation's safety. No doubt, some antis will continue to use this argument for a few hundred more years.

The *bogus reward* is a fascinating technique. Some antis offer large rewards to anyone who will prove that fluoridation is safe. If the wording is not extremely careful, however, the pros can actually collect. In 1965, a California chiropractor offered $1,000 to anyone who could produce an expert from California "who has done any conclusive research proving the safety" or who could produce documentary evidence that fluoridation is safe. A local dental group assembled a barrage of experts and more than 100 research reports testifying to fluoridation's safety and effectiveness. When the chiropractor refused to pay, the dental group filed suit and later settled out of court for $500.

A $100,000 reward offer has survived for a long time—but a close look will show why. In order to collect, pros must post a bond "to cover any costs which the offerers of the reward might incur if the proof is deemed invalid." The offer does not state who would judge the evidence, but of course the judges would be appointed by the antis themselves. If a suit were to be filed to collect the reward, the court might rule that the offer was a gambling bet which should not be enforced by a court. Such a suit would require at least $25,000 for the bond and legal fees. Even if it were won, however, there is no assurance that the money could be recovered from the individuals who sponsor the reward. Most of them are elderly and scattered widely throughout the United States and Canada.

Since the scientific community is so solidly in favor of fluoridation, antis try to discredit it entirely by use of the *conspiracy gambit*. The beauty of the conspiracy charge is that it can be leveled at anyone and there is absolutely no way to disprove it. After all, how does one prove that something is not taking place secretly? Favorite "conspirators" are the U.S. Public Health Service, the American Dental Association, the American Medical Association, the Communist Party and the aluminum industry. Apparently, in the minds of the antis, these groups could all be working together to "poison" the American people!

Local promoters are often accused of being in the employ of "vested interests." An individual is rarely accused directly since that could trigger a lawsuit for defamation of character. Instead, a question is asked: "Could it be that Dr. So-and-so is really working for the aluminum industry?" Years ago, the conspiracy gambit would work primarily with the very paranoid. But in the post-Watergate era, it may seem realistic to a wider audience.

"This is only the beginning!" is a related gambit. "First *they* will add fluoride, then vitamin pills, and the next thing you know it will be birth control pills!" Who *"they"* are does not need to be specified.

Scare words will add zip to any anti campaign. Not only the more obvious ones like "cancer" and "heart disease," but also more specialized ones like "mongoloid births" and "sickle cell anemia." *Ecology words* are currently in vogue. Calling fluoride a "chemical" (rather than a nutrient) can strike fear in the minds of many Americans who fear we are already too "chemicalized." The fact that water itself is a chemical and the fact that responsible use of chemicals can be of great help to our society will not reassure everyone. Fluoride is also called "artificial" and "a pollutant" which is "against nature." Faced with the fact that fluoridation merely copies a natural phenomenon, the antis reply that "natural" fluoride differs from "artificial" fluoride—a fact as yet undiscovered by scientists.

The "against nature" concept led to an exchange which was reported in the Lincoln, Nebraska *Star*. During the fluoridation bill debate, Nebraska State Senator Richard Proud suggested that God would have fluoridated water if He wanted it so treated. Senator Ernest Chambers answered, "And if He had wanted you to smoke, He'd have put a chimney on your head."

Suggesting *alternatives* is a common tactic. Here the antis propose that the community distribute free fluoride tablets to parents who wish to give them to their children. The suggested program sounds "democratic," but it will not be effective from a public health standpoint. Most parents are not motivated to administer the 4,000+ doses needed from birth through age 12. The plea for alternatives is often made by a "neutral" individual who sounds like he will support an alternative program if water fluoridation is defeated. Don't bet on it. Such advocacy is almost always a propaganda ploy.

Pro-fluoridationists can sometimes turn the tables on the "alternatives" argument by suggesting that unfluoridated water remain available at a special tap for residents who want it. Despite the antis' professed fears, however, such taps get little use. After Lawrence, Kansas, installed one in 1979, for example, fewer than ten people used it regularly. The Lawrence Water Department serves about 64,000 people.

Once fluoridation has begun in a community, antis can resort to the *"cause of all evil"* gambit—blaming fluoridation for everything that occurred after it started. An example of this tactic, one that backfired on opponents, took place in Cleveland on June 1, 1956. That was the day fluorides were to be added to the city's water supply. That day, the phone calls began—"My goldfish have died."—"My African violets are wilting."—"I can't make a decent cup of coffee."—"My dog is constipated." Although reactions like this would usually be recognized as psychological, this time their nature was beyond question. Last minute problems had delayed the start of fluoridation for a month!

"Let the People Decide"

The antis' most persuasive argument, both to legislators and to the public, is to call for a public vote. On the surface, this appears to be the democratic way to settle the issue. But the antis are dealing from a stacked deck. First, the people who need fluoridation the most—the children—do not vote. Second, it is not difficult to confuse voters by flooding their community with scare propaganda. The average citizen does not have the educational background to sort out claim and counterclaim or to judge which "authorities" to believe. To turn against fluoridation, he does not need to accept *all* the anti arguments—*just one*. The sheer bulk of the controversy is itself likely to arouse doubt in the minds of most voters.

Occasionally, a brave profluoridation group will attempt a referendum as a last resort to overcome the resistance of its local government. But make no mistake about it—the referendum is *primarily* an antifluoridation device. Antis who say, "Let the people decide," may sound as if they wish to use a democratic process to make the decision. But experience in many cities has shown otherwise. If fluoridation wins a referendum, the usual anti response is to work for another one. In a few states where local laws allow repeated referendums on the same subject, fluoridation has been in and out, and in and out again. When this happens, not only do children suffer unnecessary dental costs, but their tax-paying parents pay the high costs of the referendums.

Curiously, studies have shown that referendums can lose even in communities where public opinion favors fluoridation. People will usually go to the polls to vote against whatever they *don't* like. So the crucial factor in many referendums is the ability of proponents to mobilize their supporters.

The value of getting out the vote was never more strikingly demonstrated than in the 1973 referendum in Seattle, Washington. The vote was 115,000 for fluoridation and 49,000 opposed. The key to victory was an unprecedented move by Sheldon Rovin, D.D.S., who was then Dean of the University of Washington School of Dentistry. Two weeks before the election, Dr. Rovin excused students and faculty members from class so that they could participate in a door-to-door campaign. In all, 500 doorbellers saturated the city with their pleas to residents. Person-to-person contact just before the vote worked in Seattle just as it might for any political candidate anywhere—by instructing voters on how to cast their ballots and by giving them a brief opportunity to share their concerns. One homeowner agreed to vote for fluoridation if the canvassers would help him move his television set into the basement.

The Seattle fluoridation forces were extremely well-organized and were very sophisticated politically. They had a broad base of support from community organizations such as unions, the PTA and the Chamber of Commerce. But they also had *no sizable opposition!*

The Devout Anti

Most people who power local and national antifluoridation movements see themselves as saviors of their fellow men. Many of them make opposing fluoridation their single great mission in life. Others include fluoridation among a variety of causes related to health. Antifluoridationists are often active against mental health programs, compulsory immunization and animal research.

Most damaging to the cause of fluoridation are the few antis who are physicians, dentists or others who presumably should be able to judge fluoridation on its merits. Some of them are simply misinformed. Others are alienated for reasons unconnected with fluoridation, but take this cause to get back at the scientific community which they feel has "slighted" them.

What makes a devout anti tick? Three prominent psychiatrists suggested an answer in *Psychodynamics of Group Opposition to Public Health Programs,* an article which appeared in 1960 in the *American Journal of Orthopsychiatry.* Some are motivated by factors of personal power, prestige or gain. Some are driven by great anxieties or hostilities, the sources of which are unconscious. Antis commonly perceive certain health measures as a threat to their "sense of wholeness," and must passionately defend themselves against the "forcible entry" of any "foreign body" or "foreign agents"—whether this be a vaccination, an interracial contact or a wave of immigrants from overseas. Any of these is apt to be felt as a threat to their "whole way of life."

It is important to realize that a devout anti cannot be dissuaded by facts.

The National Health Federation's Cancer Scare

The most active anti in American today is John Yiamouyiannis, Ph.D. A biochemist by background, he was hired as NHF "Science Director" in June 1974 for the purpose of opposing fluoridation (see letter on next page). Since that time, he has written several reports and has traveled around the country to give speeches, testify at hearings and meet with legislators. NHF attributes the defeat of the Los Angeles referendum and many others to his vigorous leadership. In March 1980, he left NHF and set up an antifluoridation organization of his own.

Yiamouyiannis is often accompanied by Dean Burk, Ph.D., another biochemist. Burk is a retired employee of the National Cancer Institute, the highly respected branch of the U.S. Public Health Service which evaluates proposed cancer treatments to see if they work. But in recent years, Burk has been a major promoter of the worthless cancer remedy, laetrile.

Yiamouyiannis and Burk claim that fluoridation causes cancer. But their claim is based upon a *misinterpretation* of certain govern-

The National Health Federation

212 WEST FOOTHILL BOULEVARD   POST OFFICE BOX 688

MONROVIA, CALIFORNIA 91016

358-1155

November 1, 1974

Dear Friends,

FLUORIDATION IS LISTED AS OUR NO. 2 PRIORITY. Our
intentions have been handicapped by limited funds
and staff.

However, for several months plans have been in preparation for mounting an effective national campaign
which could break the back of promoters' efforts to
fluoridate more American cities.

We can reverse the trend!

On June 1st DR. JOHN YIAMOUYIANNIS was hired by the
Federation to head such an effort. Our close association with him in the intervening weeks convinces us
that he is the right man for the job. He is a totally
dedicated scientist with impressive credits and a fighting heart.

Since this program represents a commitment not budgeted,
it must be sustained through additional gifts. It must
not draw upon funds being used for programs already
under way. We now have the staff to do the job, and with
adequate funding we can mount an all out effort to achieve
our goals.

We promise to fight until victory is won. Will you help
to make this effort a winning one? Your generous contribution at this time can insure the success of another
vital NHF program.

Sincerely,

Charles I. Crecelius

Charles I. Crecelius, President

CIC:hy

A NON-PROFIT HEALTH RIGHTS CORPORATION

8

ment statistics. In true anti fashion, they compared cancer death rates in fluoridated and non-fluoridated cities. But they failed to consider various factors in each city (such as industrial pollution) which are known to raise the cancer death rate. When the National Cancer Institute did a *genuine* comparative study, it found *no* link between fluoridation and cancer. Undaunted, Yiamouyiannis and Burk charged NCI with a "cover-up." They were joined in this hoax by Congressman James Delaney, who is an anti of long standing.

Curiously, the National Health Federation has itself been concealing information about fluoridation. In 1972, NHF granted $16,000 for a study to the Center for Science in the Public Interest, a group founded by former associates of Ralph Nader. While it was under way, NHF proudly announced that the study would "put the fluoride controversy into proper perspective." When the study came out *favorable* to fluoridation, however, NHF suddenly became silent about it.

Don't Be Misled

As a public health measure, fluoridation is unusual in several ways. It is a copy of a naturally occurring phenomenon. It is supported by libraries full of articles which document its safety and effectiveness—more so than any other public health measure. It is supported by a variety of health, scientific and other civic groups which could hardly be expected to agree on any other single measure. But most significant, it is the only health measure which is often put to public vote.

If you live in a community with fluoridated water, consider yourself lucky. If you do not, don't let the poisonmongers scare you. Fluoridation is a modern health miracle.

Reprinted from *The Health Robbers* (1980). Published by the George F. Stickley Co., 210 W. Washington Square, Phila., Pa. 19106.

THE UNHEALTHY ALLIANCE

Promoters, fighting for the right to cheat.
Victims, fighting for the right to be cheated.

BY

STEPHEN BARRETT, M.D.
Chairman, Board of Directors
Lehigh Valley Committee Against Health Fraud, Inc.

From 1972 through 1976, Congress received more than a million letters urging it to *weaken* consumer protection in the field of health. Responding to this pressure, most Congressmen became sponsors of legislation which would do exactly that. This strange situation was the result of an intense campaign led by an organization called the National Health Federation (NHF).

Millions of Americans waste large amounts of money on vitamins, minerals and other "food supplements" which they do not need. Some buyers fear that the American food supply cannot give them enough nourishment. Others hope that nutritional gimmicks are the key to superior health. In 1972, after ten years of study, the U.S. Food and Drug Administration (FDA) proposed a number of marketing rules to combat this public confusion. Under these rules, many misleading tactics commonly used by "health food" marketers would have been forbidden.

NHF responded immediately with an all-out campaign to weaken the FDA. Lawsuits were filed to block the new FDA rules and Congress was urged to lessen FDA jurisdiction over food supplements and the claims which help to sell them.

NHF's Leaders

The reason for NHF involvement in this is-sue is suggested by the backgrounds of its leaders. Many of them write or publish books and other materials which support unscientific health theories and practices. Many sell questionable "health" products and some have even been convicted of crimes while engaged in this kind of activity.

• Fred J. Hart, NHF's founder, was for many years the president of the Electronic Medical Foundation. In 1954, Hart and the Electronic Medical Foundation were ordered by a U.S. District Court to stop distributing 13 electrical devices with false claims that they could diagnose and treat hundreds of diseases and conditions. In 1962, Hart was fined by the court for violating this order. Hart died in 1975.

• Royal S. Lee, a non-practicing dentist who died in 1967, helped Hart found NHF and served on its board of governors. In 1962, he and the vitamin company which he owned were convicted of misbranding 115 special dietary products by making false label claims for the treatment of more than 500 diseases and conditions. Lee received a one-year suspended prison term and his company was fined $7,000.

• Andrew G. Rosenberger, a "nature" food store operator, has been listed as NHF "nutrition chairman" and has been a featured speaker at NHF conventions. In 1962, he and his brother Henry were fined $5,000 each and were given six-month suspended prison sentences for misbranding dietary products. Their corporation, Nature Food Centers, was fined $10,000.

• Kurt W. Donsbach, chairman of NHF's board of governors, is a chiropractor and naturopath by background. In 1970, while Donsbach operated a "health food" store, agents of the Fraud Division of the California Bureau of Food and Drug observed him represent that vitamins, minerals and herbal tea would control cancer, cure emphysema and the like. Charged with nine counts of such illegal activity, Donsbach pleaded guilty to practicing medicine without a license and agreed to cease "nutritional consultation." Most of the products which Donsbach was prescribing to his "patients" were packaged by a company which he operated. After selling that company in 1973, he became president of Metabolic Products, a company specializing in "orthomolecular concepts," which he sold in 1975. According to literature from Metabolic Products, its garlic extract could "prevent cellular deterioration," its alfalfa product had "anti-toxin properties" which could help to overcome "-itis" diseases, and so on. RichLife, Inc., of Anaheim, California, currently sells *Dr. Donsbach's Pak Vitamins,* 17 different "specialized formulas" to "help make your life less complicated, more healthy." Among the products are an *Arth Pak,* an *Athletic Pak,* a *Dynamite Pak,* a *Health and Beauty Pak* and a *Stress Formula Pak.*

• Victor Earl Irons, vice-chairman of NHF's board of governors, received a one-year prison sentence in 1957 for misbranding "Vit-Ra-Tox," a vitamin mixture sold door-to-door. According to a 1978 brochure from V. E. Irons, Inc., "The *most important* procedure toward regaining Your Health is the COMPLETE and THOROUGH cleansing of the colon." The products necessary for its "Vit-Ra-Tox Seven Day Cleansing Program" can be purchased for $65.50.

• Roy F. Paxton, while serving as an NHF governor in 1963, was sentenced to three years in prison for misbranding "Millrue" as effective in treating cancer, arthritis and other serious diseases. One way Millrue was sold was by mail through ads in an NHF publication.

• Clinton Miller, NHF executive vice-president and lobbyist, had a quantity of "dried Swiss whey" seized from his Utah wheat shop in 1962. The FDA charged that the product was misbranded as effective in treating intestinal disorders. The whey was returned when Miller agreed to change its labeling. In 1976, Miller was an unsuccessful candidate for the United States Senate.

• Paul J. Virgin, NHF treasurer, is public relations director of the Alta Dena Dairy, a producer of raw (unpasteurized) milk. This dairy has been implicated several times as a source of salmonella infection in raw milk consumers in California.

• Bruce Helvie, an NHF governor, had vitamin and mineral products seized by the FDA because they were marketed with false and misleading claims for treatment of more than 25 diseases and conditions. The seized products were destroyed by consent decree in 1960.

• Bob Hoffman, another NHF governor, owns a publishing firm and sells "health" products through his company, York Barbell Co. In 1960, the company was charged with misbranding its "Energol Germ Oil Concentrate" because literature which accompanied the oil claimed falsely that it could prevent or treat more than 120 diseases and conditions, including epilepsy, gallstones and arthritis. The material was destroyed by consent decree. In 1961, fifteen other York Barbell products were seized as misbranded. In 1968, a larger number of products came under attack by the government for similar reasons. In the consent decree which settled the 1968 case, Hoffman and York Barbell agreed to stop a long list of unproven health claims for their products. In 1972, the FDA seized a shipment of three types of York Barbell protein supplements, charging that they were misbranded with false and misleading body-building claims. A few months later, the seized products were destroyed under a default decree. In 1974, the company was again charged with misbranding Energol Wheat Germ Oil Concentrate and protein supplements. The wheat germ oil had been claimed to be of special dietary value as a source of vigor and energy. A variety of body-building claims had been made for the protein supplements. The seized products were destroyed under a consent decree.

• H. Ray Evers, M.D., another NHF governor, is a major promoter of "chemo-endartectomy therapy" (also called chelation therapy) for a wide range of chronic diseases. He claims to have treated more than 15,000 patients since 1964. In 1976, at the FDA's request, a Louisiana federal judge prohibited Evers from using chelation therapy in Louisiana; but two years later, an Alabama judge allowed him to continue its use in Alabama. In 1979, Evers moved his practice to the Bahamas. According to the January 1980 *NHF Bulletin,* he left because he was "tired of FDA harassment," he faced million-dollar lawsuits by survivors of two of his patients who died, and he was unable to obtain insurance coverage as a result of these various legal actions. Weekly rates at his 80-bed clinic range from $1,750 to $2,250 for noncancer patients and from $2,250 to $2,750 for cancer patients!

• Emory Thurston, another NHF governor, has been an active promoter of laetrile, a worthless cancer "remedy." Pro-laetrile pamphlets edited by him were displayed at his booth at an NHF convention at Anaheim, California, in 1973. When approached by an agent of the California Bureau of Food and Drug, who told him she had cancer of the uterus, Thurston said he could supply her with laetrile. He instructed the agent to contact him at his office at the Institute for Nutritional Research in Hollywood. She did. During their next meeting, Thurston sold laetrile to the agent—*and advised her not to have surgery!* After additional evidence against Thurston was gathered, he was convicted, fined $500 and placed on probation for two years.

• James R. Privitera, M.D., another NHF governor, was convicted in 1975 and sentenced to six months in jail for conspiring to prescribe and distribute laetrile.

Others who now serve, or who have recently served, on the 27-person NHF Board of Governors include:

• Harald J. Taub, who was editor of *Let's Live* and *Prevention.* Both of these magazines strongly promote the use of food supplements.

• Norman W. Bassett, publisher of *Let's Live.*

• David Ajay, president of the National Nutritional Foods Association (NNFA), a trade association representing some 2,000 "health food" retailers, distributors and producers. In 1978, Ajay announced "Operation Counterattack," a series of lawsuits against "detractors of our industry who have been calling us ripoffs."

• Max Huberman, past-president of NNFA.

• John Hemauer, past-president of the California Chiropractic Association.

• John W. Noble, past-president of the National Association of Naturopathic Physicians, who died in 1976.

• L. P. DeWolf, who, according to NHF, has had "40 years of experience in the organic produce field."

• Andrew McNaughton, a leading promoter of laetrile.

• Ida Honorof, publisher of *"A Report to the Consumer,"* a newsletter which deals with health topics.

• Bernard Jensen, D.C., a leading exponent of iridology, a system of diagnosis based upon examination of the iris of the eye.

• Robert S. Mendelsohn, M.D., author of the syndicated newspaper column, *The People's Doctor.* Although he has been chairman of the Illinois state licensing board, Dr. Mendelsohn considers himself a "medical heretic." He believes that "Modern Medicine's treatments for disease are seldom effective, and they're often more dangerous than the diseases they're designed to treat"; that "around ninety percent of surgery is a waste of time, energy, money, and life"; and that most hospitals are so loosely run that "*murder* is even a clear and present danger."

• Betty Lee Morales, president of the Cancer Control Society, a group which promotes unproven cancer "remedies." She is also a publisher and a co-owner of Eden Ranch, a firm which sells *Betty Lee Morales Signature Brand* food supplements. Promotional material from Eden Ranch suggests that Americans who do not use food supplements run a significant risk of developing deficiency diseases. Among its many supplement products are *Lipotropic Plus,* to relieve "liver stress" and *Nia-Flex,* to relieve stiff joints.

Nutritional Consultation

In 1976, the Lehigh Valley Committee Against Health Fraud answered an ad in *Let's Live* magazine which offered information from Eden Ranch about its food supplements. The reply contained a two-page health questionnaire which we returned, indicating that the writer, "age 61," was in good health except that:

For several years I have had (on and off) pain and swelling in the joints of my fingers and toes. During the past few months, I have had attacks of blurred vision. Sometimes my eyes ache and I see halos around lights at night. Your suggestions would be most welcome.

The arthritis symptoms, while not specific, were compatible with a diagnosis of gout (the one form of arthritis that can sometimes benefit from a dietary program). The eye symptoms were taken from a textbook description of glaucoma, a condition that could soon lead to blindness if not treated.

Mrs. Morales' reply contained a disclaimer that her advice was for:

public education...and to assist individuals to cooperate with the doctors of their choice in building better health.. .In the event that the information is used without the supervision or approval of a doctor, that is prescribing for yourself, which is your constitutional right, but we assume no responsibility.

Her "highly personalized nutrition program" consisted of "detoxification" with a special diet and enemas, plus 15 different food supplements which could be purchased from Eden Ranch or health food stores. Based on an enclosed price list, the supplements would cost more than $40 per month. They were of no medically-recognized benefit for either arthritis or visual difficulty. *There was no apparent recognition by Mrs. Morales that the eye symptoms might be serious or require urgent medical attention.*

In 1978, NHF persuaded the California legislature to pass a law that allows any person to give nutritional advice so long as no attempt is made to diagnose, prevent or treat any disease.

Kurt Donsbach, chairman of NHF's board of governors, is also president of Donsbach University, an unaccredited school which offers "qualified students an opportunity to complete the specific requirements of the University in a substantially shortened time frame of study, with no classroom or mandatory attendance required." Tuition is $1,295 for a bachelor of science degree, $1,395 for a master's degree and $1,895 for a Ph.D., but the three degrees can be obtained in a combination program for only $3,040. Credit toward a degree is given for "life experiences" such as working in a health food store, selling food supplements, or reading approved books. The school catalogue is a four-page flyer. An iridology course costs $1,495.

Textbooks required for the "basic curriculum" include books written for the general public by Donsbach, Carlton Fredericks, Gary Null, Emanuel Cheraskin, Roger Williams, Robert Atkins (of dietary fame) and Carl Pfeiffer (promoter of megavitamins for severe mental problems). The on-campus faculty has seven members, including Donsbach, Ray Yancy (an iridologist) and Alan H. Nittler, M.D. (who, according to NHF, "lost his medical license in 1975 because he utilized nutritional therapies"). The school's advisory board has 15 members, including Mrs. Morales, Bruce Halstead, M.D. (promoter of chelation therapy), and Richard Passwater (major proponent of "vitamin B-15").

In 1979, Donsbach began publishing the *Journal of the International Academy of Nutritional Consultants,* with Dr. Nittler as its editor. The first issue had a press run of about 25,000 copies, most of which were sent free-of-charge to chiropractors. The second issue explained that Academy members could be listed in a directory, that the Academy "will in no way encourage or tolerate the practice of medicine under the guise of nutritional consultation," and would establish a legal fund to "protect our members from undue and unfair harassment by bureaucracies or agencies..."

How NHF Is Organized

The National Health Federation is a membership organization with headquarters in Monrovia, California, and a legislative office in Washington, D.C. Its members pay from $12 per year for "regular" membership to a total sum of $1,000 or more for "perpetual" membership. Many of the larger donors have financial interests in the matters promoted by NHF.

Because of the extent of its political activities, NHF could not qualify as a charitable organization so that contributions to it would be deductible for federal income tax purposes. However, NHF advertisements and letters of welcome to new members have stated otherwise. In 1972, responding to a complaint from the Lehigh Valley Committee Against Health Fraud, Inc., the Internal Revenue Service ordered NHF to stop misrepresenting its tax status.

NHF members receive a monthly 32-page *Bulletin* and occasional brief mailings. They are also invited to frequent conventions, most of which take place in the Western part of the U.S. Visitors to such meetings have noted that most of their participants are persons of middle-age or older who are preoccupied with their health. Many exhibit a rigidly suspicious outlook, fearing that government is thoroughly failing to protect them from "poisons" in their food and from exploitation by medical and drug industries. In November 1974, during a brief visit to an NHF convention in New York City, I noted that at least five of its 34 exhibitors were making misleading sales claims for their products. Most blatant was the claim that a sea-water concentrate would prevent cancer.

According to the *National Health Federation Handbook,* available for ten cents, any two members can start a local chapter by adopting the NHF constitution and bylaws, naming temporary officers and receiving clearance from NHF headquarters. The *Handbook* envisions a pyramidal national structure with local groups selecting a county board of directors, county boards selecting a state board of governors and state boards selecting one delegate each to join 27 at-large governors at the national level. This structure is mainly hypothetical, however, since the number of active chapters has generally been fewer than 100. National membership, estimated from *Bulletin* circulation figures, has averaged about 21,000 during the past five years. During the same period, NHF's annual budget rose from $345,000 to $914,660.

NHF's Philosophy

Since its formation in 1955, the steadfast purpose of NHF has been to promote what it calls "freedom of choice" by health consumers. As stated in each issue of its monthly *Bulletin:*

NHF opposes monopoly and compulsion in things related to health where the safety and welfare of others are not concerned. NHF does not oppose nor approve any specific healing profession or their methods, but it does oppose the efforts of any one group to restrict the freedom of practice of qualified members of another profession, thus attempting to create a monopoly.

At first glance, this credo may seem harmless and somehow related to opposing unfair business competition. What NHF really means, however, is that scientific methods of treatment should not be allowed to drive quackery out of the marketplace. Under this philosophy, anyone who has a product or a "treatment" which he claims can help sick people should be allowed to sell it. Proof that a particular method works should not be required. People should be free to decide for themselves which health care measures they will use. Unless a method causes immediate death or serious injury, our government should not interfere.

Put in its simplest terms, what the National Health Federation wants is for quackery to be made legal.

The Scope of NHF Activity

NHF's publications and convention programs make it clear that NHF promotes the gamut of questionable health methods and has little interest in medically acceptable types of treatment.

Nutritional fads, myths and gimmicks are given favorable mention by NHF *Bulletin* articles, by convention speakers and special mailings and by pamphlets available at conventions and by mail. Worthless cancer treatments, particularly laetrile, are promoted in the same ways. *Bulletin* articles look with disfavor upon such proven health measures as pasteurization of milk, smallpox vaccination, polio vaccination and fluoridation of water. Use of nutritional supplements is encouraged by claims that our food processing depletes its nutrients. Use of "natural" products is encouraged by exaggerated claims that our food supply is "poisoned." Chiropractic is regarded favorably. Books which promote questionable health concepts are reviewed favorably in the *Bulletin*. Underlying all these messages is the idea that anyone who opposes NHF ideas is part of a "conspiracy" of government, organized medicine and big business against the little consumer.

NHF files many lawsuits against government agencies and joins in the defense of people accused of frauds in the sale of questionable "health" products. It also has an active legislative program with a Washington-based lobbyist.

NHF was active in support of chiropractic inclusion under Medicare and in opposition to federal subsidies to communities who want fluoridation. To bolster the influence of its lobbyist, the *Bulletin* and special mailings include form letters and instructions to write to Congressmen and Federal officials in support of NHF positions. Letter-writing requests invariably contain misinformation about the issues and contain underlying themes of persecution, discrimination and conspiracy. For example, to arouse support for the anti-FDA vitamin bill, NHF suggested that FDA regulations would drive up prices, "take away our vitamins" and even make it illegal to manufacture most of the supplements now available.

Crying, "Fight for your freedom to take vitamins!" NHF organized its members and allies into unprecedented political activity. Article after article urging support of the anti-FDA bill appeared in the NHF *Bulletin*, in *Prevention* magazine and other health food industry publications, and in chiropractic journals. Letter-writing kits were distributed by chiropractors, health food stores and in special NHF mailings. At a Congressional hearing held on this issue, several Congressmen reported that they received more mail about vitamins than about Watergate! As the mail piled up, most Congressmen lost sight of why it was coming—that their constituents had been confused and frightened by health food industry propaganda. In 1976, a modified form of NHF's anti-FDA bill was passed by Congress.

In 1973, a New Jersey-based group called Citizens for Truth in Nutrition (CTN) was formed. Although apparently independent from NHF, it was led by many NHF activists. Its major activities included anti-FDA meetings, media appearances and anti-FDA lawsuits. Like NHF, CTN's promotional literature claimed falsely that its contributions were tax-deductible until it was ordered to stop these claims by the Internal Revenue Service.

Promotion of Laetrile

In February 1978, NHF began publishing *Public Scrutiny,* a monthly 16-24-page newspaper whose primary focus is on laetrile and "metabolic therapy." The majority of its staff are prominent promoters of Laetrile and three of its advisors have been convicted of Laetrile-related crimes.

Because laetrile lacks FDA approval as a safe and effective drug, it is illegal to transport it across state lines. However, cancer patients who are certified by their physicians as "terminal" may legally import a six-month supply for personal use. Each issue of *Public Scrutiny* contains a full-page ad from the Laetrile Information Center, a company near the Mexican border which will arrange for legal importation. Mexican clinics and other sellers of laetrile also advertise regularly in *Public Scrutiny*.

NHF's library is organized as a separate corporation. Contributions to it, which were tax-deductible, have been used to purchase transcripts of court cases and to support research favorable to laetrile. Early in 1978, NHF used Richard A. Viguerie to send its members a fundraising letter and poll. (Viguerie is the fundraising expert who specializes in computerized mailings for right-wing organizations.) The letter announced that "the NHF Memorial Library has just decided to make the legalization of laetrile its No. 1 priority" and would "conduct a major effort to mobilize Congressional support against the outrageous ban on laetrile." Regarding the poll, the letter promised:

Your responses along with the responses of other selected members of the community will be tabulated and released to the national press, the United States Senate Health Subcommittee and each of your senators and congressmen.

Public Scrutiny published the results of the poll in an article headlined "Americans Want Freedom of Choice." Over 90 percent of those who returned their voting cards favored NHF's position on each of the four laetrile-related questions. Hardly surprising, since only NHF members voted.

After the Lehigh Valley Committee Against Health Fraud reported the nature of Viguerie's mailing on behalf of the NHF library, the Internal Revenue Service revoked the library's tax-deductible status. (An organization whose primary activity is political action cannot have tax-deductible status for its contributions.) A 1979 Viguerie solicitation, which claimed (falsely) that gifts to NHF itself are tax-deductible, apparently stimulated more legal troubles for NHF. According to the May/June 1980 newsletter of NHF governor Ida Honorof, this mailing involved illegal use of a bulk mailing permit. The newsletter also reported that NHF received letters from the attorneys general of four states, "threatening litigation because NHF had never filed as a fund-raising organization as required by those state laws."

For many years, NHF has lobbied for legislation to enable "harmless" drugs to be marketed before they are proven effective. Recently a new type of bill was introduced by *Public Scrutiny*'s legislative advisor, physician-Congressman Larry McDonald (D-Ga.). A suit by survivors of a patient he treated with laetrile was settled in 1979 for $30,000. McDonald's bill would specifically exempt laetrile from FDA jurisdiction. After its introduction, NHF sent members another computerized fund-raiser containing petitions to Congress.

NHF furnishes support to many people involved in laetrile court cases. Appeals in *Public Scrutiny* have raised more than $5,000 to help NHF governor James Privitera, and NHF gave $5,000 toward the legal expenses of the parents of Chad Green, a 3-year-old boy with leukemia. Chad attracted nationwide attention when his family moved to Mexico in order to defy a Massachusetts court's order that the boy receive orthodox therapy. Chad's progress was closely followed by *Public Scrutiny*. Two pages in the October 1979 issue described how Chad was thriving, how his father was studying for a career as a "nutrition consultant" at the Mexican clinic where Chad was being treated with laetrile, and how Chad's mother had stopped his chemotherapy without telling the clinic doctor. A few days after the newspaper was distributed, the boy died.

NHF's Fight Against Fluoridation

Scientists know that if children get the proper amount of fluoride in their diet, they will get a lot fewer cavities in their teeth. Adjusting community drinking water to about one part fluoride to one million parts water is a safe and simple way to accomplish this. Although NHF's leaders claim to be interested in preventing disease by "proper" nutrition, they fight hard against water fluoridation.

Over the years, NHF has assembled a great many "documents" which it claims are "proof" that fluoridation is dangerous (which it is not). Close examination of these documents, however, shows that they contain reports of poorly designed "experiments," twisted accounts of actual events, statements by respected scientists taken out of context to change their meaning, misinterpreted statistics and other forms of faulty reasoning. Given enough publicity, however, these

items can convince many communities that fluoridation is too risky. Many innocent American children have NHF to thank for their toothaches.

In January 1972, NHF granted $16,000 for a fluoridation study to the Center for Science in the Public Interest (CSPI), a group led by former associates of Ralph Nader. To help raise this money, a special mailing was sent to NHF members:

SPECIAL URGENT APPEAL = NHF is proud to announce that it has undertaken to underwrite $16,000.00 in costs for the CLINICALLY controlled investigation of the long-term effects of fluorides in the human. This test is being conducted by FRIENDS of indisputable, scientific reputation. With this information we will be armed with unassailable, up-to-date, scientific data to help defeat fluoridation! There is NO such study available in the world at this time and the costs are amazingly low. The Executive Committee committed us to this obligation in emergency session...

When CSPI learned about this fund-raising message, it protested, stating that its study would be a scientific review of available knowledge and that the outcome was certainly not fixed against fluoridation. NHF apologized, claiming that the fund-raiser had been mailed "without being cleared by appropriate officials" and contained "serious errors" about the nature of the study.

In August 1972, a preliminary draft of the CSPI study was released to activists on both sides of the fluoridation controversy. This was done so that its author could get suggestions and criticisms from knowledgeable individuals before he wrote his final report. The final report was issued at about the same time as the December 1972 NHF *Bulletin* went to press stating:

A good many months ago, NHF voted a grant to the Center for Science in the Public Interest to underwrite an unbiased study of total fluoride consumption and its influence on health. This was done on the anticipation that such a study, never before undertaken by a scientific body, would put the fluoride controversy into proper perspective. That study is nearing its completion. Two preliminary, interim reports have been issued. It begins to appear as if most of the contentions of NHF on this question will be validated in this unbiased study.

CSPI's final report, however, did not "validate most of NHF's contentions." Rather, it concluded that "...the known benefits of fluoridation far outweigh any risks which may be involved."

The favorable outcome of this study was never reported to NHF members. In private communications, however, NHF claimed first that the study "was never completed" and later it was unacceptable because its author ignored too much anti-fluoridation "evidence." A Rodale Press editor suggested that the author had been "intimidated" or "bought off."

Thus, having invested $16,000 in an "unbiased" study by "FRIENDS of indisputable, scientific reputation," NHF ignored its conclusions.

During 1974, NHF announced that opposing fluoridation would be its number two priority and that a biochemist named John Yiamouyiannis had been hired to "break the back" of fluoridation promotion. Yiamouyiannis soon began issuing reports based on misinterpreted government statistics, claiming that fluoridation causes cancer. In 1978, after an article in *Consumer Reports* criticized his work severely, he filed suit for libel—but the suit was dismissed a few months later by a federal court judge.

The Unique Alliance

NHF thus stands revealed. Its policies disregard medical science and proven public health measures. Its leaders promote questionable "health" methods, often at personal profit. Its followers, although confused about the issues in which they involve themselves, are active in the arena of politics.

NHF is well-organized and working hard. Its leaders probably hold sincere beliefs in their health methods. Its followers sincerely believe they can improve their health by following the methods of their leaders.

Sincere or not, however, NHF may be dangerous to your health!

Reprinted from *The Health Robbers* (1980). Published by George F. Stickley Co., 210 W. Washington Square, Phila., Pa. 19106.

A REPORT ON FLUORIDATION

The simple truth is that there's no scientific "controversy" over the safety of fluoridation. The practice is safe, economical, and beneficial. The survival of this fake controversy is one of the major triumphs of quackery over science in our generation.

BY

CONSUMERS UNION
Publisher of Consumer Reports

"There are three kinds of lies," remarked 19th-century British statesman Benjamin Disraeli, "Lies, damned lies, and statistics." Probably every type of misrepresentation known to Disraeli, and some he may have overlooked, have been used to attack fluoridation. Misleading information about it appears regularly in a paper called the National Fluoridation News, and the entire gamut of hokum has been published in a 176-page issue of the Cancer Control Journal, a pro-Laetrile magazine based in Los Angeles. This factual report, reprinted from the July and August, 1978, issues of CONSUMER REPORTS, responds to the lies and false claims that have been made in the attack on fluoridation.

On the evening of February 10, 1976, millions of Dutch television viewers were watching their sets with more than customary attention. News of a bribery scandal in the United States had just reached Europe, along with rumors that Prince Bernard of Holland was implicated. Those who tuned in were unaware, however, that an unrelated interview later in the newscast would soon affect many of them more directly than the scandal.

The interview involved Dean Burk, Ph.D., an American biochemist formerly with the National Cancer Institute, the Federal agency that conducts or sponsors much of the cancer research in the U.S. Dr. Burk's message was a troubling one. Adding fluoride to drinking water as a dental health measure, he asserted, was causing thousands of cancer deaths annually in the U.S. He claimed that statistical studies done by himself and another biochemist, John Yiamouyiannis, Ph.D., showed a link between fluoridation and cancer. Dr. Burk expressed no reservations about his conclusion. "Fluoridation," he told the audience, "is a form of public mass murder."

Copies of the Burk-Yiamouyiannis report had been circulated to members of the Dutch Parliament before the TV appearance. Soon after, a proposal by the Minister of Health to fluoridate all drinking-water supplies in Holland died in Parliament. By September 1976, a Royal Decree ended fluoridation in Rotterdam and other Dutch cities that had been treating their water for years.

A GROWING SENSE OF ALARM

What happened in Holland is not an isolated incident. Despite widespread endorsement of fluoridation by medical, dental, and public health officials, the practice has come under increasing attack both in the United States and abroad as a potential cause of cancer and other diseases. Three years ago, after a publicity campaign linking fluoride to cancer, Los Angeles voters defeated an ordinance to fluoridate the city's water supply. Since 1973, voters in hundreds of smaller U.S. cities and towns have taken similar action, often out of fear of cancer or other disorders attributed to fluoridation.

How valid are those fears? Is there a genuine scientific controversy surrounding the safety of fluoridation? According to Representative James J. Delaney (D., N.Y.), chairman of the powerful House Rules Committee, the answer is an emphatic "yes." A long-time opponent of fluoridation, Delaney has urged Congress to halt the practice, pending further investigation of its safety. Last fall, a subcommittee of the House's Committee on Government Operations held hearings on the issue. Drs. Burk and Yiamouyiannis testified, as did representatives of the American Dental Association, the National Cancer Institute, and authorities on fluoride research. An extensive array of scientific studies and expert commentaries on fluoridation was also presented.

What emerged from the testimony, in CU's opinion, was an unmistakable sense that millions of Americans are being grossly misled about an issue important to both their health and the cost of their dental bills. Water fluoridation is the only public-health measure that many Americans vote on directly. Yet last fall's hearings received only scant coverage by the press, except in publications that commonly run anti-fluoridation series. Accordingly, in this report we will tell you the facts about fluoridation—what it is, how it developed, and what it does. We will also examine the claims about fluoridation and cancer and consider the people behind those claims. Then we'll take a look at other charges frequently leveled at fluoridation, including claims about allergies, birth defects, and heart disease.

ON THE TRAIL OF COLORADO STAIN

Fluorides are compounds containing the element fluorine. In its various forms, fluoride is found in practically all soils, plants, and animals, as well as in human blood, bones, and teeth. It's also present in at least trace amounts in all natural water supplies. The concentration in water varies widely, however. In the U.S., natural fluoride levels range from a high of about 8 parts per million (ppm) in areas of the Southwest to as little as 0.05 ppm in the Northeast.

Fluoridation is simply an adjustment of the natural fluoride content to about 1 ppm—a level of intake that strengthens tooth enamel and sharply reduces dental decay, especially among those exposed to fluoridated water from early childhood. The nominal 1-ppm level (actually 0.7 to 1.2 ppm, according to local conditions) isn't an arbitrary one. Its selection involved a scientific detective story complete with a twist ending.

The initial clue was uncovered early in the century by two scientists investigating a cosmetic defect. F.S. McKay and G.V. Black were trying to find out what caused a mottling of the tooth enamel, a discoloration variously known as "Colorado brown stain" and "Texas teeth." By 1916 they had narrowed the search to something in domestic water supplies. The next step was to identify the substance and get it out of the water. It took until 1931, however, before the substance was identified as fluoride.

Meanwhile, McKay had noticed something else. A practicing dentist, he observed that patients with mottled teeth also had remarkable resistance to tooth decay. The concern of public health officials at the time was still how to get fluoride out of the water. But McKay's observation also spurred further research by the Public Health Service to learn more about fluoride's effect on teeth.

Over the next ten years, research teams led by Dr. H.T. Dean of the Public Health Service studied the dental status of 7257 children in 21 cities having various levels of natural fluoride in their water. The results were unequivocal. The more fluoride in the water, the fewer dental cavities the children experienced. When the water contained approximately 1 ppm or more of fluoride, the children developed about 60 percent fewer cavities than did those who drank water with negligible fluoride content. Furthermore, at the 1-ppm level, the unattractive mottling did not occur. It was associated with levels above 2 ppm. Thus, 1 ppm of fluoride became the benchmark level.

Tooth decay was no minor health problem. During the war year of 1942 some 2,000,000 men were examined as potential members of the armed forces. Almost 10 percent of them were rejected because they didn't have 12 sound teeth in proper position out of a possible 32.

Although the potential dental advantages of fluoridation were obvious, there was a natural reluctance to add a chemical to community water supplies. In the early 1940's, there was no background of scientific data about possible side effects. There were some practical reassurances, though. People had been ingesting fluoride in food and water since the dawn of the human race. Many Southwesterners had been drinking water containing several times the 1-ppm level of fluoride for a lifetime without any discernible side effects except mottled teeth. Eventually, a few cities decided to take the chance.

THE NEWBURGH-KINGSTON EXPERIMENT

Among the pioneers was the New York State Department of Health. Before attempting any widespread introduction of fluoridation, the department proposed a long-term, controlled study of a limited group of children who would be carefully monitored by physicians. After considering various communities, the department chose the cities of Newburgh and Kingston as ideal candidates for the study.

Located some 35 miles apart near the Hudson River, both cities had populations of about 30,000 and were similar in racial, economic, and other demographic characteristics. Each also used reservoirs with water deficient in fluoride.

One city's water supply was to be fluoridated, the other not. Meanwhile, matched groups of children from the two cities were to be followed from infancy onward by means of comprehensive pediatric checkups to detect any side effects from fluoride. Special attention was to be given to growth rates, bone development, blood chemistry, the skin, the thyroid gland, vision, and hearing. Each child would also receive meticulous, regular dental exams.

In March 1944, the City Council of Newburgh agreed to participate in the study and approved the fluoridation of its water to 1 ppm. Kingston agreed to serve as the control city and use its fluoride-deficient water without change. A total of 817 children were enrolled in the Newburgh group and 711 in Kingston. Although most entered at the start of the study, several infants were added during each of the first three years to ensure having some children whose mothers were exposed to fluoridated water throughout pregnancy.

The study went on for 10 years, and a majority of the children in both groups participated through the final examination. The findings can be summarized briefly: The examinations disclosed no differences of medical significance between the two groups that could even remotely be attributed to fluoride. There was one difference of dental significance, however. The Newburgh children experienced nearly 60 percent fewer cavities than the Kingston children.

Numerous studies have since confirmed the benefits of fluoridation. "Fewer cavities" means fewer costly fillings, fewer lost teeth, and, eventually, fewer dentures or partial dentures. The cost of fluoridation to a community, according to a report last year in the New England Journal of Medicine, is only about 10 to 40 cents a year per capita.

THE EVIDENCE FOR SAFETY

Since the early days of the Newburgh-Kingston project, literally thousands of scientific studies have examined the effectiveness and safety of fluoride. Virtually every doubt or question that has been raised, however scanty the evidence, has been studied in depth by one or more groups of researchers. As a dentist representing the American Dental Association noted in the House subcommittee hearings last fall, "Fluoridation may well be the most thoroughly studied community health measure of recent history."

In the late 1960's, the World Health Organization accomplished the Herculean task of pulling much of the known information together. The objective was to provide an impartial review of the scientific literature on fluoridation—a vast international aggregation of population studies, experimental research, animal studies, and clinical investigations, including human autopsy studies, clinical trials, and X-ray research.

The report, "Fluorides and Human Health," came out in 1970. It addressed numerous questions raised up to that time about the possible effects of fluoride on different organs and its alleged association to various diseases. Again, the conclusions can be summarized briefly: The study found no reliable evidence that any ill effects or symptoms resulted from drinking water fluoridated at recommended levels.

Since the report's publication, the World Health Organization has uncovered no evidence to alter its judgment. In a statement issued in 1975, the organization noted: "The only sign of physiological or pathological change in life-long users of optimally fluoridated water supplies...is that they suffer less from tooth decay."

THE LOYAL OPPOSITION

No amount of study, however, has managed to quiet the criticism of fluoride that has been present from the beginning. Writing in the Journal of the American Dental Association in March 1956, the commissioner of New York State's Department of Health, Dr. Herman E. Hilleboe, told of some of the troubles his agency had encountered in the early days of the Newburgh-Kingston project. Soon after the project's approval in March 1944, the local health officer in Newburgh began receiving complaints from some of the town's citizens.

Some protested that the fluoridated water was discoloring their saucepans. Others complained that it was giving them digestive troubles. One woman complained to her dentist that the "fluoride water" had caused her denture to crack. "These incidents all occurred before fluoride was added to the water supply," notes Dr. Hilleboe. The complaints stopped abruptly after a Newburgh newspaper criticized the town's imaginary ills.

Despite fluoridation's success in Newburgh, protests against it elsewhere weren't collapsing so readily a decade later. The rise of "a vociferous minority," said Dr. Hilleboe, had succeeded in delaying, or even reversing, the start-up of fluoridation in several areas. The opposition, he reported, came chiefly from food faddists, cultists, chiropractors, and people who misunderstood what fluoridation was. But the efforts of antifluoridationists have also been aided by the caution of various physicians, dentists, and scientists of good standing who initially questioned the safety of fluoridation. Opposition has also come from other professionals and lay people who view fluoridation as a government infringement of individual freedom.

Various groups have been formed for the sole purpose of fighting fluoridation, but none has had much impact outside of its local community. Generally, the real steam behind the antifluoridation movement has come from well-funded, national, multi-issue organizations that have been able to disseminate large amounts of scare propaganda around the country. One such group is the John Birch Society. Another, up until the early 1970's, was the Rodale Press, publisher of Prevention magazine and a frequent proponent of unproved nutrition concepts. The most active and effective group today, however, is the National Health Federation, whose roots run deep into the soil of medical quackery. Those roots are worth a brief examination.

WHEN ROOSTERS HAD BAD TEETH

In the early 1950's, an organization called the Electronic Medical Foundation ran a lucrative diagnosis-by-mail service and also sold electronic treatment devices for "curing" numerous disorders. An estimated 3000 practitioners, mainly chiropractors, would send dried blood specimens from their patients to the foundation. There, the blood spot would be checked by an electronic gadget and a "diagnosis" mailed back by postcard.

This eventually aroused a certain skepticism at the U.S. Food and Drug Administration. Accordingly, the FDA arranged to send a few blood spots of its own.

The first, from a man who had lost his right leg, elicited a diagnosis of arthritis in the right foot and ankle. The blood of a dead man brought back a diagnosis of colitis, and that of a rooster resulted in a report of sinus infection and bad teeth.

The FDA inspectors also investigated the treatment devices. They found that the gadgets simply contained circuits resembling those of an electric doorbell or a small radio transmitter. None could cure anything, reports FDA historian Wallace Janssen.

In 1954 a U.S. District Court ordered the president of the firm, Fred J. Hart, to stop distributing the treatment devices. Shortly thereafter, Hart founded the National Health Federation. Hart continued to distribute the devices, however, and was subsequently prosecuted for criminal contempt and fined $500 in 1962. Between 1957 and 1963, several other officials of the NHF were convicted of misbranding dietary products with false medical claims and received fines or prison sentences. In 1963, the FDA released a report on the NHF that said in part:

The stated purpose of the federation is to promote "freedom of choice" in health matters. The record shows that what this frequently means is freedom to promote medical nostrums and devices which violate the law. From its inception, the federation has been a front for promoters of unproved remedies, eccentric theories and quackery.

In an updated report on the NHF issued in 1973, the FDA reiterated virtually the same judgment. Throughout its history, the NHF has crusaded against any Government interference with unproven remedies or treatments. At the same time, it has also opposed proven public-health measures—smallpox vaccination, pasteurization of milk, polio vaccination, and fluoridation of drinking-water supplies.

For the most part, the NHF's opposition to public-health measures has been a losing cause. Until recent years, even fluoridation was slowly gaining acceptance in more communities. About 105 million Americans now have fluoridated water. But in 1974 the NHF decided to mount a new national campaign to "break the back" of fluoridation efforts. It hired Dr. Yiamouyiannis to do the job.

RAISING THE SPECTER OF CANCER

The first big target was Los Angeles, whose City Council had voted in September 1974 to fluoridate the water supply. The NHF's ammunition was a study by Dr. Yiamouyiannis that purported to link fluoridation to an increase in cancer deaths. The study and a couple of publicity handouts that accompanied it were eventually reviewed by various public-health officials, including Thomas Mack, M.D., of Los Angeles, an associate professor of community medicine and an expert in cancer epidemiology. (Epidemiology is a branch of medicine that studies the incidence, causes, and control of a disease in specific populations.) The nature of the Yiamouyiannis study is apparent in an excerpt from Dr. Mack's review:

"I cannot begin without commenting on the form of the documents you sent me," Dr. Mack stated. "Despite the gravity of the question addressed, the form of these sheets is that of a propaganda flyer rather than a serious scientific effort. Specifically, there is no indication that any of the material was ever prepared for submission to a reputable scientific journal....All over the documents one finds...conclusions emblazoned essentially in the form of slogans, without cautious interpretation or restrictions. For these reasons, the reader must immediately presume that objectivity has never been considered....At the same time this bias is so pervasive and obvious, the mistaken logic so gross and naive, that the reader assumes the author to be, however competent in his Ph.D. field, totally unaware of the principles of epidemiology."

Most people are unfamiliar with the principles of epidemiology, however, and a Ph.D. degree can sometimes lend credibility even to claptrap. In Los Angeles it evidently did. The scare tactics of the NHF and other antifluoridationists scored a stunning victory over dental health.

Around the beginning of 1975, Dr. Yiamouyiannis also joined forces with Dr. Burk. Like the National Health Federation, Dr. Burk is a leading advocate of the worthless cancer drug Laetrile (CONSUMER REPORTS, August 1977), and he shares the NHF's aversion to fluoridation.

The collaboration produced a study claiming that 25,000 or more excess cancer deaths occur annually in U.S. cities that fluoridate their water. The assertion was based on a comparison of death rates for specific cancers in some counties that were fluoridated compared with some that were not. In July 1975, Representative Delaney entered the study into the Congressional Record and called for "an immediate suspension of all artificial fluoridation."

The National Cancer Institute reviewed the study and was unimpressed. Unlike a proper epidemiological study, it had failed to take into account widely recognized risk factors known to affect the death rate from specific types of cancers. Using the same data, the NCI reanalyzed the study, taking into account such influences as ethnic composition of the population, geographic location, socioeconomic status, and other fundamental risk factors. The purported differences in the cancer death rates promptly disappeared.

Undaunted, Drs. Burk and Yiamouyiannis bounced back with another study. This time they compared overall cancer death rates for

10 large cities that were fluoridated versus 10 large cities that were not. Again, the fluoridated cities came out second best. Over the 20-year period studied, cancer death rates in the fluoridated cities purportedly increased 10 percent more than in the unfluoridated ones. In December 1975, Representative Delaney entered the study into the Congressional Record and demanded that all fluoridation be stopped.

If anything, the new study was even more amateurish than the July entry. In the judgment of one NCI official at the House subcommittee hearings, it represented "the worst piece of work that has been done to date on fluoride." Drs. Burk and Yiamouyiannis had somehow managed to ignore the most fundamental factors involved in cancer mortality rates—age, sex, and race. Old people die from cancer more often than young people; men have a higher cancer death rate than women; and blacks a higher one than whites. Unless those factors are taken into consideration, the results of a cancer-mortality comparison would be meaningless.

When NCI scientists reanalyzed the Burk-Yiamouyiannis data, they found that the difference in the cancer death rate was due entirely to the age and racial makeup of the respective populations. Fluoridation was irrelevant.

ONWARD TO EUROPE

Rebuffed by NCI scientists, Dr. Burk took the National Health Federation studies to Holland and England. As noted earlier, the Dutch trip was a smashing success. But the British refused to panic. Both the Royal College of Physicians and Oxford University had recently completed studies of fluoridation and cancer. The Royal College of Physicians in January 1976 concluded: "There is no evidence that fluoride increases the incidence or mortality of cancer in any organ." The Oxford study reached a similar conclusion.

Moreover, British scientists had learned of the NCI's refutation of the Burk-Yiamouyiannis studies. They also were aware that an independent study conducted for the National Academy of Sciences at the University of Rochester, N.Y., had confirmed the NCI's findings.

"In the normal course of events," reported an Oxford research group, "that would have been the end of the matter. Unfortunately,

however, it has not been." What the British scientists hadn't realized was that the facts were incidental.

The real goal of antifluoridation groups, explains an American Dental Association official, "is to create the illusion of a scientific controversy." The "studies" are merely the ploy. The accuracy of that judgment was evidenced by what happened next. According to an account in The Lancet, a British medical journal, Drs. Burk and Yiamouyiannis began publicizing their cancer claims in Britain. Through the assistance of the National Anti-Fluoridation Campaign, their misleading data were circulated to members of Parliament, health authorities, and water boards as evidence that fluoridation was causing many cancer deaths.

Meanwhile, the National Health Federation began claiming in the U.S. that NCI officials were concealing data, a charge that eventually had an impact in Britain. In Parliament, one member accused British health officials of misleading the public about fluoridation and of denying people the truth "because of the Official Secrets Act."

THE NCI 'COVER-UP'

According to testimony at the House subcommittee hearings, the NCI refused to disclose certain information to the National Health Federation. That refusal, however, was far less sinister than some members of the British Parliament were later led to believe.

The NCI initially gave Dr. Burk a copy of the publication "U.S. Cancer Mortality by County: 1950-1969," which he later used in preparing the first Burk-Yiamouyiannis report. After the NCI reviewed that report, Dr. Yiamouyiannis asked for a copy of the NCI's analyses. Those were also dispatched. Then, according to NCI testimony, Dr. Yiamouyiannis used that information to attack the NCI's review. Consequently, when he requested their analyses of his subsequent study, NCI officials denied the request. They pointed out that the basic sources were routine publications of the Bureau of the Census and the National Center for Health Statistics, and they told him, in effect, to do the calculations himself. "The data," said NCI's Dr. Robert N. Hoover at the hearings, "are generally available to anyone with a public library card."

To check that claim, a CU staff member visited the local public library. All but two of the volumes needed, both from 1950, were on the shelves of a suburban library within walking distance of our offices. A phone call by one of the librarians located the two remaining volumes at another nearby branch.

As a result of the charges and the wide publicity the National Health Federation gained in Britain, Drs. Richard Doll and Leo Kinlen of the Department of Regius Professor of Medicine at Oxford decided to undertake still another study. Their reason, they explained, was "to be sure about the truth of the matter, and because we feared that Burk and Yiamouyiannis's abuse of statistics might be detrimental to the future health of British children." At the same time, the Royal College of Physicians requested a formal opinion of the cancer data from the Council of the Royal Statistical Society in Britain.

The resulting studies appeared respectively in The Lancet and in the Journal of Applied Statistics in 1977. In The Lancet, Drs. Doll and Kinlen reported that none of the evidence "provides any reason to suppose that fluoridation is associated with an increase in cancer mortality, let alone causes it." The study conducted for the Royal Statistical Society, which undertook an even more comprehensive statistical analysis than the NCI or Oxford, came to the same conclusion.

Furthermore, additional studies by the NCI in 1976, the U.S. Center for Disease Control in 1977, and the National Heart, Lung, and Blood Institute in 1977 each found no evidence linking fluoridation and cancer. In short, independent investigations by seven of the leading medical and scientific organizations in the English-speaking world have unanimously refuted the National Health Federation's cancer claims.

Meanwhile, other allegations against fluoride are in wide circulation. Fluoride is said to cause allergic reactions, birth defects, mutations, heart disease, and cancer in animals.

Since such claims are resurrected whenever fluoridation comes up for a vote, we'll discuss the most persistent ones and examine the evidence behind them.

CLAIM: FLUORIDE IS A POISON

Like iron, zinc, and several other minerals, fluorine (in the form of fluoride) is classified by the National Academy of Sciences as an essential trace element in human nutrition. And like many substances essential to life or good health—iron, vitamins A and D, oxygen, and even water itself—fluoride can be toxic in excessive quantities. At high concentrations, fluoride has been used as a poison for insects and rodents. However, at the level in fluoridated water—one part per million (ppm)—you'd have to drink at least several hundred gallons at one sitting to get a lethal dose. The water alone would kill you first.

But what about the possibility of slow poisoning—a little bit at a time over long periods? According to the National Academy of Sciences, the daily intake required to produce symptoms of chronic toxicity after years of consumption is 20 to 80 milligrams or more—far in excess of the average intake in the U.S. Such heavy doses are associated with water supplies that contain at least 10 ppm of natural fluoride, as in some parts of India. There is absolutely no danger of poisoning from imbibing water fluoridated to prevent dental cavities.

An occasional tactic in antifluoridation tracts is to run pictures of cattle or other animals harmed by fluoride poisoning. The photographs are authentic, but the impression conveyed is false. Years ago, steel mills and clay factories in England and Wales sometimes polluted nearby vegetation with tons of fluoride emissions. Similar incidents have also occurred in the U.S. Cattle and other animals that grazed on the vegetation would ingest enormous amounts of fluoride and develop bone fractures and lameness. Their pictures are the ones antifluoridationists use.

In contrast, a controlled experiment with cattle produced far different results. The cattle were fed various amounts of fluoride in their diets for nearly 7½ years. Even at fluoride levels as high as 27 ppm, the cattle did not experience fractures, lameness, or any adverse effects on soft tissues, fertility, or milk production. Nor were there any abnormal effects on their offspring through successive generations.

CLAIM: FLUORIDE CAUSES BIRTH DEFECTS

In the late 1950's, a French physician named Rapaport reported that mongolism occurred more frequently in some cities with fluoridated water than in some cities with little or no fluoride in their water. Experts who reviewed the study found it seriously flawed, however, especially in its method of locating cases. According to Dr. Rapaport's figures, the incidence of mongoloid births in both the fluoridated and unfluoridated cities was less than half the usual rate—a highly questionable finding in itself. Thus, there was a strong likelihood that Dr. Rapaport had failed to uncover the majority of mongoloid births in the cities he chose to study.

That conclusion was soon confirmed by a more carefully controlled study in England. Using more exacting methods of case-finding, the British researchers reported no difference in the incidence of mongolism whether the water was high or low in fluoride.

Since then, two extensive studies have substantiated the British findings. One surveyed virtually all mongoloid births in Massachusetts from 1950 through 1966. The results, published in the New England Journal of Medicine in 1974, showed no link between fluoridation and mongolism. An even larger study published in 1976 covered approximately 1.4 million births in six major U.S. cities. Researchers at the Center for Disease Control investigated not only mongolism, but also cleft palate, heart abnormalities, clubfoot, and other common birth defects. Again, there was no association between fluoride and any of the defects. In short, the antifluoridationists' claim is based solely on the discredited Rapaport study.

CLAIM: FLUORIDE IS MUTAGENIC

A variation on the birth-defects theme is the charge that fluoride is a genetic hazard. Until recently, this claim was based on irrelevant or questionable experiments with fruit flies and plants. Then, in 1976, two researchers in Kansas City, Mo., reported that various levels of fluoride damaged chromosomes in the bone-marrow cells and sperm cells of mice. Although experts who reviewed the experiment noted several inconsistencies in the results, the question it raised was judged important enough to warrant further research.

Accordingly, joint studies were undertaken by the Laboratory of Developmental Biology and Anomalies at the National Institute of Dental Research, the Department of Biochemistry at the University of Minnesota, and the Laboratory of Cellular and Comparative Physiology at the National Institute on Aging. The scientists conducted four separate experiments, including tests on mice receiv-

ing acute doses of fluoride and mice raised for several generations on water containing 50 ppm of fluoride. None of the studies produced any evidence that fluoride damages chromosomes, even at levels 100 times that in fluoridated water supplies.

In Germany, meanwhile, an independent group of researchers reported similar results with human white blood cells, which are especially sensitive to mutagenic agents. Not only did fluoride fail to produce damage, it also evidenced an antimutagenic effect by *protecting* chromosomes against a known mutagen.

CLAIM: FLUORIDE CAUSES ALLERGIC REACTIONS

The charge that people can suffer allergic reactions or "intolerance" to fluoride gained prominence from anecdotal accounts by George L. Waldbott, M.D., an early opponent of fluoridation who founded the National Fluoridation News. Between 1955 and 1965, Dr. Waldbott reported numerous instances of patients experiencing nausea, headaches, "spastic colitis," or various other symptoms that he attributed to fluoride ingestion.

In the World Health Organization study described last month, a review of the Waldbott reports found no reliable evidence to support his contentions. The cases were judged to represent "a variety of unrelated conditions." Following the WHO study, the Public Health Service asked the American Academy of Allergy to evaluate the issue. After a review of the existing clinical reports, the executive committee of the academy concluded unanimously: "There is no evidence of allergy or intolerance to fluorides as used in the fluoridation of community water supplies."

CLAIM: FLUORIDE CAUSES CANCER IN ANIMALS

Possibly the most absurd evidence marshalled against fluoridation is material purporting to show that fluoride induces cancer in animals. One series of studies frequently quoted by antifluoridationists was conducted by researchers in Texas in the 1950's. The first study involved a strain of mice that ordinarily gets cancer. Supposedly, the mice given fluoridated water developed tumors slightly earlier than similar mice on fluoride-free water. There were a few minor hitches in the experiment, however. All the mice were also fed a dog chow that, unknown to the investigator, contained 42 ppm of fluoride—or 10 to 100 times the amount any of the mice got in their water, thus making any comparison between the two groups invalid. A further botching occurred when the investigator miscalculated the amounts of fluoride in the water. Two scientists from the National Institutes of Health reviewed the study in 1951 and dismissed it. Other experiments by the same investigator and a co-worker have long been discredited by subsequent research. Nevertheless, opponents of fluoridation still cite the Texas experiments as significant evidence that fluoride is carcinogenic.

Another study currently getting star billing in antifluoridation tracts is an experiment conducted with fruit flies in 1963. This time, legitimate findings are being substantially distorted. In that study, two strains of fruit flies exposed to 20 to 50 ppm of fluoride in their food experienced an increased incidence of melanotic tumors. Opponents of fluoridation interpret that to mean that fluoride can cause cancer. That's not so, according to scientists working at the National Cancer Institute. While humans may be physiological cousins to the mouse and other mammals, their kinship to the fruit fly is somewhat more distant.

Specifically, a *melanotic* tumor in a fruit fly is not the same as a cancerous tumor in a human or mammal. It is more akin to scar tissue, and, unlike a cancerous tumor, it's not malignant or harmful. It can be induced by a wide range of substances, including some vitamins and even lysine and tryptophan, two amino acids essential for human growth and health. Fruit flies can also get malignant tumors, but there's no evidence that fluoride has ever caused any. Indeed, fluoride has never proved to be carcinogenic in tests on a variety of animals, including rats, mice, guinea pigs, rabbits, hamsters, dogs, and sheep.

CLAIM: FLUORIDE CONTRIBUTES TO HEART DISEASE

In Wisconsin, opponents of fluoridation have often charged that it increases the number of deaths from heart disease. They base their claim on statistics that show a rise in heart deaths in the town of Antigo, Wis., since the introduction of fluoridation there.

The National Heart and Lung Institute has called the data a "misrepresentation of statis-

tics." As one scientist points out, "The well-known fact that deaths from heart disease become more frequent as people grow older was overlooked." Since fluoridation was introduced in Antigo in 1949, the percentage of elderly people there has doubled. Between 1950 and 1970, for example, the segment of the population 75 years old or older increased 106 percent. When that factor is taken into account, the alleged effect of fluoride vanishes.

According to a 1972 study by the National Heart and Lung Institute, comparisons of fluoridated and unfluoridated communities reveal no differences in the rate of heart deaths. Furthermore, reported the institute, evidence from autopsy studies, from examinations of people exposed to acute doses of fluoride in industrial accidents, and from medical data on people who have drunk water naturally high in fluoride for a lifetime "all consistently indicate no adverse effect on cardiovascular health."

Of all the numerous ills that have been attributed to fluoridation—from cancer in humans to constipation in dogs—none has ever been shown to be valid. In fact, the only known hazard of fluoridated water has nothing to do with drinking it. Patients undergoing kidney dialysis can be exposed to about 50 to 100 times the amount of fluid consumed by the average person. Accordingly, the National Institute of Arthritis and Metabolic Disease recommends that fluoride—as well as calcium, magnesium, and copper—be removed from the tap water *before it is used in an artificial kidney machine.* Aside from that precaution, there is no genuine reason to worry about fluoridation.

In 1960, however, the residents of Antigo, Wis., didn't realize that scare stories being circulated by local opponents of fluoridation were false. Antigo voted to discontinue its 11-year practice of fluoridating the water supply. The decision eventually led to a study by public health officials, who wanted to learn what effects the end of fluoridation would have on the dental health of Antigo youngsters.

During 1960, dental personnel from the Wisconsin Division of Health examined nearly all children in the kindergarten, second, fourth, and sixth grades of Antigo's schools. The examiners recorded the number of decayed, missing, or filled teeth for each child. Four years later, they repeated the examination among children in all of the same grades except the sixth.

The kindergarteners in 1964 had a rate of dental problems 92 percent higher than their counterparts four years earlier. Among second-graders, the decay rate in permanent teeth was up 183 percent. Among fourth-graders, it was up 41 percent. A subsequent examination of sixth-graders showed a 91 percent increase in decay rates. In 1965, Antigo voted to reinstate fluoridation.

Despite persisting claims about heart deaths by local antifluoridationists, the people of An-tigo today still drink fluoridated water. Meanwhile, about 100 million Americans do not, largely because of the fears raised by opponents of fluoridation. The simple truth is that there's no "scientific controversy" over the safety of fluoridation. The practice is safe, economical, and beneficial. The survival of this fake controversy represents, in CU's opinion, one of the major triumphs of quackery over science in our generation.

LIBEL SUIT DISMISSED

A Fluoridation Lawsuit:
CU Wins Its Day in Court

In a decision reaffirming the right of the press to speak freely in a public controversy, Judge Richard Owen of the United States District Court for the Southern District of New York has dismissed an $8-million libel suit filed against CU by a prominent opponent of water fluoridation.

The suit was filed last October by John Yiamouyiannis, Ph.D., of the National Health Federation. Dr. Yiamouyiannis charged that he had been defamed by CU's two-part report on fluoridation (CONSUMER REPORTS, July and August 1978). The July report had criticized as baseless and misleading Dr. Yiamouyiannis's claims that fluoridation causes cancer. In its report, CU supported the practice of fluoridation as safe, economical, and beneficial.

In dismissing the suit, Judge Owen stated: "...the suggestion is strong that the plaintiff's object in bringing this action is to use this court to discourage the publication of opposing views."

Dr. Yiamouyiannis contended that CU, in its two-part report, had been guilty of "actual malice," a legal term meaning that the material had been published either with knowledge that it was false or with reckless disregard for whether it was false or not. In opposition, CU filed a motion for a summary judgment dismissing the complaint as meritless.

In support of that motion, CU submitted several affidavits, including extensive documentation of the facts in the report and a description of CU's research and review procedures for the report.

In granting summary judgment in favor of CU and against Dr. Yiamouyiannis, Judge Owen said:

"There is overwhelming evidence in defendant's affidavits, unrebutted by plaintiff, that the articles were prepared in a conscientious and professional manner after a thorough review of reputable sources and standard reference works on medicine and science. No serious question is raised that either the author or the editors who reviewed and approved the articles for publication had the slightest doubt as to their truth and accuracy."

CONSUMER REPORTS
AUGUST 1979

APPEAL DISMISSED

Yiamouyiannis appealed, but on March 19, 1980, the United States Court of Appeals for the Second Circuit upheld the lower court's dismissal of the suit. The three judges who heard the case concluded:

"It is clear that appellee (Consumers Union), through its agents, made a thorough investigation of the facts. Scientific writings and authorities in the field were consulted; authoritative scientific bodies speaking for substantial segments of the medical and scientific community were investigated. The unquestioned methodology of the preparation of the article exemplifies the very highest order of responsible journalism; the entire article was checked and rechecked across a spectrum of knowledge and, where necessary, changes were made in the interests of accuracy."

—Editors' Note

A LEGISLATOR'S VIEW

*If I thought there was one chance in a
million that fluoridation would harm you, I
would vote against it.*

BY
JAMES H. LINCOLN, LL.B.
City Councilman, City of Detroit
December, 1956

This memorandum is in reply to those people who have contacted me concerning the matter of fluoridating Detroit's water supply. One thing is due every citizen and that is the very clear assurance that a public official has carefully studied a problem, and has applied his very best thinking to the matter; this I have done. This is a statement of how I came to favor fluoridation of water.

Prior to becoming a member of the City Council, in November, 1954, I had little knowledge of the subject and no opinion whatsoever as to its merits. All the literature furnished me during the first part of 1955 opposed fluoridation, and I would have voted against it at that time.

For some six months, my study was directed solely to anti-fluoridation literature, which continued to arrive in the mail. I read it. With me reading and research is a habit that began on the farm with the aid of a kerosene lamp, and persisted through and beyond nine and a half years of college.

Conflicting expert testimony is an old story with me. In eleven years as an attorney, over five of which were spent in the Prosecutor's Office or the U.S. District Attorney's Office, I have had considerable experience in dealing with and challenging the statements of doctors, psychologists, psychiatrists, engineers, appraisers, etc. In their respective fields you can find a few experts who can and do testify convincingly and persuasively to what is in fact nonsense, and without the slightest doubt some of these few are sincere as they proceed with perfect logic along to the grand fallacy. No special talent for examining expert testimony is claimed by myself, other than that which may have come through experience. Certainly this experience has made me a skeptic as far as "expert opinion" is concerned—that goes for both sides of every issue.

The very first document ever given to me opposing fluoridation contained what was purported to be an excerpt from a statement issued by the U.S. Public Health Service. It would lead one to believe that the U.S. Public Health Service opposed fluoridation. As a matter of fact, this extremely conservative and cautious agency favors fluoridation. This particular piece of literature also quoted a law case in a manner that would lead one to believe that a particular State's Supreme Court had ruled against fluoridation. A check of the case showed that the good doctor who published the pamphlet was indulging in a somewhat sharp practice, engaged in by some attorneys; i.e., that of quoting a dissenting judge without indicating the ruling of the entire court. This led me to check into the legal question more thoroughly. *Those who oppose fluoridation don't have a legal leg to stand on.* Many states have upheld the practice of fluoridation; none that I find has barred it. People still continue to send me literature belaboring the legal aspect of the problem. If anyone can cite a single State Supreme Court case that has ruled against fluoridation, please send the citation to me.

The fact that something is legal doesn't necessarily make it right. But it is worthwhile noting that those who claim fluoridation can harm some people haven't been able to make their claim stick in court where they can be subjected to cross-examination. There isn't the slightest doubt in my mind that if those who oppose fluoridation were able to make even a plausible case for their claim that fluoridation can harm some people, the state courts would have long ago outlawed the use of it in community water supplies. If the courts viewed it in the nature of an experiment, you can be sure it would have been stopped. This is not enough to convince me. Some things are true even though not plausible. It is within the realm of possibility that the fluoridation of water supplies might do some harm, and the courts still rule fluoridation of water supplies legal. However, the fact that State Supreme Courts have consistently ruled in favor of fluoridation makes 9/10ths of the claims made in the literature opposing fluoridation fantastic. Those who oppose fluoridation seem to be abandoning taking the matter to court. Why? Amid all these assertions, can't some doctor come up with some evidence that will establish even a substantial possibility in the minds of the judges of one State Supreme Court that fluoridation harms people in some way? The answer to this is very clear—they can't.

The fact that some of the assertions by those who opposed fluoridation proved to be without merit did not persuade me to support fluoridation. It is an error to assume that all is false because part is false. I still felt that where there was smoke there must be fire, and I began checking footnotes, and what was supposed to be original sources in numerous publications concerning statements made by those who oppose fluoridation. We are now referring specifically to medical matters. The result was even more revealing than my check of statements concerning legal aspects of the problem. For a time I attempted to obtain reports by myself. Later I developed the habit of asking Dr. Molner, Commissioner of the Department of Health, to dig them up for me. Here is an example of how I went about to check one matter:

There is a report by F. B. Exner, M.D., F.A.C.R., entitled FLUORIDATION OF PUBLIC WATER SUPPLIES, a report prepared for the City of New York. The address is 509 Olive Way, Seattle 1, Washington. Copies are available for $1 each or less if ordered in quantity. Each Councilman must have received at least one copy of this publication. Several copies have been mailed to me by individuals who oppose fluoridation, and a considerable number of others have cited Dr. Exner's work as an authority. This particular publication is enough to scare a man out of ten years' growth. Several Councilmen have mentioned it to me. They were particularly impressed by two pictures, on page 29, of individuals having teeth about as discolored and mottled as a 26-year old horse that we had back on the farm. Dr. Exner claimed that this condition was caused by drinking water with a fluorine content of even less than that advocated by the U.S. Public Health Service. The good doctor states that he had direct evidence. One of the pictures is supposed to be a citizen of Denver, Colorado. In his statements concerning this individual, Dr. Exner made reference to an article printed in a 1933 Colorado Medical Journal. I obtained this article, and its author (Boissevain) does not have any specific example of mottled teeth in Denver, or any picture whatsoever of a Denver citizen. Where Dr. Exner obtained his picture I don't know, but he didn't get it from the article he cited. Dr. Exner's wording is such that the casual reader is led to believe that it was the Boissevain article from which he got the picture, but a careful reading indicates that there is no flat assertion to this effect. Dr. Exner cleverly leads his readers to believe something, but upon thorough investigation he leaves them completely up-in-the-air. If he has any evidence for his assertions, he wouldn't go through all these gymnastics in order to come up with nothing.

The footnote on the first page of Dr. Exner's report is quite revealing. Here is what it says:

"This study was made for the City of New York by request of Mr. Arthur Ford, Commissioner of Water Supply, Gas and Electricity. I want to express my indebtedness to Alderson Fry, LL.B., Jean Ashford, M.A., and Willford MacFadden, B.A., of the University of Washington Health Sciences Library, for invaluable assistance in securing hard-to-get references. Without their help, this work would not have been possible. FRE.''

Now I have checked a number of other of Dr. Exner's assertions and references, and they just plain don't stand-up. The sources and authority which the good doctor cites are unavailable to most people, and would be extremely difficult for me to obtain were I not a member of the Common Council.

Mr. Remus, General Manager of the Detroit Water Supply, used Mr. Ford of New York as his authority for opposing fluoridation. In Mr. Remus' report to the Common Council he even enclosed a statement from Mr. Ford. Now it is interesting to note that Mr. Ford in turn uses Dr. Exner as his authority.

I have expended considerable time and effort checking the original sources cited by those who favor fluoridation as well as those who oppose it. If you did this you would understand why those who oppose fluoridation can't make a court case stick. They just plain don't have any case. That is probably the reason why there are so many fantastic assertions in anti-fluoridation literature. This is an old technique—make so many charges that some doubt or fear is bound to rub off, no matter how baseless the charges happen to be.

I am aware of the fact that there are people who oppose fluoridation who are intelligent, educated and wholly ethical in their approach. One of these people is a relative who has a Ph.D., in Chemistry, and who has a very commanding position in one of the largest research laboratories in the United States. We have had considerable correspondence on the subject, and one conversation during the past year. Originally, he listed half-a-dozen reasons why he opposed fluoridation. A list of questions was submitted to him in order that I could more fully understand his thinking. At that time I did not favor fluoridation, but was still feeling my way on the matter.

Since then he has re-examined his original assertions and has shifted his position to the point where he says he opposes it on ''principle.'' He has abandoned his original objections which fell in the field of chemistry and medicine. I am not surprised at this course of events for I have seen the same sort of thing happen when examining or cross-examining expert witnesses in many fields. Just because

a man is highly trained in a particular field it does not mean that he is qualified to speak on some particular problem which falls in that field. He may never have had occasion to apply himself to a particular problem. Once a person decides to be against something, one excuse seems to be about as good as another.

NOW THE CASE FOR FLUORIDATION IS SIMPLE. IT STOPS TOOTH DECAY, NOT COMPLETELY, BUT IF TAKEN FROM BIRTH THROUGH THE EARLY TEENS, IT WILL ELIMINATE ANYWHERE FROM 60% TO 70% OF TOOTH DECAY. I AM NOT GOING TO ARGUE ABOUT PERCENT. IF IT WERE ONLY 50%, FLUORIDATION WOULD STILL DO A WORLD OF GOOD.

MORE THAN 30 MILLION PEOPLE IN THE UNITED STATES NOW DRINK FLUORIDATED WATER. Over 3 million of them are drinking naturally fluoridated water. As far as naturally occurring fluorides are concerned, this has been going on for generations. It is true that some people are drinking naturally fluoridated water where the fluoride content is far greater than that advocated by the U.S. Public Health Service or that which is put into the water in a mechanically controlled manner.

Drinking one part in a million or slightly more of fluoridated water has harmed no one; it has done a lot of good. The evidence to this is so overwhelming that I personally accepted it as a fact for almost six months while I still opposed fluoridation on principle.

A good many people oppose fluoridation on principle. I think I understand how they feel because of my own experience. What convinced me might well have no effect on anyone else. There is no use talking about principle until you are completely satisfied that fluoridation will do a lot of good and make a healthier generation of people. At that point you will most certainly feel compelled to examine very carefully the question of whether or not it is harmful to anyone. It is only after you have firmly convinced yourself that fluoridation harms no one; that it is a great and positive good, that you can approach the problem of principle. Personally, I felt compelled again and again to re-examine my position because it just didn't seem good horse sense to oppose a matter on principle when it would be of such great benefit to so many millions of people.

No scientific discovery that brings a great and positive good has ever been withheld from the people indefinitely. Granted that there is very apt to be great opposition to discoveries that bring any sweeping change; there is no doubt in my mind, however, that the force of a discovery that will benefit all future generations will in the end prevail. Fluoridating water does no violence to anything that was handed down from Mt. Sinai.

True, the thought of enforced mass medication is obnoxious to me. In answer to this, those who favor fluoridation point out that fluoridation of water is not mass medication, but rather a mass preventive; that it doesn't cure anything. Somehow I have never been impressed with this line of reasoning. As far as this issue is concerned, I don't see any difference between calling fluoridation mass medication or a mass preventive. Does it really make any difference? It's a distinction without a difference. Anyway it's no answer to anyone who is opposed to mass medication to tell them that fluoridation is a mass preventive. If you can't buy that answer neither can I.

But consider this—when I visited Grand Rapids and looked over their fluoridation setup, I learned that they obtained their water supply from Lake Michigan, and that Lake Michigan already has a very slight trace of fluorides in it—not enough to serve the purpose of retarding tooth decay, *but perhaps only 1/20th of what is needed.*

There is a universal presence of fluorides in water, plant and animal life; infinitesimal as it may be, it is still there. *It is self-evident that a certain amount of fluoride is entirely compatible with human health, and indeed to plant and animal life everywhere.*

Fluorides like other trace substances have been around since time began, and even the strongest opponents of fluoridation do not deny that several trace substances are needed for proper human growth and general health. Scientists have located a trace substance (fluoride) already present in many water supplies in sufficient quantities to decrease tooth decay and at the same time do no harm to people.

Scientists advocate putting this trace substance (fluoride) in other water supplies where only a "fraction of a trace" is present.

Is this mass medication? Is this a mass preventive? Call it what you will, it is neither a sin nor a shame. It is common sense.

Take another look! James Monroe fought the adoption of the Constitution of the United States "on principle." He took another look and became the 5th President of the United States. The reason I bring this up is that in some anti-fluoridation literature, I saw a quotation from James Monroe as authority for a very high-sounding principle. People don't have much difficulty in agreeing on principles, but be very careful how you apply these principles to a particular case. Monroe applied some mighty fine principles in a mighty bad manner and wound up fighting the adoption of the Constitution of the United States. But, Monroe took a second look and maybe you should, too!

The Detroit Board of Education required my children to have a card from the doctor showing that they had been vaccinated as well as inoculated against various diseases before they would be admitted to the Edgar Guest School. I am for it! and I don't mind it being called enforced mass medication or anything else.

But get this straight! Although the Board of Education asks and strongly urges students to produce a card signed by a physician indicating that they have had immunization shots for various diseases, they cannot force children to have them. Thousands of children never get this much-needed protection.

As I am writing this the Detroit newspapers are carrying stories of over 80 diphtheria cases in Detroit and five deaths so far. Many parents who should have had their children immunized against diphtheria before are now acting. Maybe it would be better if those who were concerned (the children) had a voice in this matter. It is my guess that there are some 80 children who could give a better argument against these arguments against enforced mass medication or enforced mass prevention. Of course 80 children is the wrong figure. It is too late for five of them to have any opinion on anything.

There is a difference between bad teeth and diphtheria or any communicable disease. Much is made of this by those who oppose fluoridation, and I have discussed this point in this memorandum, but right now we are discussing the principle of enforced mass medication.

Those who oppose fluoridation will have to do something more than say that fluoridation is objectionable because it is an enforced mass preventive. The graveyards are filled with people who died needlessly because of this type of thinking. It is impossible for me to embrace a line of thinking that is so clearly refuted by thousands of tombstones.

The Detroit Water Board is putting poison in Detroit's water supply every day, and it's good for you. They put chlorine in it—the stuff that they killed men with in the First World War. They put enough of it in the water supply to kill the bugs; if they didn't, thousands of people would die of dysentery or other water-borne diseases. This is an enforced mass preventive or medication or whatever you want to call it, and you are for it and you know it.

It is strongly contended that enforced mass medication may be proper where there is a communicable disease, but it is a far different thing to have enforced mass medication where no communicable disease is involved. I belabored this point in my own mind for a considerable length of time. Of course tooth decay isn't contagious, but so what? Do you claim that it is good? Of course it isn't. Bad teeth have caused a lot of discomfort and pain. Bad teeth have also caused a lot of ill health. Everyone knows this is true if they only stop and think.

There is no question that anything that will generally improve the condition of teeth, will generally improve the health and energy of the people. Many of the great afflictions of mankind are not contagious, such as poor eyesight, automobile accidents, arthritis, rheumatism, fallen arches, cancer, heart disease, and a host of other things.

I sort of grew into the position that there is no valid reason for opposing fluoridation on principle. I can only say that the real cause of my difficulty was that the matter had become somewhat fixed in my mind before I had accepted the fact that fluoridation harmed no one and was a great and positive good. Everyone is subject to abusing their mental processes with ideas that become fixed before they have carefully examined the matter. There is nothing so respected as an old abuse.

When I was a child attending a 1-room country schoolhouse, smallpox broke out in the area. My father combined farming with being the local township health officer, director of a school board, as well as being father-confessor for a number of individuals who found the game laws obnoxious to them. Father stood for no nonsense as far as smallpox was concerned. My grandmother lived with us and she was one of eleven children, four of whom were wiped out by smallpox at one crack. She allowed that smallpox was "worse than Indians on the warpath." There is no question that my father's thinking was conditioned a good deal by her description of people dying without doctors or proper care; of mass burials and the terror and tragedy that had entered her life over sixty years before.

Now a Public Health Officer has a lot of authority, even though he happens to be a farmer with an eighth grade education. Father obtained the services of a physician from the State Department of Health, and had all the citizens of the township assemble at the various country schools for mass vaccination; that is with the exception of one family who flatly refused to be vaccinated or have their children vaccinated. My father quickly ordered the children who were not vaccinated to stay home from school, and there they stayed until all danger of the epidemic had passed. As a matter of fact, none of the children who were not vaccinated got the smallpox. They lived off the immunity of their neighbors. This, also, was an enforced mass preventive.

This smallpox episode is indelibly impressed upon my mind. There was violent and bitter objection on the part of a considerable number of people to my father's mandate that either you get vaccinated or you stay home; also, his uncompromising insistence that everyone be vaccinated. A good many people got very sore arms from the vaccination; the sorer their arms got the sorer their heads got. The children at school started taking it out on me. Their parents didn't help much by saying that it was time that my father was thrown out of office. These things hit me as a small boy harder than my father, who didn't seem to mind. He knew that he couldn't get rich out of either farming or holding public office.

There wasn't really an epidemic—it was nipped in the bud. Out of a half-dozen cases, there was one death. The soreheads vanished with the sore arms. That was about 1927 and today everyone up there gets vaccinated, and no questions are asked. It's about as popular as baptism.

This first-hand experience can't help but impress me far more than it could impress anyone by telling them about it. *When people put up such a kick over vaccination which can save their lives, it is not at all surprising that there is opposition to fluoridation which can only save teeth.*

I received some very strong letters on fluoridation. But this fluoridation storm is only a summer breeze to the storm that broke about me as a child.

Fluoridation is different from vaccination, but one thing about these problems is the same. They both involve the kind of decision that once you are sure you are right you go ahead. I think this particular experience as a child, more than any other, has made me take the long view on the fluoridation matter.

Father died (1937) in office some ten years after this episode—but not from the smallpox. He had a lot of people at his funeral, some of whom wouldn't have been there if he hadn't been so mulish about this vaccination business. I hope everyone at my funeral has good teeth.

Some people complain about the cost of fluoridation. Recently, I read a report by Gerald J. Cox, Ph.D., Professor of Dental Research at the University of Pittsburgh, who said that ten cents worth of fluoridation will save forty dollars worth of dental bills; that is interesting, but I am not convinced because of this statement. For all I know, the doctor may be fifty to seventy-five percent off, but the answer is still the same. It's even a better bargain than when the white man purchased Manhattan Island from the Indians.

Some weeks ago, I spent a day in Grand Rapids inspecting their equipment and reports on fluoridation. Most of the day was spent with the chemist in their water plant, and considerable time with several physicians in their Health Department. They have been fluoridating water in Grand Rapids for over ten years. Their reports certainly give the lie to a lot of statements made by anti-fluoridation literature about what has happened there. From their death rate, and also specific death rates on specific causes of death, they might even make a case for asserting that fluoridation improved health on other than the teeth factor. However, the general health level of the people is rising all over the United States and, of course, there is really no evidence that fluoridation helps anything but teeth, but their carefully documented reports clearly refute the charges made by those who oppose fluoridation. Anti-fluoridation literature usually throws a few left hooks at Grand Rapids. I have heard all sorts of wild statements concerning death rates, and also death rates on specific illnesses in this City. The U.S. Health Service has worked with them in the particular project of fluoridation. They have carefully inspected and supervised it every step of the way. They worked with their water department and with their health department. The carefully documented reports of their health department clearly indicate that Grand Rapids is becoming a healthier place to live in all the time. There is not the slightest evidence that fluoridation has hurt anybody. There is, however, conclusive evidence that the children who have drunk fluoridated water for the maximum period have reduced their tooth decay by not less than 60%.

But let's go back to the cost argument. In Grand Rapids the cost is less than the cost of two ice cream cones a year per person of their total population; that means, roughly, 13¢ a person. What if the cost were five times this amount? The answer would still be the same. Detroit is spending about seven million dollars to widen Woodward Avenue, three blocks, only, between City Hall and Jefferson; this is supposed to make the scenery better for you when you approach the Civic Center (I voted against this widening). Anyway, this seven million dollars would fluoridate the entire City water supply, and buy all equipment, for about thirteen years. The equipment should last far beyond the thirteen year period.

To oppose fluoridation on the grounds that it is only effective when the fluoridated water is drunk when a person is in the early teens or younger is a selfish shortsighted argument when you get right down to it. So, just what is all the argument about? A good percent of what most of us earn goes for our children. What's the cost of a few more ice cream cones a year when you are spending it on something that is of some great and positive benefit? If you don't have children you pay anyway. Take a look at the school tax bill on

34

real estate; also, 1/3rd of the sales tax goes back to the schools. In case you haven't thought of it, you are paying the dentists' bills in one way or another for the children of parents who are on welfare.

It is for the children that America labors, and that's all right with me. Besides leaving the next generation with the national debt and the atomic bomb, I see nothing wrong with leaving them better teeth, particularly at such bargain rates.

Fluoridation isn't going to help you if you put your teeth in a glass of water at night, but it will help all of the children, and if you think you are paying too much for other peoples' children, then give thirteen cents or even twenty-five cents less to the community fund next year—that will cover it. Now, of course, I am not really telling anyone to give less to the community fund, but I think I am showing that the argument about cost is nonsense.

Quit arguing that fluoridating the water supply is the wrong way to do the job. It's cheap—it's the most effective way; it's the only way the job will be done. Fluoridation of the entire water supply is the cheapest and most efficient method of doing it; if it isn't done this way it just isn't going to be done. Let's quit throwing up a lot of theoretical objections and start getting practical. So what if most of it goes down the drain without being consumed by those who will benefit by it. Does this really bother you? We put chlorine in all the water now and a lot of it goes for industrial uses and other uses where it wouldn't be needed. It is still the best way. If the result is accomplished and the cost low, or within reason, then the method is efficient regardless of the amount that goes down the drain.

Anyway, why waste time arguing with an ex-farm boy that he should only spray half the potato patch. If you say it's not the same thing, I will agree, but the argument for using anything but the water supply for fluoridation makes about as much sense as spraying half a potato patch.

Most people who have talked with me and argued the cost factor have, as a matter of fact, known little or nothing about the actual cost.

Some people have written to me saying that they oppose fluoridation because they know that some other people oppose all forms of medication on religious principles,

and that I should respect their beliefs. No persons have contacted me to say that they themselves oppose fluoridation because they themselves hold a particular religious belief. When someone does state that he is speaking for himself, I will answer him. To those who prefer to speak for these individuals, I would like to ask you why you don't insist on the Detroit Water Department stopping its practice of putting chlorine in the water. This practice is equally objectionable on this particular point. In other words, if a religious principle is involved, it is as objectionable to put chlorine in the water as it is to put in fluorine. Don't back out on this just because you know that thousands of Detroit citizens would die of dysentery and other diseases if they stopped putting chlorine in the water. If you are going to speak for those who you assume oppose fluoridation on religious principles, you should be logical and also insist that Detroit cease chlorinating its water supply. Now is as good a time as any to shift your objection to some other point.

Some people object to fluoridating the water because they point out that fluorine is a poison, and that it is used to kill rats. So what?! Chlorine is also a poison, and was used to kill men in the first world war. Iodine is a poison, but when put into salt in small quantities it will stop goiters—go to the cupboard and take a look. There is a good chance that you have purchased iodized salt. You are eating poison, but taken in small quantities, it is good for you.

Everyday Detroit dumps large quantities of chlorine (poison) into its water supply, with excellent results. They dump in enough to kill the bugs, but they do not put in enough to harm anyone. Incidentally, many of the arguments used against fluoridation of water were also used against chlorination of water supplies a generation or so ago; this poison pitch is one of them, and it just doesn't add up. The real issue is whether or not one part or slightly more of fluorine to a million parts of water is harmful—it isn't! For a person to rest his case on the assertion that fluorine is a poison is something like asserting that you can drown in water and therefore don't take a bath. Kind of foolish, isn't it?

If you are dead set against fluoridation, one excuse is as good as another. Many of the people who have contacted me have clearly indicated that they never intend to re-examine their present position, and this goes for some who are for fluoridation as well as some who are against it.

Here are some national bodies that have endorsed fluoridation of water supplies:

American Medical Association, American Dental Association, American Public Health Association, American Pharmaceutical Association, American Nurses Association, American Association for the Advancement of Science, National Research Council, National Institute of Municipal Law Officers, American Water Works Association, American Hospital Association, U.S. Public Health Service, National Congress of Parents and Teachers.

The list of medical and other organizations that endorse fluoridation at the level of the various states would be much longer; the list of city and villages even longer. Detroit's Department of Health endorses fluoridation.

Again, I can't blame anyone for not accepting the word of all these various organizations. I didn't—I did my own investigating and formed my own opinion. We agree—but not because they said it, rather because they have a legal marriage with the facts.

If you believe that fluoridation will harm you, I can only say that if I thought there was one chance in a million that it would, I would vote against it. Regardless of anything that I may have said, I have a very deep and abiding respect for the opinions of other people. I even respect the beliefs of a woman who came to our home when I was a young boy and bitterly complained that the smallpox vaccination, which my father had insisted on, not only had given her a sore arm but had also greatly aggravated her rheumatism. She was certain, but the judgment of the ages is against her.

Fluoridation is not a new and untried experiment. Millions of people have drunk naturally fluoridated water for generations. Many more millions have drunk artificially fluoridated water for varying lengths of time (Grand Rapids for over ten years). Again, I repeat, over 30 million people in the United States are now drinking fluoridated water.

The United States Public Health Service; local health services; and state health services have checked and checked, and checked again. It is not only a preponderance of evidence that favors fluoridation—it is overwhelming evidence and overwhelming authority—medical and scientific.

The United States Public Health Service waited until thousands of tests were made; until they investigated case after case of alleged harm from fluoridation before they endorsed it. Why should the fact that a few doctors cry out against it disturb you in the face of such overwhelming proof? Of course, these doctors are sincere. So were the doctors who opposed putting chlorine in water; so were the doctors who opposed vaccination. When you listen to the voices of the doctors who oppose fluoridation, you are listening to the echoes of the voices of doctors who opposed chlorination of water and vaccination; they have passed the point of no return in their thinking. They will continue to make charge after charge, and cite case-after-case of some individual supposedly harmed by drinking fluoridated water, *but these charges can never stand-up against the facts. How much proof do you ask? Shouldn't the experience based on five million users be enough? Certainly, ten million ought to be enough, and if 30 million won't convince you then 100 million will never convince you. Do you give any weight to the U.S. Public Health Service in the careful and thorough investigation over many years, in many areas, and under many conditions? Do you think the doctors in the State Health Department are stupid or that they lack skill or integrity?*

Come to think of it, isn't a large amount of this anti-fluoridation literature just a bit hysterical on the face of it—some of it has to be to sell for a dollar a copy.

I have, to the best of my ability, examined this problem as conscientiously as I have examined any problem. I cannot honestly berate any person or individual for not being convinced by reason of the fact that 30 million people now use fluoridated water, or the fact that the U.S. Public Health Service; the State and City Health Departments endorse its use. I, too, was unwilling to accept their judgment. I insisted on checking the original sources and citations of authority in many articles. I insisted on going to Grand Rapids in studying the matter firsthand; in seeing the reports of their Health Department. I insisted on examining and re-examining my position again and again—all aspects of the case, including the contention that fluoridation should be opposed on principle. *I have been* *unreasonable beyond justification in the proof that I have demanded. It is with complete certainty that I will support fluoridation with all the resources at my command, because it is the only action that I can justify to myself and to you.*

THE TRUTH ABOUT FLUORIDATION

WEIGHT OF SCIENTIFIC AUTHORITY

RAT POISON

PART TWO

FLUORIDATION FACTS

AN UPDATE ON WATER FLUORIDATION
Triumphs and Challenges

BY

CORA S. LEUKHART, M.B.A.
Public Health Advisor
Center for Disease Control
Atlanta, Georgia

Status of community water fluoridation in U.S.
Extent of fluoridation

More than thirty years ago, in January 1945, Grand Rapids, Michigan, became the first community in the world to adjust the fluoride content of its water supply under the aegis of the U.S. Public Health Service.

Two other communities on this continent, Newburgh, New York, and Brantford, Ontario, joined Grand Rapids that same year to demonstrate that the dental benefits, discovered through extensive epidemiological research in naturally fluoridated communities, could be replicated by man through the upward adjustment of the fluoride content in the water.

By the end of 1975, the last time a nationwide fluoridation census was taken, it was estimated that slightly more than 105,000,000 people in the U.S had access to water fluoridated at optimum (0.7-1.2 ppm depending on the climate), or higher levels.[1] This included

Reprinted from *Pediatric Dentistry*, Vol. 1, No. 1, 1979, pp. 32-37. Copyright 1979, by The American Academy of Pedodontics.

approximately 10,000,000 people whose water supplies are naturally fluoridated at 0.7 ppm or higher. About 60% of the population who have access to public water supplies, or 50% of the total population, had fluoridated water.

Since that time, the natural population growth, the fluoridation of the Boston area, and numerous small communities have increased the number benefiting from fluoridation to at least 108,000,000.

The magnitude of the problem of extending fluoridation universally is perhaps best emphasized by the fact that this 50% of the total population is served by only about 13% of the community water supplies. Thus, to reach the last half of the population who are served by community water supplies, some 87% of the water supplies still need to be fluoridated.

There are great variations in the location and size of the communities which are fluoridating. Based on the 1975 fluoridation census, 22 states, the District of Columbia, and Puerto Rico provided fluoridated water to more than half of their population. In comparison, states in the western third of the country, the Deep South and New England,

and the state of New Jersey have been particularly slow in adopting fluoridation.

Over 9,000 areas had fluoridated water: 6,795 adjusted and 2,630 natural. Approximately 70% of all cities having a population of 100,000 or more are fluoridated. The vast majority of communities which are not fluoridated have populations of less than 25,000. It is estimated that these are served by over 50,000 community water systems.

The duration of the experience with adjusted fluoridation is impressive. At last count 108 cities with populations of 50,000 or more, distributed throughout 27 States, the District of Columbia, and Puerto Rico have been fluoridating their water supplies for 20 years or more. It is estimated that these water supplies provide fluoridated water to more than 24,000,000 people in cities such as Chicago, San Francisco, Pittsburgh, Philadelphia, Miami, Denver, Baltimore, St. Louis, Cleveland, Milwaukee, San Juan, Buffalo, Louisville, Indianapolis, St. Paul, Toledo, Oklahoma City, Tulsa, and Washington, D.C.

Over 700 communities have been fluoridated for 25 years or more, and some few have been fluoridated for 30 years or more. Among the latter group are Newburgh, New York; Grand Rapids, Michigan; Skokie and Evanston, Illinois; Lewiston, Idaho; Madison and Sheboygan, Wisconsin; and Marshall, Texas.

State laws

In 1965, Connecticut became the first state to pass a law requiring fluoridation. Many states have attempted to follow suit with varying degrees of success. At present, eight states have laws intended to provide statewide fluoridation: Connecticut, 1965; Minnesota and Illinois, 1967; Michigan, 1968; Ohio and South Dakota, 1969; and Georgia and Nebraska, 1973.

Laws of four states, Georgia, Michigan, Nebraska, and Ohio, contained provisions which allowed a community to exempt itself from compliance with the state law if a community decided it did not wish to institute this public health measure. Two states placed a time limit, which has now been passed, on the period during which referendum could be held: Michigan, 5 years; and Ohio, a maximum of 240 days.

Four states set a lower limit on the population of the community which must comply: Connecticut, 20,000; Michigan, 1,000; South Dakota, 500; Ohio, systems serving 5,000. Two states include funding provisions: Ohio and Georgia.

Kentucky statutes clearly delegated to the State Board of Health powers to adopt regulations necessary to protect the dental health of the people. Under this law, Kentucky established standards for approval of public water supplies. This is not a mandatory law since a water supply can serve the public with a Provisional rating, but the water supply must be fluoridated before an Approved rating is issued.

Puerto Rico, by the passage of legislation in 1952, provided money for adding fluoride to water supplies. This, in effect, made fluoridation mandatory in Puerto Rico.

In 1970, South Dakota fought back a challenge to rescind its law by winning a statewide referendum. The 1977 Minnesota legislature extended the deadline for further compliance with their law until July 1979, pending the results of a study by a Governmental Commission on the health effects of fluoridation. This was done as the result of pressure from the residents of Brainerd who did not want to comply with the law. After failure to obtain exemption from the State law through various procedures, including the Supreme Court, the deadline was extended by including the provision in the State appropriations bill.

In July of this year, while codifying its public health laws, Michigan passed an amendment to its fluoridation law, which now allows communities to vote to discontinue existing fluoridation programs by either council action or referendum. While the work on the laws was being conducted, the Governor had called for a study on whether or not the amount of fluoride being ingested had increased since fluoridation.

The results of the study, delivered too late to have any impact in preventing a change in the law, concluded that there was a slight increase, but that there was no evidence of any adverse health effects from such a slight increase, and that the possibility that such would occur was remote.

Five states have laws which require a public vote before fluoridation can be instituted: Delaware (1974); Maine (1957); New Hampshire (1959); Nevada (1967); and Utah (1976). This was a step backward for Delaware, which had previously passed a mandatory law in 1968, but changed it to require a referendum in 1974.

Massachusetts had a required referendum law which was repealed in 1968. The current law enables a community to implement fluoridation through a Board of Health order. Implementation is subject to a 90-day waiting period during which a petition for referendum may be filed.

Required referenda are a deterrent to fluoridation. They are costly. They frequently are only advisory and may be subsequently repealed with a reversal of the decision even after equipment has been installed. They favor the opposition, since they are conducted in an atmosphere that needs only to plant a suspicion of doubt—easily done by scare tactics and dissemination of irrelevant or misleading information.

Those states which have mandatory referenda are among those with the least fluoridation: Maine, 40.6%; New Hampshire, 13.3%; Delaware, 39.5%; Nevada, 3.0%; and Utah, 2.4%. In 1968, when Massachusetts repealed its required referendum law, fluoridation was available to only about 7% of the population. Ten years later, about 51% of the population had access to fluoridation.

In 1976, those opposed to fluoridation adopted a new technique. Three states, Washington, Oregon, and Utah, were confronted with statewide referenda. The intent was to prohibit fluoridation or make it more difficult to implement.[2-4]

It appears that these states may have been selected by the opposition in anticipation of victory because (1) their populations had limited exposure to fluoridation: Utah, 2.4%; Oregon, 10.7%; and Washington, 39.8%; (2) they were literally surrounded by states with similar limited experience; and (3) they were relatively close to the headquarters of the National Health Federation in Monrovia, California, which was actively assisting in planning and organizing the campaigns for the opposition.

Fortunately, both Oregon and Washington were able to defeat the ballot measures. In Utah, the referendum resulted in a requirement to have a public vote on fluoridation in each community before it can be implemented.

Regional action

Through the years, fluoridation campaigns have moved from the local community to the state level and now, more recently, to regional approaches. Fluoridation of Boston and some 31 communities served by the Metropolitan District Commission was accomplished by a regional approach, enlisting the support and active participation of all relevant community health departments. The strong endorsement and recommendation of the Regional Health Administrator, with the support of each State health officer in the region, is emerging as another approach.

Status of community water fluoridation in foreign countries

Much confusion has arisen over the status of fluoridation outside the U.S. It is important to know the facts, since action in foreign countries, inaccurately publicized in the U.S., can adversely impact on the fluoridation program. Inaction of a foreign government or dental association should not be interpreted as banning fluoridation; nor should political actions contrary to recommendations of health authorities be interpreted as confirmation of opponent allegations of health hazards. Some of the countries cited as banning fluoridation actually have enabling laws or fluoridation programs in effect, such as West Germany, Greece, Yugoslavia, and Switzerland.[5]

Perhaps it would not be amiss to explain the situation in Sweden, the Netherlands, and Denmark, where fluoridation currently cannot be implemented.

Sweden repealed its fluoridation enabling act in 1971. Only one community was fluoridating under this act. The National Board of Health and Welfare of Sweden has stated that the repeal of the fluoridation law in 1971 was strictly the result of general political considerations. Fluoridation lost by a 137 to 126 vote in the Parliament and the decision was against the majority report issued by the Parliament's Social Insurance Committee. Sweden now has a governmental committee reexamining the question.

Fluoridation in the Netherlands was proceeding under a 1961 Water Supply Act. Opponents of fluoridation challenged the right of the Minister to authorize fluoridation under the Act, and in 1973, the High Court ruled that fluoridation was not covered by this specific Act.

Subsequently, the Public Health Minister prepared a national fluoridation bill to be presented to Parliament. The Minister was unsuccessful in his attempt to secure the passage of the bill in 1976. This resulted in the stoppage of existing fluoridation programs.

Denmark has long had a law prohibiting the addition of fluoride to food and cosmetics. This is interpreted to prohibit water fluoridation. It is generally understood that this was done to permit control of all sources of fluoride.

Opponents of fluoridation frequently draw attention to countries which are not implementing fluoridation, ignoring the many countries that supply fluoridated water to over 155,000,000 people.[6]

It is interesting to note that, while opponents in the U.S. are trying to stop fluoridation here by claims of banning in Europe, opponents in foreign countries are trying to stop fluoridation by misinterpretation of U.S. research and claims that the U.S. is abandoning fluoridation.

School fluoridation

As a public health measure, fluoridation has one obvious limitation—it can only reach those who have access to community water supplies. Since it is estimated that some 40,000,000 people are not served by community water supplies, it becomes important to find ways in which these people might also derive fluoride benefits.

Research has shown that schools which have independent water supplies can fluoridate such supplies. These supplies, fluoridated at 4.5 times the optimum to compensate for the time that children are not in school, can provide the children with 39% fewer cavities than their counterparts in unfluoridated communities.[7]

North Carolina was the first state to follow up on the results of the research. Now, about 400 school fluoridation programs are in existence in some 14 states: Florida, Indiana, Kentucky, Maine, Montana, Nebraska, New Mexico, New York, North Carolina, Pennsylvania, Tennessee, Vermont, Wisconsin, and Wyoming.

Defluoridation

In 1974, Congress passed the Safe Drinking Water Act (PL 93-523). This Act is intended to improve the quality and safety of drinking water supplies. It required the Federal Government to set maximum acceptable levels for all "contaminants," in reality, constituents, of water supplies which could have an adverse effect on health. It also prohibited the Federal Government from mandating the addition of any substance to water supplies except for water treatment.

Communities whose water supplies naturally contain more than 2 times the optimum level of fluoride for dental health will be required to reduce the fluoride content. Opponents of fluoridation have misrepresented the intent of the law.[8] There is nothing in the law to prohibit the public health program of fluoridation, nor is it intended to imply that adverse health effects occur from fluoridation at levels recommended for dental health.

The maximum contaminant level was established based on the original research which indicated that at that level, a community might expect to have some cosmetically objectionable mottling.

Based on the information on natural fluoride levels submitted by the states in 1969, two-thirds of the states will have one or more communities requiring defluoridation. Those states having the greatest number of communities with excess fluoride are Arizona, Illinois, Iowa, Missouri, New Mexico, Oklahoma, South Dakota, Texas, and Virginia. Over 500 communities reported fluoride levels over 2 ppm and one community reported a level of 13.5 ppm.

It becomes important that in complying with the Safe Drinking Water Act, these communities reduce the fluoride level only to the optimum level in order that those currently receiving the decay-preventive benefits of fluoride are not deprived of its benefits.

The surveillance regulations necessary to assure that fluoride levels are maintained at optimal levels are not provided by this law.

Benefits

For years, the systemic caries-preventive benefits for children from fluoridation have been stressed. Such a good job has been done that those who know about fluoridation think it is good only for children.

Fluoridation does prevent 50-70% of the cavities in young children who have drunk fluoridated water from birth. Research has also shown that fluoridation can benefit children who have not had lifetime exposure.

"The 10 to 12, 13 to 14 and 16-year-old children, who were not exposed to fluoridated water all of their lives but who had continuous residency in Newburgh since May 2, 1945, had rates lower by 52%, 48% and 41%, respectively, compared with Kingston children of similar ages," (when examined 10 years after the start of fluoridation).[9]

Little attention has been given to the fact that community fluoridation also has a slight topical effect, nor has sufficient attention been paid to the 6-fold or more increase in the number of children who can be completely caries-free, or to the reduction in extractions due to caries, or to the lifetime benefits accruing to adults.

Research comparing a naturally fluoridated community (Hartlepool) with a fluoride-deficient community (York) in England, showed that the fluoridated community had a lower caries experience, a lower tooth mortality, and a smaller need for partial dentures for all ages up to 65 years. These results were apparent despite one of the lowest dentist to population ratios in the country in the fluoridated community.[10]

For years, the Naval Training Center at Great Lakes, Illinois, has been conducting a longitudinal study on caries-free recruits. In 1971, they reported that the increase in caries-free recruits was the result of gains made by the central and coastal cities, which started fluoridation in the early 1950's. There had been barely any change in caries-free recruits from the fluoride-deficient cities.

Numerous research studies throughout the world have replicated the U.S. research. It is amazing that so many countries with dietary and cultural differences and varying levels of the normal constituents of water supplies have repeatedly replicated the benefits of adjusting the fluoride content of the water supply, and without adverse health effects. Evaluatory studies are no longer limited to 5 or 10 years of experience. Such studies cover as many as 20 years.

Opposition

Repeated public opinion surveys have shown that only 10-12% of the people oppose fluoridation, while 50%-70% favor it, and the remainder are undecided. If those early researchers could have glimpsed the future to see how their work would be misinterpreted and maligned, would they have ventured into this new area of public health?

The opponents of fluoridation are adept at linking fluoridation with whatever happens to be the popular whipping boy. When fear of communism was prevalent in the 1950's, one of their most potent arguments was to allege that fluoridation was a communist plot. And in Russia, it was referred to as a capitalist plot.

Today, the allegations more frequently center around alleged adverse side effects, unknown future harm, and interference with individual rights. There has never been a clinically substantiated case of harm to anyone from drinking optimally fluoridated water. A study by the National Health Federation has alleged a relationship between fluoridation and cancer. This organization has long actively opposed fluoridation.

Their study has been repeatedly refuted both by review of their work and by independent research studies conducted in Canada[11] and England,[12] and by the National Cancer Institute,[13] the National Heart, Lung, and Blood Institute[14] of the National Institutes of Health, and the Center for Disease Control.[15]

Evidence of the safety of fluoridation has been examined critically and repeatedly, and specific allegations of injury and hazard have been carefully evaluated. The conclusions reached in every instance have been the same—fluoridation is safe. Comprehensive reviews of the extensive scientific literature by both the American Medical Association and the Royal College of Physicians in England continue to support fluoridation.[16,17]

No court of last resort has ever ruled against fluoridation, regardless of the charge. The "individual rights" question has been repeatedly dealt with by the courts which have repeatedly found in favor of fluoridation. Opponents who object to the addition of fluoride to fluoride-deficient waters to prevent caries could also consider the removal of excess fluoride from high-fluoride bearing waters to prevent mottling as equally infringing on their rights. Both are public health measures designed to improve the overall health of the Nation.

In raising the issue of the right to vote on fluoridation, one must recognize that those who stand to benefit or lose most, children, are not voters. The health benefits denied children by a negative action are lost forever and cannot be recovered by the children when they attain voting age.

A two-part report appears in the July and August issues of *Consumer Reports* under the titles of "Fluoridation: the Cancer Scare" and "The Attack on Fluoridation—Six Ways to Mislead the Public." This report puts the opposition in perspective and concludes that there is no scientific controversy, but that the continuing attack on fluoridation is a major triumph of quackery over science.[18]

Fluoridation continues to have the support of virtually every health and scientific organization with competence in the field. One of the most recent strong endorsements is that of the Nutrition Consortium, representing the American Dietetic Association, the American Institute of Nutrition, the American Society for Clinical Nutrition, Institute of Food Technologists, Society for Nutrition Education, American Academy of Pediatrics and the Food and Nutrition Board of the National Academy of Sciences—National Research Council.

The following excerpts emphasize their support:

"The use of this system (fluoridation) to provide an essential nutrient, fluoride, to the diets of children susceptible to dental caries who otherwise would have no fluoride, is a most laudable public health development.... It is not in the best interest of the health of the people of the United States to discontinue or to delay utilization of fluoridation of community water supplies. To delay is to deny good dental health to children and encourage the continued development of dental caries at all ages of the population."[19]

There are many challenges to be met if the full benefits of fluoridation are to be realized:
—Dental health must be given a higher priority in our value system.
—Apathy of many health professionals and reluctance to become involved in fluoridation campaigns must be overcome.
—A multifaceted approach which recognizes the political ramifications needs to be developed.
—A more effective and extensive method of communication is needed to convey information on the benefits of fluoridation and to counteract the misinformation circulated by the opposition.
—And an effective system of monitoring approved programs to assure maintenance of optimum fluoride levels must be implemented.

Perhaps the greatest triumph is that despite an unprecedented attack, and the dragging of public health into the political arena, 50% of the people can now benefit from fluoridation.

References

1. U.S. Department of Health, Education, and Welfare, Public Health Service, Center for Disease Control, Atlanta, Georgia: *Fluoridation Census 1975.*

2. Evans, A., Jr., and Pickles, T.: "Statewide Antifluoridation Initiative: A New Challenge to Health Workers," *Am J Public Health,* 68:59-62, 1978.

3. Rosenstein, D. I., Isman, R., Pickles, T., and Benben, C.: "Fighting the Latest Challenge to Fluoridation in Oregon," *Public Health Rep,* 93:69-72, 1978.

4. Dwore, R. B.: "A Case Study of the 1976 Referendum in Utah on Fluoridation," *Public Health Rep,* 93:73-78, 1978.

5. U.S. Department of Health, Education, and Welfare, Public Health Service, Center for Disease Control, Atlanta, Georgia: "Status of Fluoridation in European Countries," FL 92, April 1977.

6. Backer Dirks, O., Kunzel, W., and Carlos, J.B.: "Caries-Preventive Water Fluoridation," *Caries Res,* 12:Suppl. 1, 7-14, 1978.

7. Horowitz, H. S., Heifetz, S. B., and Law, F. E.: "Effect of School Water Fluoridation on Dental Caries: Final Results in Elk Lake, Pennsylvania, After 12 Years," J.A.D.A. 84:832-838, 1972.

8. U.S. Department of Health, Education, and Welfare, Public Health Service, Health Resources Administration, Bethesda, Maryland: "Misin-

terpretation of 'Safe Drinking Water Act'," FL 77, July 1975.

9. Hilleboe, H. E., Schlesinger, E. R., Chase, H. C., Cantwell, K. T., Ast, D. B., Smith, D. J., Wachs, B., Overton, D. E., and Hodge, H. C.: "Newburgh-Kingston Caries-Fluorine Study: Final Report," J.A.D.A. 52:290-325, 1956.

10. U.S. Department of Health, Education, and Welfare, Public Health Service, National Institutes of Health: "Adult Dental Health Benefits from Fluoridation Documented in New American and British Reports," PPB 35, February 1972.

11. Department of National Health and Welfare, Environmental Health Directorate, Health Protection Branch, Brooke Claxton Building, Ottawa K1A OK9, Canada: "Fluoridation and Cancer," 1977.

12. Kinlen, L.: "Cancer Incidence in Relation to Fluoride Level in Water Supplies," *Br Dent J,* 138:221-224, 1975.

13. Hoover, R. N., McKay, F. W., and Fraumeni, J. F., Jr.: "Fluoridated Drinking Water and the Occurrence of Cancer," *J Natl Cancer Inst,* 57:757-768, 1976.

14. Rogot, E., Sharrett, A. R., Feinleib, M., and Fabsitz, R. R.: "Trends in Urban Mortality in Relation to Fluoridation Status," *Am J Epidemiol,* 107:104-112, 1978.

15. Erickson, J. D.: "Mortality in Selected Cities with Fluoridated and Non-Fluoridated Water Supplies," *N Engl J. Med,* 298:1112-1116, 1978.

16. Shupe, J. L., Leone, N. J., and Fletcher, D. C.: *Efficacy and Safety of Fluoridation,* Chicago: American Medical Association, 1975.

17. Royal College of Physicians: *Fluoride, Teeth and Health,* A Report and Summary on Fluoride and Its Effect on Teeth and Health from the Royal College of Physicians of London, Kent, Pitman Medical Publishing Co., Ltd., 1976.

18. *Consumer Reports.* "Fluoridation: The Cancer Scare," July 1978, pp. 392-396; "The Attack on Fluoridation: Six Ways to Mislead the Public," August 1978, pp. 480-482.

19. U.S. Department of Health, Education, and Welfare, Public Health Service, Center for Disease Control, Atlanta, Georgia: "National Nutrition Consortium Endorses Fluoridation," FL 91, March 1977.

FLUORIDATION:
100 QUESTIONS AND ANSWERS

*The best way to separate fact from fiction
in a fluoridation controversy is to find out
from a trusted professional which side is
telling the truth.*

BY
ALAN M. SLUTSKY, D.M.D., M.B.A.
Instructor
SHELDON ROVIN, D.D.S., M.S.
Professor and Chairman
and
NORMA A. KAPLIS, D.D.S., M.P.H.
Assistant Professor
Department of Dental Care Systems
University of Pennsylvania

This chapter answers most questions that are commonly asked about fluoridation. For your convenience, they are organized into eight general topics:

TOPIC	QUESTION NOS.
Definition, methods and chemistry	1-17
Benefits and effectiveness	18-33
Safety	34-72
Cost	73-76
Fluoridation alternatives	77-79
Social and legal issues	80-86
Opponents of fluoridation	87-90
Politics of fluoridation	91-100

Individual questions may be located by using the table of contents on the following page. References are located at the end of the chapter.

CONTENTS

DEFINITION, METHODS AND CHEMISTRY

1. **Q.** What is "fluoride"?
   A. Fluor*ine* is a chemical element which is chemically too active to exist in nature in a free state. Instead, it is combined with other elements to form fluor*ide* compounds—substances which are widely distributed in nature and found in many of the foods we eat (62, 115). In water, fluoride compounds dissolve to form fluoride ions which can benefit teeth.

2. **Q.** What is fluoridation?
   A. Fluoride is found naturally in most public water supplies. Fluoridation is the adjustment of fluoride concentration to reach an optimum level to build healthier teeth (123).

3. **Q.** Why is water fluoridation called a "primary preventive measure"?
   A. Fluoride in water has a direct effect on teeth: it unites with their hard outer layer (enamel) to make them more resistant to decay (19, 35, 62, 74, 78, 82, 93, 123, 154). Even opponents of water fluoridation seldom dispute fluoride's direct role in preventing tooth decay.

4. **Q.** Why is water fluoridation needed as a public health measure?
   A. Dental decay is one of the nation's most widespread diseases, affecting 98% of our population. Water fluoridation is the best method of protecting against decay because it is effective, safe and inexpensive (1, 6, 10, 50, 51, 59, 62, 64, 72, 105, 115, 144). It is ideal as a public health measure because it requires no special effort by the people who receive its benefits. No health mea-

sure has been more thoroughly substantiated by scientific research.

5. **Q.** How is water fluoridated?
   A. Natural fluoridation occurs when fluoride compounds dissolve into water as it passes through rocks and soil. Water fluoridation is simply an adaptation of this natural process. Fluoride compounds are added to water by means of a carefully controlled feeder and pump system, in much the same way that water purifiers are added. Water plants are equipped with automatic controls to maintain the correct concentration of fluoride in the water (62).

6. **Q.** Can fluoride tablets or drops work as well as fluoridated water?
   A. Fluoride tablets reduce tooth decay about 35%—about half as much as fluoridated water. But to be effective, they must be administered daily from birth through age 12 (38). Very few parents have the motiviation to do this. Community-wide programs in which tablets are offered free-of-charge have not been successful. In Clifton, New Jersey, for example, only 500 of 21,000 children had parents who chose to participate, and only 2.3% of the tablets needed for maximum prevention were dispensed (59).

7. **Q.** What other methods of fluoride administration have been proposed?
   A. The following have been suggested or tried: addition of fluoride to salt, milk, bread or some other food; fluoridation of

school water supplies; fluoride gels or pastes applied to teeth by dentists; mouth rinses; and toothpastes (11, 73, 84, 93, 96, 97, 98, 137, 145, 155, 158, 160). All of these methods may work to varying degrees. However, none has the overall effectiveness, safety, economy, simplicity and reliability of water fluoridation.

8. **Q.** How are (topical) fluoride treatments given in a dental office?

   A. A paste or gel is applied to the teeth for several minutes. It is then removed and the patient is instructed not to rinse for half an hour. Ideally, the procedure is done twice a year. In unfluoridated areas, fluoride treatments result in a 30-40% reduction in dental decay—about half the effect of community water fluoridation (115).

9. **Q.** Why fluoridate *all* water if only a small percentage is actually drunk?

   A. Simple economy. It is much cheaper to fluoridate a community water supply than to create a system in which only water that is drunk has fluoride added. The same principle applies to all water safety measures, such as chlorination and other purification procedures.

10. **Q.** Can people remove fluoride from their own water?

    A. Yes. A home-made defluoridator has been described by Fremlin and Challin (68). It uses treated bone or synthetic bone filters to remove fluoride without affecting calcium, magnesium or chloride. These devices have not been commercially successful because there has been little public demand for them.

11. **Q.** Is there a difference between artificial and naturally occurring water fluoridation?

    A. Because of its natural distribution in rocks, soil and vegetation, calcium fluoride is sometimes referred to as "natural" fluoride while manufactured compounds such as sodium fluoride or stannous fluoride are termed "artificial" (62, 115). Actually, all of these compounds yield the same fluoride ion in water. However, the manufactured compounds dissolve much more easily and are therefore much more practical to use.

12. **Q.** Is fluoride an essential nutrient?

    A. Yes. The Food and Nutrition Board of the National Research Council/National Academy of Sciences is the scientific body that issues the widely used guidelines known as "Recommended Dietary Allowances (RDAs)." The Food and Nutrition Board considers fluoride "essential for the growing organism on the basis of its proven beneficial effects on dental health." Its 1980 report states: "It is evident that the daily fluoride intake in many areas of the United States is not sufficient to afford optimal protection against dental caries. Standardization of water supplies by addition of fluoride to bring the concentration to 1 mg/liter has proved to be a safe, economical, and efficient way to reduce the incidence of tooth decay—an important nutritional public health measure in areas where natural water supplies contain less than this amount" (65).

13. **Q.** What concentration of fluoride is used in fluoridated water?

    A. About one unit of fluoride per million units of water. This concentration is usually referred to as "one part per million" or "1 ppm." In visual terms, this would be the equivalent of less than one grain of salt dissolved in a gallon of water.

14. **Q.** How much fluoride occurs naturally in our food and drink?

    A. The concentration of fluoride has been analyzed for most foods and found to be quite low—well under 1 ppm (115, 121). It is possible that a slight increase (still well below 1 ppm) has taken place during the past 10 years because fluoridated water is used in food processing. Seafood made with unfluoridated water contains about 1 ppm of fluoride and tea usually contains 1-2 ppm. Water fluoridation is necessary because there is not enough fluoride in our overall diet to prevent tooth decay.

15. **Q.** Does calcium intake affect the body's absorption or retention of fluoride?

    A. If large amounts of calcium are consumed (by taking pills or eating large amounts of dairy products), calcium compounds can combine with fluoride to reduce its absorption. The converse is not true. High fluoride intake does not deprive the body of calcium and retard bone growth. The average person in the

United States consumes 500-1,000 times as much calcium as fluoride. Increasing fluoride intake even tenfold would have no effect on calcium absorption (115).

16. **Q.** Does fluoride affect the taste of coffee, tea, water or any foods?

A. No. Fluoride does not affect in any way the taste, odor or color of food or water. In one study, when fluoride was added to water at 10 times the recommended strength (10 ppm), about 5% of the subjects could detect a slight taste. However, at 1 ppm no one could taste or smell the fluoride (31).

17. **Q.** Is fluoridated water acidic?

A. No. Although fluoride-containing acids may be used to accomplish fluoridation, the amount of acid used is too small to change the acidity (pH) of a community water supply (115).

BENEFITS AND EFFECTIVENESS

18. **Q.** What are the health benefits of fluoridation?

A. More than 50 years of research and practical experience have proved beyond a reasonable doubt that fluoridation is effective in preventing tooth decay. Hundreds of studies have demonstrated reductions in tooth decay of 60-70% in communities with either natural or controlled fluoridation (1, 6, 10, 50, 51, 62, 64, 72, 105, 115). Recent research also suggests that fluoride may be helpful in preventing or treating certain bone diseases, especially in older people (15, 16, 19, 70, 89, 90, 95, 162).

19. **Q.** Is tooth decay a serious enough disease to warrant water fluoridation?

A. Yes. Tooth decay, which affects 98% of the U.S. population, is a chronic disease that destroys teeth and can produce pain, discomfort, fever and infection. Loss of teeth can make people look less attractive. It can also make eating much less pleasurable, which can even contribute to malnutrition (particularly in the elderly).

20. **Q.** Does fluoride help teeth after they are formed?

A. Yes. Although maximum benefits of water fluoridation are achieved from 0-12 years of age (while teeth are forming), fluoride does offer some additional protection throughout adult life by acting directly upon tooth surfaces (131).

21. **Q.** Does fluoride have any additional oral health benefit?

A. Yes. Fluoride may protect against periodontal disease, the leading cause of tooth loss in adults. Recent evidence suggests that fluoride alters bacterial "plaque" that forms around the teeth and causes periodontal disease. Further research is needed; but the initial evidence is very encouraging (126).

22. **Q.** Does fluoride prevent decay or merely postpone it?

A. It prevents decay. This question is important because opponents of fluoridation are prone to claim that it merely postpones decay. To make this claim, they have constructed tables which supposedly compare decay rates of people of various ages in fluoridated communities. But these tables include data on older children or adults who have been exposed to fluoridation for only *part* of their lives. To be valid, a study must compare people who have received fluoride *from birth onward* with those who have not. Studies of both decay rates and dental treatment costs have been carried out in naturally fluoridated communities as well as in some which began controlled fluoridation 25-35 years ago. These studies indicate conclusively that fluoridation's decay reduction benefit is permanent (35, 44, 62, 92, 99, 108, 115, 124, 135). The chart below illustrates how decay rates are affected by the age at which exposure to fluoridation begins.

23. **Q.** Does fluoride have any additional benefits?

A. Large dosages of fluorides are being used to treat osteoporosis, a disease in which bone density and strength are reduced (22). At present, however, it does not appear that water fluoridated at 1 ppm prevents osteoporosis.

SOME DENTAL HEALTH STATISTICS FROM GRAND RAPIDS, MICHIGAN, FOR CHILDREN UP TO AGE 15

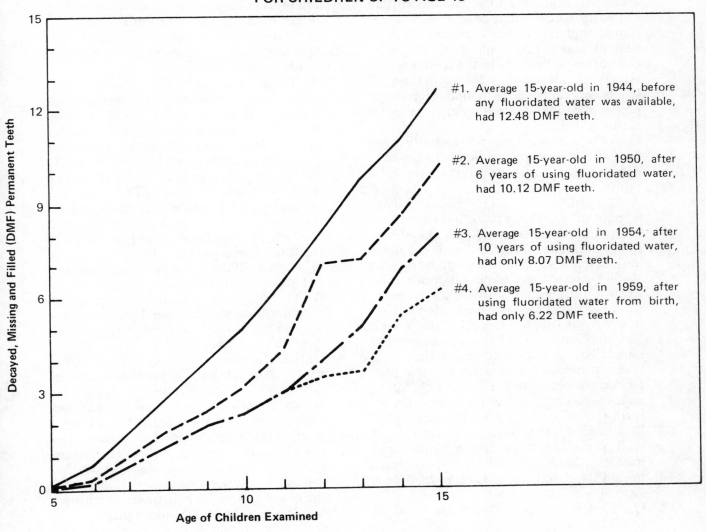

#1. Average 15-year-old in 1944, before any fluoridated water was available, had 12.48 DMF teeth.

#2. Average 15-year-old in 1950, after 6 years of using fluoridated water, had 10.12 DMF teeth.

#3. Average 15-year-old in 1954, after 10 years of using fluoridated water, had only 8.07 DMF teeth.

#4. Average 15-year-old in 1959, after using fluoridated water from birth, had only 6.22 DMF teeth.

24. **Q.** How was it discovered that fluoridated water prevents tooth decay?

A. In the late 19th century, health officials in the U.S., Great Britain and Italy noticed that some individuals in certain geographical areas exhibited a light brown staining of their teeth. They observed further that individuals in these areas had relatively little tooth decay. In the early 1930's, other researchers determined that the factor common to these regions was a very high (8-14 ppm) concentration of fluoride in the drinking water (115). Later it was found that lower levels of fluoride provided significant protection against tooth decay without staining teeth.

25. **Q.** Which major studies initially confirmed the relationship between reduced dental decay and water fluoridation at 1 ppm?

A. In the late 1930's, U.S. Public Health Service officials observed that some children in areas of Texas, South Dakota, Illinois, Arizona, Colorado and Arkansas had much less dental decay. Extensive studies were then done on more than 7,000 children in 21 American cities to discover the lowest concentration of naturally occurring fluoride in water which had maximum dental decay prevention effect. This was determined to be 1 ppm (115). In the mid-1940's, three major projects were begun in Grand Rapids, Michigan; Newburgh, New York; and Brantford, Ontario; to see whether controlled fluoridation at 1 ppm would work as well as natural fluoridation. It did, and many subsequent studies have confirmed its effectiveness (1, 5, 6, 28, 56, 63, 72, 108, 116, 144, 151).

26. **Q.** What is meant by "optimal level" of fluoridation?

A. The optimal level is the concentration which gives maximum benefit while allowing a comfortable margin of safety. This level is about 1 ppm. Where fluoride concentration is below 1 ppm, less dental benefit occurs. Raising the concentration above 1 ppm may produce additional dental benefit, but not enough to justify the risk of staining the teeth which occurs in communities with natural fluoride levels above 3 ppm (45).

27. **Q.** Does the optimal fluoride level vary according to the climate?

A. Yes. Calculation of the optimal level takes into account individual variations in water and food consumption and allows a fair margin of safety (62). Since people drink more water in warm, dry climates, fluoride levels there are set lower than they are in cool climates. The differences are not great, however. Concentrations range from 0.7 to 1.2 ppm.

28. **Q.** How does fluoride work to prevent tooth decay?

A. There is considerable evidence that when fluoride content is increased, tooth enamel (the hard outer shell) is less prone to breakdown by acids in the mouth. As enamel incorporates fluoride into its structure, it becomes more resistant to demineralization and therefore more resistant to decay. There is also evidence that fluoride may help reduce the ability of plaque (a sticky bacterial film which produces decay) to form on the tooth surfaces (123, 127).

29. **Q.** Is water fluoridation equally effective in hard and soft water?

A. Yes. Many studies have shown that communities with similar fluoride levels but differing water hardness have similar dental decay rates (35, 77).

30. **Q.** Can the effects of fluoride in preventing tooth decay be attributed to delays in eruption of permanent teeth?

A. No. Fluoride does not affect eruption patterns of primary ("baby") teeth. Permanent teeth may erupt a little earlier in non-fluoridated areas. However, careful statistical analyses have shown that this probably occurs because children in these areas lose their primary teeth earlier as a result of tooth decay (82).

31. **Q.** Can fluoride cause faulty tooth enamel?

A. In areas where natural fluoride concentration exceeds 3 ppm, mottling appears as a brown stain of the tooth enamel (62). This discoloration occurs during tooth development and does not become worse with age. Where fluoridation is 1 ppm, mottling is slight, its incidence is low and it produces no cosmetic defects. Slight mottling is difficult for untrained observers to detect and can actually improve the appearance of teeth by making them look whiter. Many other factors besides fluoridation can cause mottling. They include injuries, childhood infections and fevers, congenital defects and some antibiotics.

32. **Q.** Can excess fluoride cause so much damage to teeth that it actually promotes decay?
A. No. Excessively high concentrations of fluoride in the water can cause severe staining and/or pitting of the enamel, but the teeth are still resistant to decay (62).

33. **Q.** Do dental insurance rates reflect confidence in fluoridation?
A. Yes. Some dental insurance companies offer reduced premiums in fluoridated communities. This can result in great savings to employers and labor unions which purchase insurance for large groups of people.

SAFETY

34. **Q.** How do scientists define the concept of drug safety?
A. The toxic level or median toxic dose ("TD50") of an ingested substance is the level or amount which would made about half the population sick. The therapeutic level or median effective dose ("ED50") is the amount or level which would benefit about half the population. The *therapeutic index* or *margin of safety* is determined by dividing the median toxic dose by the median therapeutic dose—TD50/ED50. The higher this number, the safer the therapeutic substance. Fluoride, which has a therapeutic index of well over 125, is extremely safe (62).

35. **Q.** What are the known toxic effects of fluoride?
A. Acute fluoride poisoning, caused by *very large* amounts of directly administered fluoride, has been demonstrated in animals. Its symptoms include thirst, vomiting, abdominal pain, diarrhea, excessive salivation, sweating and respiratory paralysis. A human volunteer who ingested 250 milligrams of fluoride at one time (equivalent to the amount of fluoride contained in 62 gallons of water at 1 ppm) experienced nausea and vomiting that began within two minutes and continued throughout the following day (62).

36. **Q.** Can acute fluoride poisoning result from drinking too much water which is fluoridated at 1 ppm?
A. No. An intake of approximately 31 gallons would be required to obtain the amount of fluoride (125 mg) needed to make an adult sick. It is estimated that 20 times this amount would be needed to reach a fatal dose of fluoride (62).

37. **Q.** Can chronic fluoride poisoning result from drinking too much water which is fluoridated at 1 ppm?
A. No. Chronic fluoride poisoning can result in increased bone density, calcification of ligaments and a variety of signs and symptoms including stiffness and pain, particularly in the spine. It is estimated that a daily intake exceeding 20 mg for many years is needed to bring about chronic fluoride poisoning (62). This has happened to certain workers exposed to fluoride in industrial dust and fumes, but it cannot happen as a result of drinking water fluoridated at 1 ppm.

38. **Q.** Is it safe to use fluoridated toothpaste or other topical fluorides if water is fluoridated?
A. Yes. The amount of fluoride ingested by proper use of fluoridated toothpastes, rinses or treatments in a dental office is small. These methods may provide additional benefit even in fluoridated communities (66).

39. **Q.** Can fluoride in the food supply be harmful if one drinks fluoridated water?
A. No. Almost every food and water supply contains traces of fluoride. But calculation of the optimal level of fluoride in the water takes into account individual variations in water and food consumption and allows *a considerable margin of safety*. Even when individuals in fluoridated areas ingest large amounts of seafood and tea (the two foods with the most fluoride), they still would be well within safety limits (62, 115).

40. **Q.** Does boiling of fluoridated water make it unsafe to drink?

A. No. Although boiling of fluoridated water does increase its fluoride concentration, the effect this has on overall fluoride intake is not significant. Most water that people drink is not boiled. Even when water is used to make coffee or tea, only a small amount of water is usually boiled off. When vegetables or other foods are cooked for a long time in boiling water, the remaining water will have its fluoride concentration increased, but this water is usually discarded. Even if it were not, the total amount of fluoride could not exceed what was in the water originally. Even in areas where natural fluoridation is highest, boiling has never produced any harmful effects.

41. **Q.** Does fluoride harm human growth and development?

    A. No harmful effect has ever been found on human growth and development. Nor does fluoride cause any birth defects (64, 88, 129, 148).

42. **Q.** Does fluoride inhibit growth of cells in tissue culture?

    A. Considerable skill is required to produce reliable results in experiments with tissue cultures. Although a claim was published in the early 1960's that small amounts of fluoride added to tissue culture media inhibited the growth of two types of cells, this claim has not been confirmed. Subsequent investigators found that concentrations of 10-15 ppm were needed to interfere with metabolic functions (112).

43. **Q.** Is fluoride "mutagenic" in animals?

    A. No. In 1976, two researchers (Mohamed and Chandler) reported that fluoride given to adult mice caused an increase in chromosomal abnormalities. But elaborate and better-designed experiments by others have shown no such effect, even with a fluoride concentration of 50 ppm (1).

44. **Q.** Is fluoride poisonous to body enzymes?

    A. No. Although high concentrations of fluoride can inhibit certain enzyme systems, the human body has built-in mechanisms which maintain fluoride concentration in the blood at very low levels. There is no evidence that optimally fluoridated water has any adverse effect upon enzyme action in the body (64, 87, 105, 130).

45. **Q.** Does fluoridation shorten life expectancy?

    A. No. Many studies have compared fluoridated and non-fluoridated communities. No study has shown any relationship between fluoridated water and life expectancy or death rates (21, 23, 24, 40, 44, 47, 54, 62, 92, 95, 115, 159).

46. **Q.** Does fluoridated water affect the baby before it is born?

    A. No harmful effect on either mother or baby has ever been shown to result from ingestion of water containing 1 ppm of fluoride by pregnant women; and stillbirth and infant death rates are not affected by fluoridated water (64, 74, 105, 129, 130). The placenta, which is richer in fluoride in fluoridated areas, appears to regulate the supply of fluoride to the developing baby. Several dental researchers postulate that placental transfer of fluoride may benefit teeth that are forming before birth (55, 71).

47. **Q.** Does fluoridation lead to an increased incidence of Down's syndrome (mongolism)?

    A. No. This question arose in the 1950's because of studies by a French physician named Rapaport. He claimed that the prevalence of mongoloid births was 2-3 times higher for women living in fluoridated Illinois cities than it was for women living in non-fluoridated cities. His studies were so poorly designed, however, that they are considered worthless. (For example, his "fluoridated" group included mothers from non-fluoridated areas who traveled to fluoridated cities to give birth.) Properly designed studies by others have shown no relationship between water fluoridation and the incidence of Down's syndrome (62, 115).

48. **Q.** Is fluoridation harmful to a breast-fed baby?

    A. No. The fluoride concentration of breast milk has never been demonstrated to exceed 0.2 ppm regardless of the fluoride intake of the mother. Even this low level of fluoride may benefit developing teeth (64, 99, 111, 128). Infants fed with prepared formulas receive 5-10 times as much fluoride as do breast-fed infants. This concentration (0.5-1.0) has never been shown to be harmful to infants (12, 132).

49. **Q.** Are some people allergic to fluoride?
A. Allergy to fluoride would be theoretically surprising because of the nature of its chemical properties. Allergy to fluoride has not been reported among the millions of tea drinkers or among people who come into contact with sea water (1.4 ppm fluoride). Thus if allergy to fluoride in water exists, it must be *extremely* rare and mild—or it would have been widely reported by now. A few physicians who are rabid antifluoridationists claim they have seen patients who are allergic to 1 ppm of fluoride (150); but their claims are given no credibility by the scientific community (7, 52).

50. **Q.** Does fluoridated water cause hemophilia or other difficulties with blood clotting?
A. No. Hemophilia is a hereditary disease. High concentrations of fluoride can prevent clotting of blood in a test tube, but no evidence exists that water fluoridation has any adverse effect on blood formation or clotting in humans or animals (64, 87).

51. **Q.** Does fluoride affect skin, muscle or other soft tissues in any way?
A. No. Studies have shown that fluoride does not accumulate in human soft tissues (60, 91, 133). No soft tissue changes related to fluoride concentration have ever been reported.

52. **Q.** Does fluoride accumulate in bones and damage them?
A. People exposed to industrial pollution or very high fluoride concentration for many years (8 ppm for 20 years) may develop abnormalities of their bones (64, 88, 89, 90, 125, 162). However, prolonged exposure to water containing less than 4 ppm of fluoride does not lead to such changes (9, 64, 88, 89, 90, 162). Some areas which have more than 1 ppm of fluoride have a lower incidence of osteoporosis (15, 16, 88, 89).

53. **Q.** Does high fluoride intake lead to arthritis?
A. No. Very high and prolonged intake of fluoride can result in pain and stiffness of joints. But no evidence exists that fluoridated water (even at 8 ppm as found in naturally fluoridated areas) causes arthritis (62, 115).

54. **Q.** Does fluoridation affect eyesight?
A. No. There is no evidence that water fluoridation affects any part of the eye. Even in cases where large amounts of fluoride are used to treat osteoporosis, no eye difficulties have been reported.

55. **Q.** Can fluoridated water lead to deafness?
A. No. In fact, there is evidence that a few hearing problems may be treatable with fluoride as part of the therapy (9, 34, 64, 88, 122).

56. **Q.** Does fluoride affect the endocrine system (pituitary gland, thyroid, reproductive organs, etc.)?
A. No. Fluoride at 1 ppm does not affect human endocrine gland function in any way (64, 69, 70, 86, 87, 88, 105). Humans drinking water fluoridated at 8 ppm have shown no evidence of thyroid dysfunction (64, 75, 88, 89). In fact, animals who received up to 100 ppm for more than 7 years showed no reproductive changes as a result (64, 86, 88, 128).

57. **Q.** Are diabetics at increased risk in fluoridated areas?
A. No. No relationship has ever been found between fluoride and any disease of the pancreas. If a diabetic were so uncontrolled that he had tremendous thirst and had to drink large quantities of water, he would become severely ill from diabetes long before he could be endangered by excess fluoride. With proper care, diabetics do not suffer from excessive thirst.

58. **Q.** Does fluoridated water have any adverse effect on peptic ulcers?
A. No evidence has ever been reported that fluoridation affects the incidence of peptic ulcers or any other gastrointestinal illness.

59. **Q.** Does fluoride adversely affect the liver?
A. No. Fluoride up to 100 ppm in the diet does not influence the structure or function of the liver (64, 128, 161).

60. **Q.** Can water fluoridation lead to heart disease?
A. No. Studies to date show no evidence that fluoridation is a factor in the development of any form of cardiovascular disease (43, 140).

61. **Q.** Does fluoride cause cancer?

A. No. Cancer is one of the few diseases for which there are reliable long term data on incidence. The National Cancer Institute has stated categorically that fluoridation does not increase the risk of cancer (117). Many studies have shown no relationship between water fluoridation and cancer frequency in either humans or animals. Eight recent large studies are summarized below:

Research Shows No Fluoridation-Cancer Link

Source and Date	Title and Author	Summary of Findings
British Dental Journal, March 1975	"Cancer Incidence in Relationship to Fluoride Level in Water Supplies," by Leo Kinlen	Cancer incidence and death rates throughout all of England and Wales showed no cancer-fluoride link.
California Tumor Registry Board, October 1975.	"Analyses Testing the Hypothesis That Fluoride in Drinking Water is Related to Human Cancer," by Donald Austin	Extensive mortality data from California and other U.S. areas showed no cancer-fluoride link.
Journal, National Cancer Institute, October 1976	"Fluoridated Drinking Water and the Incidence of Cancer," by Hoover et al.	Mortality data from 269 U.S. counties over a 25-year period showed no significant differences between fluoridated and non-fluoridated areas.
Austrian Journal of Stomatology, September 1977	"Fluoride in Drinking Water and Frequency of Cancer," by Binder et al.	Austrian mortality data over a 20-year period showed a *lower* cancer death rate in high-fluoride areas than in low ones.
American Journal of Epidemiology, February 1978	"Trends in Urban Mortality in Relation to Fluoridation Status," by Rogot et al.	473 cities, each with a population of 25,000 or more, showed no relationship between fluoridation and cancer death rate trends.
Public Health Reports, February 1978	"Fluoridation and Mortality," by Tokuhata et al.	24 Pennsylvania communities with a total population of 3,500,000 showed a slightly *lower* mortality from cancer in fluoridated communities.
Environmental Toxicology Division, Canadian Health Agency, March 1978	"An Analysis of Canadian Drinking Water Fluoridation and Cancer Mortality Data," by Becking et al.	Mortality data from 70 Canadian city groups over 20 years showed no differences before and after fluoridation, or between fluoridated and non-fluoridated cities.
New England Journal of Medicine, May 1978	"Mortality in Selected Cities with Fluoridated and non-Fluoridated Water Supplies," by J.D. Erickson	Mortality data from 26 cities containing 27,000,000 people showed no cancer-fluoride relationship.

62. **Q.** Does drinking fluoridated water lead to kidney disease?
A. No. Water fluoridated at 1 ppm does not damage or otherwise affect the kidneys of healthy persons, diabetics or even individuals with kidney disease (64, 86, 138, 161).

63. **Q.** Do elderly people have trouble excreting excess fluoride?
A. No. Older people actually excrete a greater percentage of excess fluoride taken orally than do younger people (153).

64. **Q.** Does fluoridated water cause impactions or losses of "wisdom teeth" (third molars)?

A. No. The jaws of modern man seem to have evolved somewhat smaller than those of our ancestors. If a full complement of teeth is kept into the late teens, the wisdom teeth—which are the last to erupt—will be less likely to have room. This is more likely to happen in fluoridated communities because the lower decay rates help people retain their other teeth (82).

65. **Q.** Can the fluoride in fluoridated toothpaste present a health hazard?
A. The concentration of fluoride is approximately 1 gram per quart of toothpaste. An individual who ate a full tube of toothpaste at one time could theoretically get sick enough from fluoride to have nausea and vomiting; but this has not been reported. Fluoride toothpastes contain an ingredient (an "emetic") to induce vomiting if too much toothpaste is swallowed. This is supposed to happen if a child, for example, were to ingest 3 ounces of fluoridated toothpaste. The usual size tube of toothpaste is 7 ounces. It is estimated that five 7-ounce tubes would have to be eaten to cause death (8).

66. **Q.** Has anyone ever died as a result of drinking fluoridated water?
A. No. A spill of hydrofluosilicic acid into the Annapolis, Maryland, public water supply on 11/11/79 contributed to the death of a man who had severe heart disease. Two days after the spill, the man received kidney dialysis water containing 50 ppm of fluoride (50 times the usual concentration). Seven other patients who had dialysis the same day became ill but recovered. A few workers at the fluoride plant where the spill occurred experienced mild symptoms, but no symptoms suggesting fluoride intoxication were reported in the community at large. Subsequent investigation revealed that a worker had failed to close a valve, that the system was not properly designed to render this error harmless, that the spill was not reported, and that the artificial kidney was not equipped, as many are, to remove fluoride from its fluid before it enters the patient. One week after the spill, water samples were analyzed throughout Annapolis and found to contain less than 1 ppm of fluoride (3).

67. **Q.** Has anyone ever died as a result of fluoride poisoning during a dental treatment?
A. In 1974, a 3-year-old Brooklyn boy died after ingesting more than 435 mg of fluoride as a result of negligence in a dental office. The child, left unsupervised, swallowed a quantity of *undiluted* fluoride mouthrinse. Prompt treatment might still have saved his life, but he was kept waiting unnecessarily after being taken to a hospital.

68. **Q.** Should fluoridation be considered a form of pollution?
A. No. In 1973, the U.S. Environmental Protection Agency issued the following statement in response to the charge that fluoridation is pollution:

> Since the safety and efficacy of water fluoridation have been well established, the Environmental Protection Agency endorses the principles of such practice. The Environmental Protection Agency does not consider the adjustment of the fluoride content of drinking water for purposes of dental decay reduction to be a form of pollution. By definition, water pollution is the addition of a substance to water which makes such water unfit for its intended use. Since adjusting the natural fluoride content of drinking water to a level which is optimal for reduction of dental decay does in no way make the water unfit for drinking, water fluoridation cannot be considered to be pollution.
>
> At the concentration used in water fluoridation, the fluoride ion has no detrimental effects on the environment. Fluoride is a natural constituent of fresh water, soil, sea water and most living organisms, often at higher concentrations than are used in water fluoridation. A recent study on the environmental impact of fluorides, conducted by the National Research Council under contract to the Environmental Protection Agency, has confirmed that the only hazard to our environment from fluoride is from industrial discharges.

69. **Q.** Is fluoridated water harmful to fish or other marine life?

A. No. All forms of fresh water marine life have lived happily for years in aquarium tanks filled with fluoridated water from public water supplies. Sea water is already "fluoridated" at 1.4 ppm.

70. **Q.** Can fluoride corrode water pipes?
A. No. In a study done in England, engineers determined that water pipe systems are unaffected even by high concentrations of fluoride (13). No corrosion takes place and no incrustations form on the pipes (25).

71. **Q.** Does adding fluoride affect other water treatments?
A. No. More than 35 chemicals may be added to public water supplies to remove objectionable bacteria, remove odor and taste, remove color, remove metals, salt, excess minerals, etc. None of the additives is affected by the addition of fluoride.

72. **Q.** Does fluoride interfere with any industry-related products or services?
A. No. Fluoride does not interfere with food processing, photographic development, electroplating, manufacturing of glass or plastics, laundering of clothes, manufacture of ice, or other commercial processes (44).

COST

73. **Q.** How much does water fluoridation cost?
A. The initial cost depends upon the amount and type of equipment that is used. A reasonable estimate is 50-55¢ per person for the first year (including equipment) and 20-25¢ per year after that (62).

74. **Q.** How does water fluoridation affect the cost of dental treatment?
A. In Sheboygan, Wisconsin, the average cost for dental care for children from birth to age 14 was $172.32 per child before fluoridation. After 20 years of fluoridation, the average cost dropped to $46.39. The Wisconsin State Board of Health estimated that the saving of $124.93 per child represented a benefit of $55.77 for every $1 invested in fluoridation (61). The Michigan Department of Health recently estimated that a family with two teenagers should save close to $400 in dental bills at a cost to the community of $12-16 for fluoridation while the children are growing up (115). Many other studies show that the cost of dental treatment drops drastically in areas which introduce fluoridation (1, 4, 5, 24, 28, 35, 37, 54, 62, 73, 78, 80, 81, 100, 107, 134, 136, 142).

75. **Q.** How much can Americans expect to save in dental bills if all of our public water supplies are fluoridated?
A. At present, only half of our population is drinking fluoridated water (37, 103). It is conservatively estimated that if the entire country were fluoridated tomorrow, an additional 25 million families might save at least $25 per family per year on dental bills. The total saving would be $625 million, about 7% of current annual dental expenditures in this country. This figure does not include the value of time no longer lost from school or work, or the social value of having more attractive teeth.

76. **Q.** Where can money be obtained to pay for fluoridation?
A. Money has never been a problem for communities that are sincerely interested in fluoridation. Sources have included federal, state, county and municipal governments; national, state and local dental societies; other health organizations; insurance companies; private industries; and foundations and other charitable organizations.

FLUORIDATION ALTERNATIVES

77. **Q.** How many Americans cannot receive fluoridated water?

A. About 35 million people (14% of the U.S. population) cannot benefit from fluoridated water because they do not obtain their water from a central water supply system (5).

78. **Q.** What alternatives exist for communities who cannot fluoridate their water supplies?

A. Several alternatives exist which can be implemented separately or in combination:

1. School water fluoridation.
2. Fluoride tablets or drops administered by parents.
3. Fluoride tablet and rinse programs in schools.
4. Topical fluorides applied 2-4 times a year by dentists or dental hygienists (5, 76, 101, 144).

79. **Q.** What are the relative cost and benefit of community-sponsored alternatives to fluoridation?

A. Water fluoridation is by far the most effective, cheapest, safest and easiest method of preventing tooth decay (1, 5, 6, 72, 116, 144, 151). The following table summarizes how it compares with other methods:

Community Alternatives to Fluoridation*

Method	% Reduction of Decay	Cost per Person per Year	Cost/Benefit Ratio**
Community water fluoridation	50-70%	20-25¢	1:50
School water fluoridation	40%	75¢	1:20
School fluoride tablets	25-35%	$1.44-$3.00	1:5
School fluoride rinse	25-35%	90¢	1:18

*Adapted from Allukian (5) and Gish (144).
**The cost/benefit ratio tells how many dollars of dental care cost are saved for each dollar invested in a fluoride program.

SOCIAL AND LEGAL ISSUES

80. **Q.** Does fluoridation violate individual liberty?

A. No. Courts in more than half the United States have heard cases based upon the contention that fluoridation violates individual rights. No court of last resort has ever ruled unfavorably on fluoridation regardless of the issues involved. Basically, the courts have reasoned that safe, proven public health measures—such as vaccination, chlorination and fluoridation—should take precedence over the wishes of "the individual." Although opponents of fluoridation assert that dental disease is not life-threatening, the courts have ruled that dental decay causes enough pain, discomfort and loss of money and time to justify fluoridation as a preventive public health measure (14, 27, 57, 113, 136).

81. **Q.** Does fluoridation violate religious liberty?

A. No. Persons claiming that fluoridation at 1 ppm violates their religious freedom have been unable to demonstrate any adverse personal effects from this alleged violation (27, 136). The fact that fluoridation occurs naturally and has no ill effects greatly weakens their argument.

82. **Q.** Is fluoridation a form of compulsory mass medication?
    A. No. Fluoride should not be considered a medication at all, because at 1 ppm in water its purpose is *prevention*, not treatment (99). Moreover, it is an essential nutrient which is found naturally in almost all foods and water supplies (65). It is a settled principle of law that a community has the right to fluoridate its water supply and is not practicing medicine by doing so (18).

83. **Q.** What trends in our society should help to promote fluoridation?
    A. People are becoming much more interested in what can be done to prevent disease and lower the cost of health care. Fluoridation is one of the best ways to accomplish both (146). Sound teeth also enhance the quality of life.

84. **Q.** What trends can make promotion of fluoridation more difficult?
    A. Distrust of government has been rising and many people wish they had more individual freedom. Distrust of "organized medicine" and others who are perceived as "running our health care system" has also been increasing. Feelings of this sort can cause people to lose sight of the health benefits of fluoridation when it is attacked as an act of "big government" or the "medical establishment."

85. **Q.** What types of judicial decisions have facilitated the implementation of fluoridation?
    A. Many state supreme court decisions have upheld the constitutionality of fluoridation and the right of state governments to mandate it. All 12 cases that were appealed to the U.S. Supreme Court were dismissed for lack of merit or failure to raise a substantial federal question (57). Three Pennsylvania cases are noteworthy. In one case, referendums on matters of public health and safety (such as fluoridation) were decreed invalid (157). In another, the court ruled that state health authorities have discretionary power to order statewide fluoridation (33). In a third, the court ruled that once a community has begun fluoridation, state health authorities may deny permission to stop it because such action would "lower the level of the public's health" (85).

86. **Q.** What problems have the courts made for fluoridation?
    A. The chief problem has been delay. After government bodies or private water companies decide to fluoridate, antifluoridationists can sometimes obtain a court order to delay implementation until whatever issues they raise have been settled. The appeal process can sometimes delay fluoridation for years (4). In a recent case (Aitkenhead vs. Borough of West View), despite overwhelming testimony to the contrary, a maverick judge concluded that fluoridation causes cancer and issued a temporary injunction against fluoridation by a private water company in suburban Pittsburgh. The order was quickly nullified by the Pennsylvania Department of Environmental Resources. Fluoridation will continue while the case is appealed on the grounds that the lower court judge lacked jurisdiction to hear the case (29, 30). Although the side of fluoridation is expected to prevail, antifluoridationists are citing the judge's decision as "proof" that fluoridation is dangerous.

OPPONENTS OF FLUORIDATION

87. **Q.** What are the main reasons why people oppose fluoridation?
    A. Some devout antifluoridationists seem to see themselves as saviors of their fellow men through opposition to fluoridation (32, 94). Others (including a few trained health professionals) seem motivated by distrust of government and alienation from the scientific establishment (119). Some opponents appear to perceive certain health measures as threats to their sense of physical or psychic wholeness (sometimes referred to as their "life space"). Such individuals may

also defend themselves against "forcible entry" of any perceived "foreign body"—whether it is fluoridation, vaccination, a mental health proposal or interracial contact (94). Most people opposed to fluoridation, however, are not devout opponents. They have simply become confused by the shrill claims of its opponents (17, 67, 118). Senior citizens, who tend to worry a great deal about their health, may be particularly vulnerable to antifluoridation scare tactics.

88. **Q.** Who are fluoridation's most active opponents?

A. Since it began, fluoridation has encountered opposition from scattered groups and individuals. Many have been associated with the "health food" industry—which aligns fluoridation with its general propaganda that our food supply is "poisoned" (10). Chiropractors have opposed fluoridation as an interference with "free choice of health care." Christian Scientists have regarded fluoridation as "forced medication," and right-wing groups such as the John Birch Society and the Ku Klux Klan have seen it as an unwarranted government intrusion (17, 94). Rodale Press, publisher of *Prevention* magazine, opposed fluoridation vigorously until the death of its founder, J.I. Rodale, in 1971. *Prevention*'s current executive editor realizes that fluoridation prevents cavities, but the magazine has not so informed its readers (10).

The most effective antifluoridation group is the National Health Federation (NHF), a health food industry organization whose activities are described in detail in Chapter 2 of this book. In 1974, NHF announced that opposing fluoridation would be its number two priority and hired a biochemist named John Yiamouyiannis to do the job (102). For more than five years, Yiamouyiannis served effectively as a consultant to most local and state groups which fought against fluoridation. In March 1980, after a falling out with other NHF leaders, he left the organization.

89. **Q.** Why are antifluoridationists often successful?

A. Devout "antis," though few in number, tend to be persistent, highly vocal and politically sophisticated. Their battle plans require only a small number of people to carry them out effectively (10). Proponents tend to underestimate the amount of effort needed to secure fluoridation.

90. **Q.** What tactics do antifluoridationists use?

A. The basic technique is to create doubts in the minds of citizens by blaming fluoridation for a large number of diseases and other problems. Even though these claims are baseless—or even boldfaced lies—if they are repeated often enough, many people will feel there is some truth to them.

POLITICS OF FLUORIDATION

91. **Q.** What is unique about fluoridation that sets it apart from other public health measures?

A. Fluoridation has four unique attributes:
   1. It is a copy of a naturally occurring phenomenon.
   2. More than 20,000 studies support its safety and effectiveness.
   3. It is endorsed by a variety of civic and scientific groups which could hardly be expected to agree on any other single measure (10).
   4. It is the only public health measure

which has been subjected to public vote.

92. **Q.** By what actions may fluoridation be obtained?

A. The laws applying to fluoridation vary from state to state. Fluoridation may be ordered by state legislatures, local government bodies, boards of health, water company officials, or other officials who are empowered to do so. Referendums are permitted in most states and are required in a few.

93. **Q.** How many states have laws intended to provide statewide fluoridation?

A. Eight: Connecticut (1965), Minnesota (1967), Illinois (1967), Michigan (1968), Ohio (1969), South Dakota (1969), Georgia (1973) and Nebraska (1973).

94. **Q.** How was the decision made in communities which are fluoridating?

A. As of 1975, there were 9,425 American communities drinking fluoridated water (5). Natural fluoridation accounted for 2,650 of these. The rest obtained it as follows:

Vote of governing body	4,899 (72%)
Public vote	503 (7%)
Decision of utility commission	219 (3%)
Other means	290 (4%)
Not reported	884 (13%)

95. **Q.** How do most citizens feel about fluoridation?

A. Most people favor fluoridation but do not regard it as a high priority issue. As a result of education by dental professionals and frequent exposure to television commercials for fluoride toothpastes, almost everyone knows that fluoride prevents cavities. Left alone, most people are content to have government officials follow expert advice in routine technical matters. A well organized antifluoridation scare campaign can mobilize doubts, particularly when political leaders are indecisive. But once fluoride is in the water, all but the most devout antis will give it little thought. Some fluoridated communities have installed special non-fluoridated taps in response to anti demands for "freedom of choice," but use of such taps is minimal. Brainerd, Minnesota, is a city which resisted a mandatory state law for more than 10 years. After fluoridation was begun, only 2 people per thousand used the special tap. Sales of bottled water did not increase and home appliances to filter out the fluorides went unsold.

96. **Q.** How do most public officials feel about fluoridation?

A. Most public officials understand the benefits of fluoridation and favor it—at least privately. To vote for it, they either have to be statesmen or feel there is little or no political risk in supporting it openly. Few citizens perceive fluoridation as important enough to base their vote solely on a legislator's stand on this one issue, but the commotion made by devout antis sometimes makes legislators overestimate the risk of acting on fluoridation's behalf. The key to convincing a legislator is understanding the bottom line of his concern. A demonstration of widespread public support for fluoridation may be necessary to secure his help.

97. **Q.** Why do antifluoridationists like referendums?

A. Referendums take the decision-making process away from public officials who are likely to consult experts and reach a correct understanding of the issue. Voters are much easier to confuse. Referendums also give status to the antis and provide a forum for their scare tactics. A citizen doesn't have to believe *all* the false claims made against fluoridation in order to vote against it in a referendum. One unresolved doubt may be enough.

98. **Q.** Do antifluoridationists usually accept the results of a public vote if fluoridation wins?

A. No. Quite often they will seek another referendum or file suit to prevent fluoridation from starting.

99. **Q.** How can a citizen separate fact from fiction in a fluoridation controversy?

A. The best approach is to find out from a trusted professional person (such as a physician) which side is telling the truth.

100. **Q.** How do U.S. Congressmen feel about fluoridation?

A. Federal legislators are not eager to involve themselves in a controversy as volatile as fluoridation if they can avoid it—particularly when there is considerable public feeling that government is already too intrusive in our lives (152). On the other hand, many Congressmen realize that fluoridation is beneficial and can help reduce both public and governmental expenses for dental care (116). The "compromise" so far has been to make federal funds available on a voluntary basis to support new fluoridation efforts at the state and community levels. Although a federal law to mandate fluoridation throughout the nation would be of great benefit, it will be a difficult thing to achieve. During the 1979 budgetary hearings, while Congressmen were considering an increase in financial support for fluoridation, they were blitzed by a National Health Federation campaign but received almost no mail favoring fluoridation (143). Passage of a national fluoridation law would require a vigorous campaign by a coalition of major health organizations backed by considerable grassroots support.

REFERENCES*

1. A two-part report on fluoridation. Consumer Reports, July-Aug., 1978.

2. ADA News. Chicago, Apr. 14, 1980., p. 4.

3. APHA Newsletter, Dental Health Section. Washington, May, 1980, p. 5.

4. Allukian, M. et al. Community organization and a regional approach to fluoridation of Greater Boston. Presented at the 104th Annual Meeting, APHA, Oct. 1978.

5. Allukian, M. Effective community prevention programs (Chap. 14). In Handbook of Preventive Dentistry, DePaola, D.P. and Cheney, J.G. (Eds.). Publishing Services Group, Inc., Littleton, Mass., 1979.

6. Allukian, M. Fluoridation. An essential component of a health service plan or state health plan. DHEW, HRA 230-76-0078, p. 5.

7. AMA Re-emphasizes Endorsement of Fluoridation. Dept. HEW, FL-73, Feb. 1975.

8. Austin, A. (Technical manager, Proctor & Gamble, Cincinnati) Personal communication.

9. Azar, H.A. et al. Skeletal sclerosis due to chronic fluoride intoxication. Ann. Intern. Med. 55:193, 1961.

*10. Barrett, S. (Ed.) The Health Robbers (2nd Ed.) Chapters 2, 5, 12, 16, 19). George F. Stickley Co., Philadelphia, 1980.

11. Bawden, J.W. et al. Current concepts of fluoride therapy. N.C. Dent. J. 60(4):21-4, Autumn, 1977.

12. Behrmann, G. et al. Do human breast milk fluoride levels reflect water fluoride levels? Chronicle 41(9):170-5, Nov., 1978.

13. Bellack, E. Fluoridation engineering manual. Environmental Protection Agency, Water Supply Programs Div. (1972), Chapter IX.

14. Bergen, R.P. Legal status of fluoridation. JAMA 211:555,1970.

15. Bernstein, D.S., Sadowsky, N., Hegsted, D.M., Guir, C.D. and Stare, F.J. Prevalence of osteoporosis in high- and low-fluoride areas in North Dakota. JAMA 198:499-504, 1966.

16. Bernstein, D.S. and Cohen, P. Use of sodium fluoride in the treatment of osteoporosis. J. Clin. Endocr. 27:197-210, Feb. 1967.

17. Bickel, H.W. The politics of fluoridation. J. Prev. Dent. 6:107-111, 1980.

18. Butler, H.W. Legal aspects of fluoridating community water supplies. JADA 65:653, 1962.

19. Call, R.A., Leone, N.C. and Davis, R.V. Summary of histopathological and chemical findings with respect to fluorides. Utah Study Arch. Ind. Hygiene 21:341, 1960.

20. Cariostatic mechanisms of fluorides: Summary and recommendations for research. Caries Res., 11 Suppl. 1:322-7, 1977.

21. Castaldi, C.R. and Pelletier, B.A. A 22-year follow-up study of fluoridation in New Britain, CT. (Presented April 1975 at the American Association for Dental Research, New York.)

22. Charen, J. et al. Bone fluoride concentrations associated with fluoridated drinking water. Calcif. Tissue Int. 27(2):95-9, Apr. 17, 1979.

23. Cholak, J. Current information on the quantities of fluoride found in air, food and water. AMA Arch. Ind. Hlth. (21)312-315, 1960.

24. Chrietzberg, J.E. Georgia's water fluoridation program. J. Am. Dent. Assoc. 65:643-647, 1962.

25. Clarification of the relationship between fluoride compounds and corrosion in potable water distribution systems. Dept. HEW, PHS, CDC, FL-89, Aug. 1976.

26. Clark, C.A. Fluoridation: The Cleveland experience, an epidemiological classic and the status in Ohio. Ohio Dent. J. 51(9):40-5, Sept., 1977.

27. Clark, R.E. and Sophy, M.M. Fluoridation: The courts and the opposition. Wayne Law Review 13:338-375, 1967.

*References marked with an asterisk are especially recommended.

28. Cohen, A., Soricelli, D.A. and Ship, I.I. The effects of fluoridation on dental caries in Philadelphia Public School Children, 1954-1964. PA Dent. J. 32(2):47-55, 1965.

29. Commonwealth of Pennsylvania: Letter to Deputy Secretary for Environmental Protection by the Secretary of Health, Dec. 21, 1978.

30. Court Cases: HEW, PHS, CDC, DDPA/April, 1980.

31. Cox, G.J. and Nathans, S.W. J. Am. Water Works Assn. 44:940, 1952.

*32. Crain, R.L. et al. The politics of community conflict, the fluoridation decision. Bobbs-Merrill, Indianapolis, 1969.

33. Crawford vs. Speller, Commonwealth Court of Pennsylvania, 1973.

34. Dace, O., Kramer, L., Wiatrowski, E. and Spencer, H. Dietary fluoride intake in man. J. Nutr. 104:1313-1318, 1974.

35. Dean, H.J. Dental caries fluorine. Am. Assn. Adv. Sav., Washington, 1946.

36. Dental health after ten years of fluoridation. Connecticut Health Bull., Spring, 1979.

37. Dowell, T.B. The economics of fluoridation. Brit. Dent. J. 140(3):103-6, Feb. 3, 1976.

38. Driscoll, W.S. et al. Dosage recommendations for dietary fluoride supplements. Am. J. Dis. Child 133(7):683-4, 1979.

39. Duckworth, S.C. et al. The ingestion of fluoride in tea. Brit. Dent. J. 145(12):368-70, Dec. 19, 1978.

40. Dudney, G.R., Rozier, R.G., Less, M.F. and Hughes, J.T. Ten years of fluoridation in Asheville, NC. N.C. Dent. J., Autumn, 1977, pp. 11-16.

41. Dunning, J.M. Current status of fluoridation. N. Eng. J. Med. 272:30-34, 84-88, Jan. 7 and 14, 1965.

42. Dwore, R.B. a case study of the 1976 referendum in Utah on fluoridation. Publ. Health Rep. 93:73-8, Jan.-Feb. 1978.

43. Ekstrand, J. Relationship between fluoride in the drinking water and the plasma fluoride concentration in man. Caries Res. 12(3):123-7, 1978.

*44. Elwell, K.R. and Easlick, K.A. Classification and appraisal of objections to fluoridation. University of Michigan, Ann Arbor, MI, 1957.

45. Englander, H.R. Is 1 ppm fluoride in drinking water optimum for dental caries prevention? J. Am. Dent. Assoc. 98(2):186-7, 1979.

46. Erickson, J.D., et al. Water fluoridation and congenital malformations: No association. J. Am. Dent. Assoc. 93(5):981-4, 1976.

47. Erickson, J.D. 1978 Mortality in selected cities with fluoridated and non-fluoridated water supplies. N. Eng. J. Med., May 18, 1978, pp. 1112-1116.

48. Ericsson, Y. Report on the safety of drinking water fluoridation. Caries Res., Suppl. 8:16-27, 1974.

49. Evans, C. and Pickles, T. Statewide antifluoridation initiatives: A new challenge to health workers. Am. J. Public Health 68:59-62, 1978.

*50. Facts about fluoridation. American Dental Association Council on Dental Health Publication, Aug., 1978.

51. Faine, R.C. An agenda for the eighties: Community and school fluoridation. Presented at The Amer. Assoc. Dental Research Annual Meeting, March 20, 1980.

52. Feingold, B.F. Fluoridation: On balance, it becomes evident the benefits far outweigh any potential risks. Dept. HEW, 00-3209 FL-100, July, 1978.

53. Fidler, P.E. A comparison of treatment patterns and costs for a fluoride and non-fluoride community. Community Health (Bristol) 9(2):103-13, 1977.

54. Flavan, B.M. Minnesota Dept. of Health, Publication Document, Feb. 1977. Benefits of eleven years of fluoridated water—The Winona Report.

55. Fleen, F.B. Immunity conveyed by sodium-fluoride supplement during pregnancy: Part II. ASDC J. Dent. Child. 46(1):17024, 1979.

56. Fluoridation. CDC Atlanta, DDPA Report, Apr. 1980.

57. Fluoridation: A constitutional issue. Univ. Minn. School of Dentistry, 1977.

58. Fluoridation facts. American Dental Association, 1974, p. 17.

*59. Fluoridation facts. American Dental Association Publication, 1979.

60. Fluoridation in Newcastle and Northumberland. Brit. Dent. J. 142, June 21, 1977.

61. Fluoridation News. Wisconsin State Board of Health (3), No. 2, Apr. 1966.

*62. Fluoridation of water supplies. The British Dent. Assoc., Jan. 1976.

63. Fluoridation: Slow diffusion of a proved preventive measure. Washington, DC, N. Eng. J. Med. 296(19):1118-20, May 12, 1977.

64. Fluorides and Human Health. World Health Organization, Geneva, 1970.

65. Food and Nutrition Board of the National Research Council. Recommended Dietary Allowances, 1980.

*66. Forrester, D.J. and Schultz, E.M. Transcript of the International Workshop of Fluorides and Dental Caries Reduction. Dept. of Pedodontics, University of Maryland School of Dentistry, Baltimore, 1974.

67. Frazier, J.P. Fluoridation: A review of social research. Presented at the Amer. Assoc. Dental Res. Annual Meeting, March, 1980.

68. Fremlin, J.H. and Challin, L.P. Brit. Dent. J. 114:497, 1963.

69. Geever, E.F., Leone, N.C., Geiser, P. and Lieberman, J. Pathologic studies in man after prolonged ingestion of fluoride in drinking water. I. Necropsy findings in a community with a water level of 2.5 ppm. JADA 56:499-507, 1958.

70. Geever, E.F., Leone, N.C., Geiser, P., Lieberman, J. Pathologic studies in man after prolonged ingestion of fluoride in drinking water. II. Findings in bones in communities with water levels from 1.0 to 4.0 ppm fluoride. Public Health Rep. 73:721-731, 1958.

71. Glenn, F.B. Immunity conveyed by a fluoride supplement during pregnancy. J. Dent. Child. 44(5):391-5, 1977.

72. Healthy People. The surgeon general's report on health promotion and disease prevention. U.S. DHEW Publication No. 79-55071.

73. Heifetz, S.B. et al. Effect on school water fluoridation on dental caries; results in Seagrove, NC, after eight years. J. Am. Dent. Assoc. 97(2):193-6, 1978.

74. Hodge, H.C. and Smith, F.A. Fluorides and man. Ann. Rev. Pharmacol. 8:395-408, 1968.

75. Hoogstratten, B., Leone, N.C., Shupe, J.L., Greenwood, D.A. and Lieberman, J. Effect of fluorides on hematopoietic system, liver and thyroid gland in cattle. JAMA 192:26-32, 1965.

76. Horowitz, H.S. School water fluoridation for the prevention of dental caries. Int. Dent. J. 23:346.

77. Jackson, D. et al. Brit. Dent. J. 139:119, 1975.

78. Jordan, W.A. Eighteen years of fluoridated water as a caries inhibitor—Red Lake Falls. Northwest Dentistry 49:231-234, 1970.

79. Jowsey, J., Riggs, B.L., Kelly, P.J. and Hoffman, D.L. Effect of combined therapy with sodium fluoride, vitamin D and calcium on osteoporosis. Am. J. Med. 53:43-49, 1972.

80. Keene, H.J. et al. Prevalence of caries-free naval recruits from cities with fluoridated and non-fluoridated water supplies. J. Dent. Res. 55(4):704, 1976.

*81. Knutson, J.W. Water fluoridation after 25 years. JADA 80:765-9, 1970.

82. Kunzel, W. Influence of water fluoridation on the eruption of permanent teeth. Caries Res. 10(2):96-103, 1976.

83. Larson, R.H. An extensive review of animal studies relating to caries inhibition by fluoride. Caries Res., J. European Org. for Caries Res. (ORCA), Vol. 11, Suppl. 1, 1977.

84. Lawson, J.S. et al. The dental health revolution: The dramatic improvement in dental health of school children in the northern metropolitan region of New South Wales. Med. J. Aust. 1(3):124-5, Feb. 11, 1978.

85. Lebanon Decision. Commonwealth v. City of Lebanon, 393 A.2d 381 (Pennsylvania). Supreme Court of Pennsylvania, Oct. 5, 1978.

86. Leone, N.C., Geever, E.F., Moran, N.C. Acute and subacute toxicity studies of sodium fluoride in animals. Public Health Rep. 71(5):459-467, 1956.

87. Leone, N.C., Hoogstratten, S. and Shupe, J.L. The effects of fluoride on the hematopoietic system. A 7½ year study. JAMA 192:112-118, 1965.

88. Leone, N.C., Shimkin, M.B., Arnold, F.A., Stevenson, C.A., Zimmerman, E.R., Geiser, P.A. and Lieberman, J. Medical aspects of excessive fluoride in water supply. A 10 year study. Public Health Rep. 69:925-936, 1954.

89. Leone, N.C., Stevenson, C.A., Hilbish, T.F. and Sosman, M.C. A roentgenologic study of a human population exposed to high fluoride domestic water. A 10 year study. Amer. J. Roentgen. 74:874-885, 1955.

90. Leone, N.C., Stevenson, C.A., Besse, B., Hawes, L.E., Dawber, T.R. and Claffey, W.J. The effects of the absorption of fluoride. II. A radiologic investigation of 546 human residents in an area in which the drinking water contained only a minute trace of fluoride. AMA Arch. Ind. Health 21:326-327, 1970.

91. Leone, N.C., Stinson, J. and Sunbury, R.T. The effects of the absorption of fluoride. Comparison of the physiologic and pathologic characteristics. Comparison of two cases. AMA Arch. Ind. Hygiene 21:335, 1960.

*92. Leukhart, C.S. An update on water fluoride: Triumphs and new challenges. National Symposium on Dental Nutrition. S.H.Y. Wei (Ed.) DHEW, HSA, Office of Maternal and Child Health. Project No. 347, pp. 36-46, 1979.

93. Mainwaring, P.J. et al. A three-year clinical study to determine the separate and combined caries-inhibiting effects of sodium monofluorophosphate toothpaste and an acidulated phosphate-fluoride gel. Caries Res. 12(4):202-12, 1978.

*94. Marmor, J., Bernard, V.W. and Ottenberg, P. Psychodynamics of group opposition to health programs. Amer. J. Orthopsychiatry, 1960, p. 339.

95. McClure, F.J. Water fluoridation. The search and the victory. U.S. Dept. of Health, Education and Welfare. National Institutes of Health, National Institute of Dental Research, Bethesda, MD, 1970.

96. McQueen, P.R. Fluorides: Past-present-future. Canad. Forces Dent. Serv. Q. 19(2):5-8, 1978

64

(Eng. Fre.).

97. Melberg, J.R. et al. Short intensive topical APF applications and dental caries in a fluoridated area. Community Dent. Oral Epidemiol. 6(3):117029, 1978.

98. Messer, L.B. et al. Fluoride mouthrinses. Northwest Dent. 57(2):96-100, 1978.

99. Mitchell, J.D. Fluoridation: Scientific, economic and medicolegal aspects. J. Miss. State Assoc. 14:483-487, 1973.

100. Moncrief, E.W., Jr. Results of eleven years of fluoridation in Fayette, AL. J. Ala. Dent. Assoc. 54:18-25, 1970.

101. Murray, J.J. Fluoride supplements—alternatives to water fluoridation. R. Soc. Health J. 97:48-51, 1977.

102. National Health Federation. Letter to its membership dated November 1, 1974.

103. Nelson, W. et al. Cost-benefit analysis of fluoridation in Houston, TX. J. Public Health Dept. 36(2):88-95, Spring, 1976.

104. Newbrun, E. Fluorides and Dental Caries. Charles C Thomas Pub., Springfield, IL, 1973.

*105. Newbrun, E. The safety of water fluoridation. JADA 94:301-304, 1977.

106. Oswald, J.D. Fluoridation—the present case. The economics of fluoridation or how better to spend our pounds. R. Soc. Health J. 97:45-47, 1977.

107. Palmer, C.A. Fluoridation economics—reason enough to pick up where we left off in the 1960's. J. Am. Dent. Assoc. 99(1):59-60, 1979.

108. Parviainen, K. et al. Occurrence of dental caries and gingivitis in low, medium and high fluoride areas in Finland. Community Dent. Oral Epidemiol. 5(6):287-91, 1977.

109. Petterson, E.O. The decision to fluoridate: The impact on the elected officials and the community power structures. J. Publ. Health Dent. 29:153-169, Summer, 1969.

110. Philadelphia shows dramatic drop in decay. Bull. Phila. City Dent. Soc. 41(5):4, 1976.

111. Phillips, P.H., Hart, E.B. and Bohstedt, G. The influence of fluoride ingestion upon the nutritional qualities of milk. J. Biol. Chem. 105:123, 1934.

112. Proffit, W.R. and Ackerman, J.L. Science 145:932, 1964.

*113. Quimby, F.P. Fluoridation: A modern paradox in science and public policy. Washington, DC, The Library of Congress Legislative Reference Service, Feb. 17, 1970, pp. 92-103.

114. Rapaport, I. Bull. Acad. National Med. 140:529, 1956.

*115. Reizen, M.S. Michigan Dept. of Pub. Health Policy Statement on Fluoridation of Community Water Supplies and Synopsis of Fundamentals of Relation of Fluorides and Fluoridation to Human Health, 1979.

116. Report to the Congress. Reducing tooth decay—more emphasis on fluoridation needed. U.S. General Accounting Office, HRD-79-3, Apr. 13, 1979.

117. Research shows no mutagenic effects from fluoride. Dept. HEW, FL-95, 00-3092, Sept. 1977.

118. Sapolsky, H.M. Science, voters and the fluoridation controversy. Science 162:427-433, 1968.

119. Sapolsky, H.M. Social science views of a controversy in science and politics. Am. J. Clin. Nutrition 22:1397, Oct. 1969.

120. Schamschula, R.G. et al. Contribution of length of exposure to fluoridated water to explanation of variation in caries experience. Caries Res. 13(4):238-40, 1979.

121. Schulz, E.M. et al. Fluoride content of popular carbonated beverages. J. Prev. Dent. 3(1):27-9, 1976.

122. Shambaugh, G.E. Ten years experience with fluoride in otosclerotic patients. Ann. Otol. 83:635-642, 1974.

123. Shannon, I.L. Biochemistry of fluoride in saliva. Caries Res. 11 Suppl. 1:205-25, 1977.

124. Shannon, I.L. The fluoride concentration in drinking water of fluoridating communities in Texas. Tex. Dent. J. 96(6):10-2, 1978.

125. Sharma, R.P. et al. Fluoride accumulation in bone and the effect on their physical properties in guinea pigs given different levels of fluoridated water. Clin. Toxicol. 11(3):329-39, 1977.

126. Sheiham, A. Prevention and control of periodontal disease. Section 6 in International Conference on Research in the Biology of Periodontal Disease, 1977, pp. 309-368.

127. Shimura, N. et al. The effect of NaF on the bacterial production of hydroxyapatite. J. Dent. Res. 57(9-10):928-31, 1978.

128. Shupe, J.L., Miner, M.L., Greenwood, D.A., Harris, L.E. and Stoddard, G.E. The effect of fluorine on dairy cattle. II. Clinical and pathologic effects. Am. J. Vet. Res. 24:964-984, 1963.

129. Shupe, J.L. and Alther, E.W. Handbuch der experimentellen pharmackologe. Vol. XX/1, Pharmacology of Fluorides, Chapter 6. Springer-Verlag, Berlin, 1966, pp. 307-354.

130. Shupe, J.L. Clinical and pathological effects of fluoride toxicity in animals. In Carbon-fluorine Compounds; Chemistry, Biochemistry and Biological Activities. Cilia Foundation. Associated Scientific Publishers, Amsterdam, 1972, pp. 357-388.

131. Shupe, J.L., Nicholas, J.L. and Fletcher, D.C.

Efficacy and safety of fluoridation. AMA Publication #0138:502-L, 1975.

132. Singer, L. et al. Total fluoride intake of infants. Pediatrics 63(3):460-6, 1979.

133. Smith, F.J., Gardiner, D.E., Leone, N.C. and Hodge, H.C. The chemical determination of fluoride in human soft tissues. AMA Arch. Ind. Hygiene 21:330-332, 1960.

134. Spears, N.D. Reconsidering the 1975 census of the U.S. communities which provide naturally fluoridated waters. J. Public Health Dent. 19(2):102-11, Spring, 1979.

135. Stamm, J.W. and Banting, D.W. Comparison of root caries prevalence in adults with life-long residence in fluoridated and non-fluoridated communities. J. Dent. Res., March, 1980, Abstr. 552.

136. Strong, G.A. Liberty, religion and fluoridation. JADA 76:1398, June, 1968.

137. Svatum, B. Plaque-inhibiting effect of dentifrices containing stannous fluoride. Acta Odontol. Scand. 36(4):205-10, 1978.

138. Taves, D.R., Terry, R., Smith, F.A. and Gardner, D.E. Use of fluoridated water in long-term hemodialysis. Arch. Intern. Med. 115:167-172, Feb. 1965.

139. Taves, D.R. University of Rochester, 1977.

140. Taves, D.R. Fluoridation and mortality due to heart disease. Nature 272(5651):361-2, March 23, 1978.

141. Ten years of fluoridation in Perth, Western Australia. Australian Dental J. 23, No. 6, Dec. 1978.

142. Teuscher, G.W. Fluoridation in an era of limited expenditure for health care (Editorial). ASDC J. Dent. Child. 45(5):355, 1978.

143. The Nation's Health. March, 1980, p. 7.

144. The relative efficiency of methods of caries prevention in dental public health. Proceedings of a workshop at the University of Michigan, June 5-8, 1978. Brian Burt (Ed.). Also, Gish, G.W., pp. 49-54.

145. Tijmstra, T. et al. Effect of socioeconomic factors on the observed caries reduction after fluoride tablet and fluoride toothpaste consumption. Community Dent. Oral Epidemiol. 6(5):227-30, 1978.

146. Training manual on Community Organization for Preventive Programs: Fluoridation: An example of how to organize a communal program for reduction of disease/injury. Dept. Health and Human Services, PHS, CDC, Atlanta, GA.

147. Tweedle, J. and Lagstein, M. Fluoridation debate. J. Bergen Cty. Dent. Soc. 41(4):9-11, Jan. 17, 1975.

148. USPHS Report. Fluoride: An essential mineral nutrient. PPB67, 1974.

149. Wadden, J.V. The Winona fluoridation success story. Northwest Dentistry, May-June, 1977, pp. 127-128.

150. Waldbott, G.L. Int. Arch. Allerg. 12:347, 1958.

151. Walsh, D.C. Fluoridation: Slow diffusion of a proved preventive measure. N. Engl. J. Med. 296:1118-20, May 12, 1977.

152. Washington Explained. J. Dent. Child. 46:345-8, July-Aug. 1979.

153. Weatherall, J.A. In Mineral metabolism in paediatrics (Ed. by Bartrop, D. et al.). Blackwell Publ., Oxford, 1969.

154. Weatherall, J.A. et al. Assimilation of fluoride by enamel throughout the life of the tooth. Caries Res., 11 Suppl., 1:85-115, 1977.

155. Whittle, J.G. et al. Dental health and treatment needs of Birmingham and Salford school children. A comparison in a fluoridated and non-fluoridated area. Brit. Dent. J. 147(3):67-71, Aug. 7, 1979.

156. Why we recommend fluoridation. Amer. Dental Assoc. Publication, 1979.

157. Williamsport Decision. Commonwealth Court of Pennsylvania, 434 (1969), filed April 7, 1972.

158. Woodhouse, A.D. A longitudinal study of the effectiveness of self-applied 10 percent stannous fluoride paste for secondary school children. Aust. Dent. J. 23(5):422-8, 1978.

159. Yacovone, J.A. and Parente, A.M. Twenty years of community water fluoridation: The prevalence of dental caries among Providence, RI, school children. Rhode Island Dent. J., June, 1974, pp. 3-7, 18.

160. Zharan, M. Effect of topically applied acidulated phosphate on dental caries. Community Dent. Oral Epidemiol. 4(6):240-3, 1976.

161. Zipkin, I. and Leone, N.C. Fluoride content of urinary and biliary calculi. Proc. Soc. Exp. Biol. and Med. 97:650-653, 1958.

162. Zipkin, I., McClure, F.J., Leone, N.C. and Lee, W.A. Fluoride deposition in human bones after prolonged ingestion of fluorides in drinking water. Public Health Rep. 73:732-640, 1958.

PART THREE

FIGHTING FOR TEETH

FLUORIDATION CAMPAIGN TIPS

*A successful fluoridation campaign is
likely to require many years of hard work
by many people.*

STEPHEN BARRETT, M.D.
Chairman, Board of Directors
Lehigh Valley Committee Against Health Fraud, Inc.

and
SHELDON ROVIN, D.D.S., M.S.
Professor and Chairman,
Department of Dental Care Systems
University of Pennsylvania

The most important ingredients in a fluoridation campaign are hard work, organization and persistence. Although this chapter is written in an authoritarian tone and presents a "cookbook" approach, there is actually no single success formula.

The chapter is intended to be comprehensive. While it contains most of the ingredients for a successful campaign, it would be unrealistic to expect everyone to do everything it describes. You should implement the ideas that seem most suitable for *your* community.

The ultimate goal of a campaign, of course, is either to persuade appropriate government officials to implement fluoridation or to win a referendum. If you have a choice, it is better to avoid a referendum. Persuading intelligent government officials is much simpler than winning a referendum where the public will be subjected to the scare tactics and distortions of antifluoridationists.

Since fluoridation offers great benefits at minimal cost with virtually zero risk, you might think that convincing a small group of local officials is an easy task. Just present the facts, and your dedicated public servants will quickly put them to use. While this does happen occasionally, in most communities it will not. *A successful fluoridation campaign is likely to require many years of hard work by a lot of people.* For a referendum, you can *never* have too many volunteers.

The First Step

The best way to begin your campaign is to form a steering committee composed of people willing to invest 5-10 hours a month for as long as it takes to complete the job. The committee should be small at first, about 6-8 members, but it can be expanded to 8-12 members after the first few months. If too few people are involved, an undue burden will fall on each one. *The committee should meet twice monthly at set times until it is clear that meeting less often will not interfere with its effectiveness.* Without routinely scheduled meetings, a group is unlikely to become cohesive enough to work smoothly under stress.

The steering committee's role will be to explore the situation, to design a campaign plan and to oversee implementation of the plan. An ideal committee would include persons from a variety of ethnic, racial and occupational backgrounds. An attorney, a dentist, a physician, a public health official, a teacher, a communications expert and an experienced executive could each provide valuable perspective. Someone who has had experience in managing a political campaign or working for an elected official could also be invaluable. *However, the most important characteristic of a good committee member is the willingness to make a firm commitment of time and energy.* There is no room for deadwood on a steering committee!

The committee's first task should be a community assessment or preliminary survey which includes the following subjects:

1. What is the existing level of fluoride in the community water supply?
2. How can it be adjusted to the effective range?
3. Who has the legal authority to order the adjustment?
4. Who would implement such a decision?
5. Have there been any previous attempts to gain fluoridation for the community? What took place? What was done right? What was done wrong?
6. What health professional organizations might support fluoridation?
7. What other community organizations will endorse it?
8. Is there more than just professional support? How can this support be mobilized?
9. Which prominent or influential citizens might endorse, work actively or help lead the fluoridation campaign? How should these individuals be approached?
10. Who might be opposed to fluoridation? What is their strength?
11. What are the community's media out-

lets? A complete list of TV and radio stations, newspapers and magazines should be compiled. The names, mailing addresses and telephone numbers of key media officials (station managers, editors, news directors, producers and talk show hosts) should be recorded.
12. Tooth decay rates, dental disease costs and dentally related absence rates from work and school are important data. Are these data available? If not, can they be obtained? (Health Systems Agencies can often be helpful in this regard.)
13. How can funds be raised for the campaign?
14. What literature might be useful in explaining fluoridation to community leaders and to the general public? A supply of basic publications should be on hand for the next step.

If governmental action is your ultimate goal, it is unlikely to take place unless the involved officials feel that fluoridation will be accepted by the community. This will require a program of community education. Such a program will be even more important if a public vote on the issue is necessary. The next step is therefore to organize a citizen's committee for the purpose of conducting an educational campaign. This committee will need knowledgeable professionals as members, but *its composition should reflect all of the forces that can influence your community's attitudes.*

The Citizens' Committee

Physicians and dentists will obviously be needed to help with the scientific side of fluoridation. Other health professionals—nurses, pharmacists, podiatrists, dietitians, optometrists, dental hygienists, medical and dental assistants, hospital administrators and other health organization executives might also provide strong support for the committee's efforts. An engineer and a chemist could provide advice on the technical aspects of fluoridation. One or more attorneys should be recruited who will offer advice and other services free-of-charge. Teachers or school administrators could be very helpful in overseeing an educational program in the school system. Science teachers might also be interested in helping with public speaking. An expert in public relations is also essential to help with media relations and speaker training.

Besides these professionals, you will want persons who represent a cross-section of the community—people who have talent, experience and influence. As you look at your community power structure, think in these terms. You may have large religious or ethnic groups. Business and labor are both potent elements. All age groups should have spokespeople. The same goes for all economic and educational levels. Where possible, people with political know-how should be enlisted in the cause.

Many organizations in your community should be represented. Parent-teacher and child welfare groups may be particularly important. The Chamber of Commerce, luncheon and civic clubs, religious organizations, lodges, social clubs, women's groups, youth groups and senior citizen organizations may be interested.

In every community there are people who do not hold formal office in organizations or government but who do wield considerable influence. They should be identified and asked for help.

Don't forget that you will need more than just "big names" in the community. You will need citizens who are liked, respected and willing to work. You need people who know their way around and who know how to get things done. Such people can be found in any organization or occupation and at every economic level.

As the list of prospects for the citizens' committee is being developed, a member of the steering committee should make contact with each one. A personal meeting (over lunch or in the prospect's home) will be the best way in most instances. Prospective committee members should welcome a chance to exchange ideas and get a feeling for the campaign by meeting one of its involved leaders. Basic fluoridation literature should be provided, and each prospect should be asked about his ability to attend meetings and participate in committee projects.

Once a sufficient number and diversity of people have agreed to join the citizens' committee, an organizational meeting should be called. A member of the steering committee should serve as temporary chairman. Communication will be facilitated if each participant is given a nametag. The meeting should follow an agenda which begins with a brief discussion of the need for fluoridation and the goals of the committee (community education followed by governmental action and, if necessary, a referendum). A name for the committee should be selected, officers should be chosen and subcommittees should be formed.

Selection of a permanent committee chairperson is a key decision. The ideal chairperson should be one of the community's most respected citizens, someone who is above reproach, above suspicion and above politics. He or she should be highly motivated and have a knowledge of the community's power structure. The best choice would be someone other than a physician or a dentist—a person who advocates fluoridation for reasons other than scientific training. Selection of a co-chairperson, possibly the leader of the steering committee, might be a wise idea. (Here again, someone other than a physician or dentist is advisable.) A secretary and a treasurer should also be chosen.

The next item of the agenda should be the selection of a name for the committee. "Anytown Committee for Fluoridation" is a simple, effective title. So is "Citizens for Fluoridation." "Citizens for Dental Health" is another good name, particularly if the committee wishes to promote other aspects of dental care. The prefix "pro" (as in pro-fluoridation) should be avoided in the title because it implies there is a "con." The words "ad hoc" and "temporary" should also be avoided.

The final item on the agenda should be the organization of subcommittees according to function. A tentative list of functions, prepared in advance by the steering committee, could include the following:

Scientific	Medical/Dental
Legal	Endorsements
Research	Finance
Education	Political Action
Speakers' Bureau	Volunteer Recruitment
Publicity	

If a smaller number of subcommittees seems more practical, the above functions could be combined into six categories:

1. Scientific/Research/Education
2. Legal
3. Publicity/Speakers' Bureau
4. Medical/Dental
5. Finance/Endorsement
6. Volunteer Recruitment

A member of the steering committee should belong to each subcommittee and could act as its temporary or permanent chairman. Additional subcommittee members should be recruited from within and without the citizens' committee. *It is vital that all participants feel assured that they will have plenty of help, even though they may have to work hard initially to secure enough active workers.* Ideally, subcommittees should meet once a week until it is clear that meeting less often will not interfere with their effectiveness. A small task should be assigned to each involved individual each week.

Although the first citizens' committee meeting will be newsworthy enough to get good media coverage, publicity is not advisable at this time. It is better to organize quietly and thoroughly without tipping off potential opponents about what you are doing. However, if you should wish to issue a news release, or if you think it may become necessary to release one, a draft should be prepared in advance by the steering committee (preferably with the help of a public relations consultant!) so that final copies can be mailed or delivered to all media outlets as soon as possible after the meeting.

The Scientific Subcommittee

The purpose of this subcommittee is to develop local expertise to supply information about the safety and efficacy of fluoridation. Its membership should include at least one dentist, one physician, a local public health official, a science teacher and an engineer. The steering committee will already have investigated educational materials and collected some useful publications. The scientific subcommittee should expand upon this work, gathering scientific papers as needed. It should stockpile publications for later use and should consider whether to prepare additional position statements for use in the campaign.

The scientific subcommittee should establish liaison with the local and state dental societies (which may have fluoridation committees), the state department of health, and the following individuals:

Gordon H. Schrotenboer, Ph.D.
Director of Fluoridation Activities
American Dental Association
211 East Chicago Avenue
Chicago, IL 60611
Telephone: 312-440-2549

James J. Collins
Public Health Advisor
Dental Disease Prevention Activity
Room 110
Center for Disease Control
Atlanta, GA 30333
Telephone: 404-262-6513

John Scott Small
Office of the Director
National Institute of Dental Research
Building 31, Room 2C21
Bethesda, MD 20205
Telephone: 301-496-4261

Stephen Barrett, M.D.
Chairman, Board of Directors
Lehigh Valley Committee Against Health
    Fraud, Inc.
P.O. Box 1602
Allentown, PA 18105
Telephone: 215-437-1795

The scientific subcommittee should also investigate the technical aspects of fluoridation installation. Although this job would normally be done by a city engineer after action by local government, this process may be expedited if the citizens' committee does preliminary research.

The Legal Subcommittee

This committee should consist mostly of attorneys who agree to perform one or more of the following functions without pay:

1. Incorporate the citizen's committee as a nonprofit corporation.
2. Outline the legal steps necessary to obtain fluoridation.
3. Draft a fluoridation ordinance or resolution for use by local government. (If a referendum will be required, its exact wording for the ballot should be drafted before *any* approach to government officials is made.)
4. Answer legal questions as they arise.
5. File lawsuits when necessary.
6. Challenge unfair election tactics used by antifluoridation groups, such as questionable petitions and unfair ballot wording.
7. Seek endorsement by the local bar association.
8. Encourage attorneys to provide educational materials in their waiting rooms.

Research Subcommittee

This committee should include a dentist, a

teacher, someone with expert knowledge of statistical techniques, and others who are willing to work hard to collect local information.

All physicians and dentists in your community should be asked how they feel about fluoridation. Each one who favors it should be asked to sign a statement allowing his support to be made public by the citizens' committee at an appropriate time. Unanimous or near-unanimous support from these trusted professionals will be a key factor in any campaign.

It is helpful to be able to publicize how the dental health of your unfluoridated community compares with that of nearby fluoridated ones. Or, if your community has fluoridation which the antis are trying to stop, it is helpful to show how fluoridation has improved dental health. A scientific survey is therefore good to have unless the time involved in doing it is too much of a burden. Remember, the results need not be publishable in a scientific journal—they need only be useful for local comparison. Useful information can include decayed, missing and filled teeth (DMF) rates, school absenteeism, Head Start and Medicaid expenditures, and the percentage of children with decay-free mouths.

Public opinion polls, although they also require considerable work, can help guide committee efforts. A community-wide poll may be obtained by college students, other volunteers or paid professional workers. To be valid, it should be designed by someone who has expert knowledge of both statistics and polling techniques. A few workers covering several shopping centers can get a lot of information in a single day. Several people using telephones can conduct a poll from within their homes.

Another simple type of survey can be conducted periodically if dentists are willing to cooperate. Each dental office can be given a supply of forms which contain the following questions:

1. Have you ever heard or read about the fluoridation of public drinking water?
___Yes
___No
___Don't know.

2. Is the drinking water in this area fluoridated?
___Yes
___No
___Don't know

3. What is the purpose of water fluoridation?
___To purify water
___To prevent tooth decay
___Other reason
___Don't know

4. What is your opinion about fluoridating public water supplies?
___Very good idea
___Good idea
___Bad idea
___Very bad idea
___Don't know
___Don't care

Patients should be asked to complete the questionnaire before seeing their dentist so that the answers can be a starting point for discussion with the dentist. Completed forms can then be collected and tabulated once a week by committee members. This type of survey and discussion will not only provide valuable data on community attitudes but will also lead to increased public support for fluoridation.

Dates when the forms are filled out should be recorded so that the research committee can measure the effect of the campaign on public attitudes. Patients' names and addresses should also be noted so that individuals who are highly favorable can be approached at an appropriate time to help with the campaign.

Education Subcommittee

The purpose of this committee is to ensure that facts about fluoridation are taught in the local school system(s). Its members might include school nurses, teachers, other school officials, dental hygienists and a dentist. A high-ranking school administrator could be very valuable.

The education subcommittee should begin its work by surveying public and private schools and colleges to see what is being taught. Teacher training, educational materials and visiting speakers can be offered as needed.

In some communities, opponents of fluoridation may attempt to make the teaching of fluoridation facts (like sex education and evolution) into a political issue. This is less likely to happen if the initial approach to the school system is made well in advance of any public controversy.

Speakers' Bureau

Dentists, physicians, dental hygienists, science teachers and public health officials are likely to be good candidates for the speakers' bureau. Outstanding laypersons might also be capable of good presentations. Laypersons often have greater impact because they are perceived to be closer to the audience. For example, a Travelers Insurance Company agent who tells why his company gives discounts on dental insurance in fluoridated communities might be a very effective speaker.

Speakers will have to be well-versed in every aspect of fluoridation. They should be able to anticipate every argument against fluoridation as well as possible disruptive tactics by opponents in the audience.

Expert knowledge is not enough, however. The speakers must be able to put their points across to their audiences. People who lack formal training in public speaking usually make elementary errors which interfere with maximum effectiveness. For this reason, *members of the speakers' bureau should undergo basic training by an expert in the fields of communication and public speaking.*

It might be advisable for some speakers to cover fluoridation as just one aspect of an overall talk on dental care. Some audiences will find this type of presentation more interesting. It is also more difficult to disrupt because it is less "political" in nature.

Publicity Subcommittee

This committee should include (and possibly be led by) a professional communicator who will know how much publicity is needed and how to obtain it most effectively. Committee activities, speaking engagements and organizational endorsements can all be used to generate publicity which can help promote fluoridation to the community. But publicity though the media is a two-edged sword. Although it can reach people who will not be exposed to the fluoridation committee's other educational efforts, it can also stir up opponents and increase their access to the media. (When a topic becomes controversial, the media are likely to give equal time or space to the other side—in a spirit of "fair play.") Moreover, education is actually more effective when provided on a person-to-person basis in schoolrooms and offices where information is delivered by trusted professionals.

For these reasons, *publicity should not be obtained prematurely or haphazardly but should be carefully timed as part of the overall campaign plan.*

Medical-Dental Subcommittee

The purpose of this committee is to generate maximum support from the physicians (medical and osteopathic) and dentists in the community. These professionals have unique opportunities to educate their patients and may also be the main source of financial support for the fluoridation campaign.

Dentists have an ideal opportunity to educate their patients about fluoridation. They have the knowledge and can easily talk to their patients while working. Physicians are unlikely to do this, but they may be willing to use other means of effective communication. *One goal of the medical-dental subcommittee should be to inspire each dentist to educate his patients in depth and each physician to personally hand each patient a piece of fluoridation literature.*

One of the best ways to inspire a high level of professional support is to present a brief report of the campaign's progress at each meeting of the professional society. Visibility and enthusiasm are powerful persuaders!

Endorsements Subcommittee

The steering committee will already have developed a list of organizations whose endorsements will help the campaign. Members of the endorsements committee should follow through by contacting officers or other key members of these organizations. Organizational leaders should be thoroughly educated so that they will become enthusiastic supporters of fluoridation. Endorsing organizations not only add prestige to the campaign but may also be a source of money and/or manpower for political action.

Influential individuals should also be approached for endorsements.

Finance Subcommittee

An educational campaign can be conducted with modest amounts of money. A successful referendum campaign is likely to be expensive. A finance committee should be set up to raise whatever funds are needed. Its work will be facilitated if some of its members have local fundraising experience.

Because they are philosophically antagonistic to disease, dentists and physicians are likely to be the major source of funds for fluoridation. There are four good ways to raise money from these professionals:

1. Local or state societies may give lump

sum contributions.

2. Individuals can be solicited, using the "money tree" technique described in Chapter 9. (Key leaders each recruit 10 contributors, each of whom also telephones 10 others to solicit contributions.)

3. Society members can vote to assess themselves a stated amount, either once or annually.

4. Society members can set up a voluntary fluoridation fund to which each member can contribute once a year when he pays his dues. (The key here is to be sure that the voluntary contribution is listed on the annual dues statement and included in its total.)

Health insurance companies which might benefit from a reduction in dental disease might be another source of campaign funds. Even if these companies won't contribute money, they will often endorse fluoridation and include information about it in mailings to subscribers or policyholders. Unions are another potential source of funds, as are the United Way and Easter Seal Societies. The finance committee should also find out whether government grants might be available for educating the community or buying fluoridation equipment.

In addition to money, the committee can try to line up contributions in the form of goods and services that might otherwise have to be purchased. Examples include space for a campaign headquarters, printing and duplicating, use of office equipment, and piggybacking of material for distribution.

Political Action Subcommittee

If all goes well, the educational campaign will gradually develop a broad base of public support for fluoridation. The function of the political action subcommittee will be to mobilize the forces necessary to convince government decision makers that the support exists. At the same time, it must lay the groundwork for a referendum if one is necessary.

The steering committee will already have determined which individuals (the mayor, city councilmen, water authorities, etc.) have a role in deciding fluoridation's fate. While the steering committee develops a plan for approaching these officials, the political action subcommittee should prepare to generate citizen communication to them by letter, telephone, petitions or other means. Letters

to the media will also be necessary, and many additional workers will have to be obtained if there is a referendum.

Volunteer Recruitment Subcommittee

You may or may not need a separate committee to recruit volunteers to perform specific tasks or help with the overall campaign. You will certainly need all the help you can get. Whether or not each subcommittee does its own recruiting or a separate committee is set up for this purpose, you should devote considerable effort to recruitment of volunteers.

When the citizen's committee is organized sufficiently, it should print a letterhead which indicates the diversity of its membership. A post office box should be obtained, office space should be found for storage of literature and research files, and access to a copying machine should be arranged so that documents can be produced quickly and easily.

Letters to the Editor

At some point in your campaign, letters to the editor(s) from local opponents are likely to be published in your local newspaper(s). If you ignore them, their charges will go unanswered. If you respond tit-for-tat, the public will be exposed to arguments on both sides, but a letter battle may develop which can create the illusion that fluoridation's safety is a matter of scientific controversy. If you blitz the newspaper with "pro" letters, you may get more space for your ideas; but if the antis respond in kind, they too will get more exposure. It almost seems that any action you take will make matters worse!

There is, however, another strategy that may help. *Early in your campaign, you should visit newspaper editors to request that they investigate what is sent to them to find out who is lying and who isn't. Your approach should make it clear that many members of the community will admire a firm stand on the part of the newspaper.*

A meeting with an editor should be attended by several of the most prominent members of your organization, including the citizens' committee chairman, the steering committee chairman and the editor's dentist and personal physician. A small amount of written material which has key points highlighted for easy reading should be sent a few days beforehand.

Begin the meeting by stating that you need

his help. Ask whether he has any doubts about the safety and benefits of fluoridation, whether he has any suggestions for your campaign and whether he would like to become a member of the citizen's committee. (He will probably decline on the grounds that joining an action group could interfere with his journalistic objectivity—but there is no harm in asking.) Then point out the nature of antifluoridation propaganda and ask whether he can follow antifluoridation letters with editor's notes explaining their fallacies. Indicate that you realize your request is unusual, but that fluoridation controversies are sufficiently unique to warrant special handling by the media. (It may help to draw an analogy between a false cry of "Fire!" in a crowded theater and a false cry of "Poison!" in a public statement. Both can do great harm.)

If the editor agrees to help you, your political action subcommittee should generate letters congratulating him on this decision. If he does not, and letters are published which claim that fluoridation is dangerous, the newspaper should be bombarded with a steady stream of letters (not for publication) suggesting that irresponsible claims should be curbed. In addition, at every contact between committee members and reporters, a plea should be made to ignore anti claims of dangerousness when writing news reports.

Key people at local radio and television stations should be approached and educated in the same manner before any controversy becomes heated.

Public Speaking

Although there is no substitute for formal training under the supervision of a skilled instructor, a few basic ideas may help you:

1. Don't try to cram too many facts into your presentation. Your goal should be to identify and deal with the concerns of the people with whom you are talking. Additional information can be provided in the form of literature to take home.

2. Be brief. Twenty to thirty minutes should be enough.

3. It is neither necessary nor advisable to prepare a whole speech which can be read. *Reading a speech is likely to undermine your effectiveness.* You may sound dull and your audience may wonder whether you really know your subject matter. Most good speakers work ex-

temporaneously from a bare outline.

4. Since your audience will be as interested in you as in your topic, *be sure to include some personal experiences*—including how you became involved in promoting fluoridation. (A dentist should also describe some of the rampant tooth decay he has seen in fluoride-deficient patients.)

5. The content of your talk should also be adapted to your audience. A senior citizens group could be reminded of how difficult it is to cope with dentures, and how nice it would be to protect future adults from this problem. Parents could be told of fluoridation's savings in terms of discomfort and expense. Cost-effectiveness and good investment can be stressed to businessmen. Attorneys can be informed that no court of last resort has ever ruled that fluoridation is unsafe or undemocratic. The long-range saving of tax dollars may be a timely topic for most audiences.

6. To gain the most from your speaking engagements, tape record them and share your experiences with other members of the speakers' bureau. If time permits, rehearsals can also be valuable.

A simple yet effective talk can be prepared by writing down 10-20 commonly asked questions about fluoridation. You can then tell your audience, "To prepare for this talk, I jotted down a few questions that people have been asking"—and proceed to ask and answer them. Before completing your prepared questions, invite the audience to ask questions and they will probably bring up more than enough to fill your allotted time.

During the question period you may be confronted by someone who wishes to give an antifluoridation speech or engage you in lengthy debate. There are a number of good techniques that can be used in this situation. One is to ask the person his name. (It is always nice to know with whom you are talking.) If he gets defensive, he will lose credibility. If he tells you, the confrontation will probably become less emotional.

You should never allow any one questioner to dominate the meeting. This is unfair to the rest of the audience and they will get angry *with you* if order is not maintained. Most people can be politely limited by inviting them to contact you after the meeting or by suggesting that others would also like a turn. *Before the meeting begins, there should be a clear understanding that its chairman will intervene firmly when needed.* If you anticipate considerable hostility from an audience, the meeting will be easier to control if all questions are submitted in writing.

Should You Debate?

Experienced fluoridation campaigners have found there is nothing to be gained by engaging in face-to-face debates with antifluoridationists. Regardless of who delivers the better argument, the very fact that the debate takes place tends to convey the idea that fluoridation's safety and effectiveness are scientifically controversial.

Early in the campaign, the citizen's committee should prepare a formal policy statement for use in declining debates. The statement should describe fluoridation's solid support from the scientific community, tell why debating is inappropriate, and offer a positive presentation at a separate time.

Although debating should be avoided if at all possible, there may be occasions when you decide it is necessary. Some radio or TV stations, more interested in controversy than accurate representation of the issue, may put antifluoridationists on the air alone. When you ask for equal time, the only way they will allow a response is through a debate. If the listening audience is small, then a debate is still not worthwhile. On the other hand, an audience of many thousands should not be allowed to listen to antifluoridationists without hearing some rebuttal.

How To Debate

If you must debate, it is important to nail down rules well ahead of time and have them announced at the beginning of the debate. The more structured the format, the better off you are likely to be. The usual rule for a formal debate is that the pro side goes first in order to define the issue. It is also customary for the pro side to make the final statement so that the anti side does not have the last word throughout the debate. Here are some additional tips:

1. *Be well prepared.* Expect the worst. Expect your opponent to use distortion, innuendo, unfounded allegations and other scare tactics. A typical opponent will state that the AMA and ADA do not really support fluoridation or perhaps that dentists are not really scientists and therefore know nothing about it. You can be certain that your opponent will charge that fluoridation causes cancer. You must be able to counter such false statements in an unemotional, matter-of-fact manner without losing sight of your own objectives.

2. Select your best spokesperson, someone who has had experience in a freewheeling debate. If you can't find such a person, don't debate. A fluoridation debate is no place to break in a novice.

3. Regardless of your opponent's tactics, get your message across. Your opponent will try hard to distract you. Focus on *your* message, not his.

4. The key issue is credibility—whom to believe. Your presentation should make it clear that the overwhelming majority of scientists support your position. (Mention that fluoridation is endorsed by all major health departments and health organizations in the United States. Also indicate the extent of local support as tabulated by your research subcommittee.)

5. Your opening remarks can indicate how opponents of fluoridation try to create an illusion of scientific controversy. A good way to do this is to explain how the scientific community works (as described in the "Truth-Seekers" chapter of *The Health Robbers*).*

6. Your opponent can mention more supposed dangers of fluoridation in one minute than you can completely rebut in one hour. So be prepared to focus on one or two such claims. The claim that fluoride is a "rat poison" is a good one to rebut. By pointing out how poison is a matter of amount, you can make your opponent sound quite foolish.

7. If you get too nasty, the audience may sympathize with your opponent. On the other hand, if you stick strictly to scientific issues, you are likely to lose the debate. So be prepared to play rough if you have to. Your opponent is certain to make the claim that fluoridation causes cancer. This claim is a concoction of the

The Health Robbers, published by George F. Stickley Co., 210 W. Washington Square, Philadelphia, Pa. 19106 (1980)

National Health Federation, an organization which promotes quackery. Twelve of its leaders have been in legal difficulty for promoting questionable "health" ideas with false claims. Five of them have received prison sentences for such activity. Be prepared to expose NHF for what it is, using data from the "Unhealthy Alliance" chapter of either *The Health Robbers* or *The Tooth Robbers*. In a televised debate, *The Health Robbers* should be displayed and referred to for documentation.

8. Insist that the prearranged rules be followed. Both sides should receive equal time. If your opponent tries to speak beyond his allotted time, assert your rights. (Bring a stopwatch so you can protect your right to equal time.) If your opponent interrupts you, say quietly but firmly: "I didn't interrupt you. Please don't interrupt me." If this happens several times, you will destroy his credibility by showing he cannot stick to the rules.

9. Some other tactics, if used properly, may also be effective in winning over an audience. When your opponent makes an outlandish remark, smile and say: "Come now, _____, (using his first name if you know it), we both know that's not true." Or, "Are you still saying that _____? I though you knew better." Another response is "(first name), you don't really expect our listening audience to fall for that, do you?" These kinds of responses tell the audience that you know your opponent and how he argues. (If you can obtain copies of what he has previously said, that will help you prepare.) It also tells your audience that you give them credit for being able to tell who is credible and who is not.

10. Almost all debates are associated with referendums. Therefore *stress how to vote* and keep stressing this throughout the debate.

11. Remind your audience that if they have any doubt about who is telling the truth, they should ask a health professional whom they trust, such as their dentist or personal physician.

Approaching Government Officials

The key to convincing an elected official is determining what matters to him. If he is *unsure of the facts*, you will need to educate him. If he considers fluoridation a matter of *low priority*, you will have to persuade him that citizens care about it. This can be done by letters, telephone calls and petitions. If he believes the *public should decide*, you will have to convince him that statesmanship is needed. Fluoridation is really an issue that people do not want to decide. If forced to vote in a referendum, they may vote it down because of doubts raised by scare tactics. But if leaders judge it safe enough to put in the water, very few citizens will protest.

If an elected official *fears political repercussions*, you will have to convince him that supporting fluoridation is politically safe. (Even though their voices are loud, the number of antis is small.) The broad base of political support you have generated may be enough. If it isn't, letters, telephone calls and petitions may help. (A petition signed by more than 50 percent of the registered voters might be decisive yet easy to obtain in a small community.) You may also have to become deeply involved in the election process, helping good candidates get elected both in primary and general elections.

The manner and timing of your approach to elected officials will depend upon your assessment of local political factors. You will probably want to wait until your educational program has generated a broad base of political support. But you should also try to make sure that no official takes any public position until he has a clear picture of the facts. The approach of the citizen's committee should include a face-to-face meeting which is attended by prominent citizens who are known and trusted by the official—including his personal physician and dentist. As soon as one official is convinced, he can help you persuade the others.

If all goes well, you will convince a majority of the officials to vote for fluoridation. What happens then will depend upon the applicable laws. Some jurisdictions will require a public hearing. Others may require a public vote. Regardless, you should help the involved officials to move quickly. *The antidote to fear is firm leadership.* The faster fluoride gets into the water, the less public reaction there will be.

Increased Political Action

The fact that fluoridation has been promised should be reason to rejoice, but not to rest. *The closer you get to success, the harder the antifluoridationists will work to defeat you.* Political officials are notoriously fickle, and you must see to it that they have constant political reassurance from the time they promise to help you to the time that fluoridation is actually begun—and even afterward. Strange as it may seem, the most important time to pressure an official is *after* he agrees to help you. If you fail to do this, he may change his mind.

The type of support that is needed will be easy to generate if the community's dentists have been well-organized and motivated by the citizen's committee. An enormous amount of helpful communication can result if each dentist asks only a few patients per day to send a letter (even a prepared form letter!) or make a telephone call from the dentist's office. (Most phone callers should merely leave their names, addresses and give brief statements of support to the official's secretary. If hundreds of callers ask to talk with the official, he might get very angry.)

In case you wonder whether organized communication of this type will be effective, the answer is yes. Public officials will feel reassured that so many people are still being "educated."

Every professional office should also be asked to permanently display a poster promoting fluoridation. These can be printed inexpensively and installed *permanently* under a 1/16" plexiglas shield by workers from the political action subcommittee. A "prescription" theme, like the one pictured below, will attract attention and stimulate trust:

R̲x̲ ——

For Better Teeth
Support Fluoridation!

Your Doctor

The job of generating political support should not be limited to health professionals. The effort should be aided by prominent citizens, unions, PTAs and other civic organizations. It cannot be emphasized enough that the most effective way to achieve *and retain* fluoridation is through a broadly-based community effort.

If A Hearing Is Needed

A public hearing on fluoridation should really not be the time that government officials get educated about fluoridation. That job should be done well ahead of time, in private, on an individual basis. What will be needed, if you have lobbied effectively, is a presentation that is politically appropriate. Public officials want their constituents to feel that they have carefully reviewed the facts and that there is public support for their ultimate decision. A few of your speakers should be health professionals who focus on facts, but most should be citizens who convey public support.

Experts, preferably from several disciplines, should present a *brief* summary of the facts, including benefits, safety, cost, why alternatives are impractical, and how strongly the scientific community supports fluoridation. A few well-designed visual aids can convey authority as salient points are made. Someone should also describe how opponents of fluoridation use misleading tactics to confuse the public. (This can be illustrated by explaining the fallacies of one or two antifluoridation claims and indicating that many such claims will be made during the public hearing.) Another expert can ask whether the officials have any doubts about the safety of fluoridation. It can be very helpful to uncover and deal with this type of fear if it is present.

The rest of your speakers should be individuals or leaders of endorsing organizations who tell why they favor fluoridation. They do not need to rebut the false claims that opponents of fluoridation make at the hearing. A far better tactic would be to say that they simply do not believe the claims—that they believe their doctors and want fluoridation. A petition with many signatures would be very effective.

The person responsible for the hearing should be asked ahead of time to establish rules of conduct and to see that they are followed rigidly. Antifluoridationists tend to play by their own rules unless otherwise constrained. In some instances, they have virtually "taken over" a hearing by overwhelming the presiding official. This can be prevented if the official is forewarned. Ground rules are even more important if the presiding official is opposed to fluoridation. If you anticipate this circumstance, try to enlist the help of a favorably inclined official to keep the hearing fair.

Hearings may be shorter and more orderly if a policy is established that only residents of the community are allowed to speak. Since there are very few antis who have scientific credentials, such a rule may make it impossible for them to present someone who can claim to be an "expert."

If representatives of the media are present, assign one or more members of your committee to stay with each one at all times. This will make it much harder for the antis to influence them when you are not looking. Last, but not least, try to fill the room with people who are on your side. This will not only indicate public support for fluoridation—it will also make it difficult for antis to gain media coverage by being disruptive.

Increasing Your Media Coverage

The key to effective publicity is timing. An educational campaign about fluoridation should generally be low-keyed and conducted through channels (like professional offices, health insurance company mailings and union mailings) which are essentially "off limits" to fluoridation's opponents. Too much publicity can stimulate opponents to work harder, and by making the issue more newsworthy, it can increase access to the media for their misleading views.

Should a time come when you wish to maximize publicity—a few weeks before a critical vote, for example—it is important to be able to do it. Your steering committee should already have compiled a list of media outlets, and the publicity subcommittee will have prepared mailing labels and arranged for duplicating equipment so that mailings can be quickly prepared. Any public speaking engagement or organizational endorsement can be used as a springboard for a news release. Other suitable topics might include: "Fluoridation Committee Forms," "Com-

mittee Elects Officers," "Fluoridation Needed, Says…," "Poll of Dentists Released," "Citizens' Poll Favors Fluoridation," "Petition Drive Underway," "Petitions Urge Fluoridation," "Council Asked To Act."

If A Referendum Is Needed

Intelligent officials are more likely to make a rational decision than are average citizens faced with a scare campaign. So if the law does not require a referendum to initiate fluoridation in your community, you should try very hard to persuade your local officials to order fluoridation themselves rather than submitting the issue to public vote.

Timing can be a critical factor in the outcome of a referendum. The smaller the voter turnout, the more chance for antifluoridationists to exert influence out of proportion to their number. General elections are therefore better for you than primaries, and presidential elections are best of all.

Wording of the ballot is also an important factor in a referendum. The most favorable wording is one which helps voters understand exactly what they are voting for. "Shall we adjust the fluoride content of our water supply to prevent tooth decay as recommended by the state department of health?" is the best wording. Any wording where "Yes" is a vote against fluoridation and "No" is a vote for it will confuse many voters. (Your attorneys can help you challenge ballot wording that is inflammatory or misleading.) Linking fluoridation to a bond issue is also undesirable.

If local officials insist upon holding a referendum, they can at least choose voting conditions favorable to your side. So *be prepared to suggest them during your early contacts!*

A referendum will require expansion and intensification of your educational campaign, changing it from low key to high gear. If you have been working effectively, you should have a closely-knit leadership group, a large number of active workers, and the names of *many* other citizens who might help your campaign. Endorsing organizations should also be asked for volunteers who can help with mailings, display bumper stickers, form telephone trees, hold coffee klatches, go door-to-door and to shopping centers with literature, hand out voting instructions at the polls, etc. *A few retired persons who can do-*

nate large amounts of time could work wonders for your campaign.

If your community contains a dental school or other schools at a university-based health sciences center, seek their help. Such schools should have lots of students and faculty members who can supply volunteer manpower as well as expertise. Some professional schools have excused everyone from classes to enable them to work actively in a referendum campaign!

Your preliminary campaign (1-2 years) should have loaded your guns. Now is the time to fire them! Distribute your dental health surveys to the media and hold news conferences about them. Get featurettes and editorials into print. Posters and educational handouts should be displayed at every professional location—including offices, hospitals, and pharmacies. Prescription-sized voting instructions, similar to the illustration on this page, should be inserted in bills and handed *personally* to each patient by every dentist and physician. Pharmacists can give them out with filled prescriptions. Postal cards like the type pictured below can be distributed throughout the community.

I SUPPORT FLUORIDATION BECAUSE OF ITS SCIENTIFICALLY PROVEN DENTAL HEALTH BENEFITS, AND AUTHORIZE THE USE OF MY NAME IN ENDORSEMENTS.

I ALSO WILL HELP BY:

☐ Displaying Bumper Stickers.   Send me_____.

☐ Displaying a window sign or poster.   Send me_____.

☐ Working on campaign.   Contact me_____.

☐ Helping financially: $1 ☐ ; $5 ☐ ; $10 ☐ ; other $_____

Signature_____

Name Printed_____

Address_____ Phone_____

No Postage Stamp Necessary If Mailed in the United States

BUSINESS REPLY MAIL
FIRST CLASS PERMIT NO. 811   SAN RAFAEL, CA. 94902

Postage will be paid by:
MARIN CITIZENS FLUORIDATION CAMPAIGN
Post Office Box 143
San Rafael, Calif. 94902

80

Your media strategy at this point will depend upon your assessment of local factors. Endorsements should be obtained from as many media outlets as possible. (The groundwork for these should, of course, be laid during the early stages of your educational campaign.) Radio and TV endorsements should be aired close enough to the election that opponents do not have time to organize responses.

Letters should be sent to newspapers for publication, and a few paid ads should be inserted. Since credibility will be an issue, readers should be encouraged to question health professionals whom they trust. A very effective ad is one which endorses fluoridation, tells how to vote for it, and is signed by virtually every physician in the community. (The groundwork for such an ad should have been laid months in advance by the research subcommittee's effort to have each physician sign a pledge of support.)

Radio spots should be directed primarily toward groups of people in the community who have not come in contact with your educational campaign and are unlikely to read the newspaper ads. Public service messages may be possible on some stations. If so, they should be prepared months ahead of time (so nothing gets fouled up), but broadcast close to election day. TV spots can be very effective, but also very expensive. *All advertising messages should be very simple and prepared with professional help. They should stress how to vote.*

Remember that most voters have short memories. Do not place your ads prematurely—no further than 3 or 4 days before the election. The same applies for editorials. An editorial the day before an election is ideal.

News events can have considerable publicity value. One community, for example, held a "Mother's Day Run" just prior to a June referendum. Practicing dentists can reserve half a day to go door-to-door with their office staffs on the day before the election. If enough do this, the community might be so moved by their dedication that the election would be clinched then and there.

During the final stages of the campaign, spokespeople should be carefully designated. A campaign headquarters and a paid, full-time coordinator are good to have if you can afford them.

Handling NHF

It is important to realize that there is no such thing as a *local* fluoridation campaign. Advice and scare propaganda from the National Health Federation (NHF) are certain to be used by your local opponents. John Yiamouyiannis, Ph.D., NHF's former "Science Director," is a very personable, intelligent man who appears sincere and credible to laymen when he claims that fluoridation causes cancer. If your community is large enough (or your opponents are willing to defray expenses), you can expect a visit from Dr. Yiamouyiannis or from someone currently associated with NHF.

Your efforts to counter NHF activity should begin during the early part of your campaign as you inform media leaders about the nature of antifluoridation propaganda. If you expect a visit from Dr. Yiamouyiannis or a current NHF leader, distribute information about NHF to all talk show hosts and news directors. Our *Fluoridation Prevents Cancer* flyer should be distributed at public meetings where NHF propaganda may be involved.* If someone associated with NHF is interviewed, observe what is said, request a direct opportunity to respond to it, give the reporter appropriate portions of *The Tooth Robbers,* and say:

> Before you publicize these claims that fluoridation is dangerous, please read this material and decide whether doing so is a responsible thing to do. We realize that this is an unusual request, but this is an unusual situation. The National Health Federation is an organization which promotes quackery. Twelve of its leaders have been in legal difficulty and five of them have received prison sentences for questionable "health" activities.

Only your most knowledgeable and articulate people should be used to deal publicly with Dr. Yiamouyiannis or with current representatives of NHF. If your community has no dentists or physicians opposed to fluoridation, be sure to point out that the antis' case is so weak that they had to reach across the country (or wherever) to find someone who could speak for them!

---

*This pamphlet should be folded in thirds so that the headline FLUORIDATION PREVENTS CANCER!!! appears on top.

After The Vote

If the vote is favorable, don't make the mistake of resting on your laurels. Many things can go wrong. The opponents may file a lawsuit to delay implementation. They may persuade an administrator to hold things up. They may try to persuade future candidates for office to act against fluoridation if they get elected. They may try to secure another referendum.

The best way to reduce further controversy is to begin fluoridation as soon as possible. Implementation can be greatly facilitated if the necessary permit is obtained before the issue is voted.

Educational efforts should still be maintained. Brief messages should be inserted in water bills for several years. Your speakers' bureau should continue to schedule talks about dental health with fluoridation mentioned within them. And a delegation from the citizens' committee should continue to educate all those who run for offices that could affect fluoridation's fate.

One thing is certain. In many communities, antifluoridationists will not give up easily. Three years after losing a referendum in Seattle by a plurality of 70 percent, they tried again by going statewide. They failed again, but only because the machinery that had previously been so effective was still essentially intact. The lesson here is that while your steering committee does not have to meet frequently after fluoridation is in place, it should remain intact and ready to resume action on a moment's notice.

Most people who begin fluoridation campaigns find out too late how difficult they can be. The suggestions in this chapter may seem overly elaborate, but many communities will require tremendous effort to promote fluoridation. Not everything that has been mentioned will be applicable to your situation, but much of it will be. You should select what seems most suitable for your community.

What To Do In An "Emergency"

Sometimes antifluoridationists will attempt to remove fluoridation or block its implementation by means of a referendum which is suddenly announced. In the state of Washington, for example, the issue was placed on the ballot only three weeks before an election. If you are confronted with such a situation, the following strategies may be best:

1. If you have an existing committee, activate it immediately. Plan on *daily* meetings (or at least daily communication by telephone) and concentrate on what is needed to win an election—*getting votes!*

2. If no committee exists, take no more than 48 hours to recruit 10-20 people of diverse backgrounds to serve as a steering committee. The more people with experience in political campaigns, the better. Quickly convene a meeting to select a leader, pick a committee name, make assignments and *establish deadlines for their completion.* Committee members should be able to act independently since there will be little time for group decisions. Members will have to recruit their own helpers and form their own subcommittees.

3. Raise funds using the sources mentioned earlier in this chapter. Activate telephone trees if time permits, but also go directly to the presidents of health professional societies for both money and endorsements.

4. Obtain informational materials. You are unlikely to have time to develop your own. Obtain materials which have been used successfully in other communities and adapt them to your needs. Call the people listed in this chapter for help in this regard.

5. Use whatever funds you raise to engage an expert in public relations, to buy advertisements and to pay for printed materials.

6. Hold news conferences, send information to media outlets and make members of the steering committee available to the media at all times. Place your ads just a few days before the election. Ads in shopping newspapers are cheap but reach many people. If your funds are limited, try at least to place a half-page newspaper ad endorsing fluoridation, signed by as many physicians and dentists as you can get. The ad should clearly tell readers how to vote.

7. If the referendum is part of a general election, try to get candidates from both sides to endorse fluoridation.

STATESMANSHIP

Prominent citizens may help you influence the candidates.

8. Try to get prominent citizens to endorse fluoridation. A sports hero might be very influential.

9. Canvassing door-to-door, at shopping centers, at sporting events and the like can be organized in a matter of days. As discussed earlier in this chapter, students from health professional schools, senior citizen groups, unions, PTAs and the like might provide volunteers. You should also try to piggyback on other electioneering activities. For example, if flyers are being distributed to potential voters, your material might be added.

10. If your community is already fluoridated, try to present data from a survey which shows how its children have benefited. If data are not available, a survey of several hundred schoolchildren can be completed within a week if permission to conduct it is obtained from the superintendent of schools.

11. Use other recommendations from this chapter that seem appropriate for your community and for the limited time you have available. Remember, when time is short, use of the media is most important.

Please do not hesitate to contact us for help in planning your campaign.

Recommended Reading

Fluoridation for Your Community and Your State, by Donald R. McNeil, Ph.D. (A 44-page booklet of campaign tips, published by the American Dental Association.)

VICTORY IN SEATTLE

BY
PETER K. DOMOTO, D.D.S., M.P.H.
Associate Professor & Chairman, Pedodontics
University of Washington School of Dentistry

ROBERT C. FAINE, D.D.S, M.P.H.
USPHS Regional Dental Program Director,
Seattle, Washington;
and
SHELDON ROVIN, D.D.S, M.S.
Professor & Chairman, Department of Dental Care
Systems, University of Pennsylvania School of
Dental Medicine

In November of 1973, the citizens of Seattle overwhelmingly voted in favor of retaining fluoridation for the city's water supply. There were a number of factors directly or indirectly responsible, or both, for the success of this campaign, which should be documented for the benefit of other communities involved in similar efforts. The Seattle campaign capitalized on the availability of hundreds of dental students, dental hygiene students, and others to implement an aggressive doorbelling campaign. Campaign emphasis was initially on the building of broad-based community support and then concluded with a strong focus on how to vote. In fact, voting instructions outweighed dental health education efforts. During the campaign, a political perspective was emphasized. This approach proved to be well suited to this particular community. It is the intent of this paper to present an overview of the strategy, methods, and results, in addition to an assessment of the victory. Because of the number of other people involved in this successful endeavor, the authors claim no particular credit for the victory.

In 1952 and 1962, two unsuccessful attempts were made to fluoridate Seattle's water supply before acceptance of fluoridation was finally achieved in 1968 by a 57% margin. Significantly, the 1968 victory represented the efforts of a very broad-based campaign that included lay people as well as health professionals. This bears special emphasis since the 1973 election had the same broad-based community support.

In the 1973 election, a landslide victory in which nearly 70% of the votes cast favored retaining fluoridation was a most gratifying result. The lowest winning margin in any legislative district was a substantial 63%. It is noteworthy that the highest winning total was nearly 80% and represented the district that received the most intense doorbelling and public-speaking coverage. Extensive planning was made to achieve this successful result.

Organization

The battle for retaining fluoridation was joined in July of 1973 after publication of a newspaper announcement from the antifluoridationists who prosaically called themselves the "Anti-Pollution" Committee. In their challenge, the opponents claimed to have collected 23,000 signatures supporting the move to stop fluoridation and for the dismantling of all existing equipment. After this announcement, several persons primarily responsible for the 1968 victory met to discuss this new challenge to fluoridation.

The initial meeting was attended by approximately 35 people, most of whom were health professionals. This professional domination was recognized, and the primary activity of the group was to recruit and expand the base of support throughout all areas and levels of the Seattle community. An agreement was reached at this stage of mobilization that the fluoridation campaign should be a community-political venture, and this proved to be one of the most significant factors for its success. Also during the initial meeting, a series of organizational planning sessions were developed, and campaign responsibilities were assigned.

At the second meeting about two weeks later, there was a substantial increase in the number of nonprofessional participants. A steering committee was established, cochairmen for the campaign were elected, and various committee assignments were made. Also, a campaign slogan, "Save Seattle Fluoridation," was selected by the steering committee. It bears mention that professional degrees were neither viewed as a prerequisite to chairmanship appointments nor as a guarantee of leadership qualities.

A sound committee structure was developed to guide the campaign. The organizational format was structured around five working committees, and they are as follows: financial, speakers' bureau and professional relations, correspondence and publicity, materials and literature distribution, and scientific. Although these committees functioned and made decisions independently, they frequently made status reports to the steering committee.

Strategy

After the committee structure was established and the informational tasks were completed, the major concern of the steering committee was to formulate an operational strategy. The dean of the School of Dentistry, University of Washington, had committed every dental and dental hygiene student to an active role in the campaign. Therefore, it was clear that the base of the campaign strength lay in the availability and energy of 400 health service students.

The basic strategy was to conduct a low-key campaign initially and then build enthusiasm and exposure in the two weeks before the election. *Low-key* was defined as the avoidance of any confrontation or notoriety in the early weeks of the campaign. The first stages of the campaign were designated as the time for broadening the base of support in the community at large and intensifying efforts to organize and develop materials.

Some of the community groups involved in the campaign were: Seattle Model City Projects such as Environmental Health, Pre-Paid Health, and the Odessa Brown Children's Clinic; Group Health Cooperative of Puget Sound; Head Start; free clinics; Seattle Chamber of Commerce; Parent-Teacher Association; labor unions; League of Women Voters; Washington Dental Service Corporation; Seattle-King County Medical and Dental Societies; and others.

Information and materials from previous campaigns from cities all around the country were beneficial. Specifically, it was decided to stress how to vote rather than emphasize the scientific aspects of fluoridation. Thus, the political nature of the campaign was beginning to emerge.

It was determined that four main points were needed to be communicated to the public:
- how to vote on the issue;
- the importance of a large voter turnout;
- the effectiveness of water fluoridation; and
- the safety of water fluoridation.

Because of the reverse wording on the ballot—"Shall the initiative measure requiring the city to discontinue fluoridation of the municipal water supply be enacted as an ordinance?"—it was imperative that the public be informed that a *no* vote was required to keep fluoridation for Seattle. The Save Seattle Fluoridation Committee thus faced a dual challenge. It had to overcome the effects of the misleading wording of the initiative in addition to providing facts about the benefits and safety of the measure. Therefore, the proponents of fluoridation were committed to using the most effective political techniques in order to retain fluoridation for the city.

The specific strategy used in this campaign is summarized in these points:
- distribution of an informational brochure;
- saturation doorbelling, using volunteers to

deliver a campaign tabloid to 65% of voting precincts;

—nonpaid publicity through news conferences, news releases, and an appeal for editorial integrity in the news media;

—paid newspaper advertising;

—posters for display throughout the community; and

—general community exposure through speakers' bureau activities.

An important adjunct to the process of strategy formulation was an informal consultation with two experienced political campaign strategists who had been active in both local and national political campaigns. The meeting was a tremendous opportunity for one of the cochairmen to integrate the vital elements of the 1973 campaign into a clear perspective. In this short brainstorming session, these "consultants" brought clearly into focus the need for capitalizing on the bandwagon aspect of the issue. Fluoridation should be considered a nonpartisan issue—even the bitterest of rivals agree that fluoride is effective, safe, and economical. The consultants validated the rudimentary 1973 plan in such a positive way that it gave the cochairpersons more confidence to pursue a direct strategy.

Methods of campaigning

Doorbelling: The overwhelming success of the campaign to retain fluoridation was attributable, in great part, to the effective personal contacts accomplished through the doorbelling activity of students and of other volunteers. To show the detailed planning involved in executing a doorbelling campaign, the following steps were required: political consultants contacted; voter profiles examined; precinct maps drawn up; district chairmen selected; distribution points determined; literature packets assembled; volunteers assigned; and precinct coverage verified.

The doorbelling activity was planned and implemented through the leadership of a young dental laboratory technician and his wife, a former dental assistant. Their chief consultant was a politically experienced high school senior who had been involved in a similar operation for a local political candidate. This type of broad-based cooperation was characteristic of the profluoride forces.

Through the committee structure, a city-wide system for saturating the precincts with printed profluoride material emerged. Through the assessment of previous election records, high voter turnout precincts were identified. Also, consultation with members of the League of Women Voters assisted in the selection of priority areas. This information was combined to identify specific precincts that responded well to the doorbelling technique. Because the campaign could depend on the volunteer involvement of about 500 "doorbellers," it was possible to establish central distribution points in each of the nine legislative districts. From these points, the doorbellers picked up the written material, which was to be distributed to the householders with every visit. The doorbelling began fifteen days before the election. Systematically, pairs of dental and dental auxiliary students from the University of Washington, the Shoreline Community College, and the Seattle Community College reported to the distribution centers on specific days. Other doorbelling volunteers included Head Start parents, Vista volunteers, free-clinic volunteers, and a variety of health project employees in the Seattle area. They were given packets with sufficient numbers of tabloids based on total residents. Each pair of volunteers was responsible for two precincts. They were cautioned not to become involved in lengthy discussions with occupants. The tabloids also were distributed to hospitals, community clinics, health department facilities, and schools, as well as residences.

Anecdotally, one of the homeowners who was contacted agreed to vote for fluoridation if the canvassers would help him move his television set into his basement. It seems that the only real problem with the doorbelling campaign was unfriendly dogs. Feedback from the doorbellers indicated that this form of communication with citizens was penetrating and effective. Additionally, the doorbellers felt that they had really contributed to a very meaningful project by doing this kind of thing. In short, the human interaction seemed to be the highlight of the entire process for most of the participants.

Speakers' bureau: Although the total public speaking thrust was not given as high a priority as the doorbelling activities, it is important to develop a cadre of speakers to respond to the requests of interested groups desiring in-

86

formation about fluoridation. Dentists, physicians, and community volunteers were asked to participate in this endeavor.

The speakers presented information to as many groups as possible, such as the PTA, political party caucuses, volunteer organizations, service clubs, and Head Start parent groups. A retired dentist spoke at several retirement centers and was quite effective. By taking the offensive and making fluoridation a public issue at these various forums, the speakers had the opportunity to answer questions from the audiences. Discussing the questions openly was very helpful in allaying the concerns of the people. Members of the speakers' bureau also spoke on local television and radio talk shows, and they debated.

The position of the Save Seattle Fluoridation Committee regarding debate reversed itself during the campaign. Initially, it was decided not to engage in debate or to directly confront the anti-fluoridationists. This decision was based on experiences of past campaigns and on advice from other sectors, which caused our speakers to feel that the distortions and misrepresentations used by the antifluoridationists would not allow "reasoned" debate.

However, some confrontation was inevitable, and it turned out to be successful because the profluoridation speakers learned how to control the situation. The formula was simply this:
—Be well prepared with information.
—Do not be distracted by the distortion and misrepresentation, no matter how emotional it becomes.
—State the message clearly and positively, inserting as often as possible how the people should vote.
—If directly attacked, state calmly that the opponent is incorrect or is distorting the facts, and constantly revert to the correctness of your position.

Informational brochures: At the outset it was recognized that specific groups and individuals required positive, concise information regarding the validity and safety of water fluoridation. One of the coordinators of the campaign quickly obtained suitable *Reader's Digest* reprints, which were appropriately circulated.

A very important role was played throughout the campaign by one of the coordinators, Helen Danforth, who served as a "clearinghouse" for requests of information from both groups and individuals.

A blue-colored brochure, titled *Fluoridation Facts in Seattle,* was developed, which clearly spelled out the benefits, safety, and low cost of water fluoridation. Dentists, physicians, nurses, and other health-oriented groups distributed several thousand of these brochures.

Subsequent to the limited distribution of the blue brochure to interested and supportive individuals and groups, another brochure, designed to influence the labor group, was produced. The resulting labor-directed brochure was distributed in cooperation with Group Health Cooperative of Puget Sound, Washington Dental Service, and other insurance groups. Several thousand of these brochures went out with mailings from the aforementioned groups. They clearly proclaimed that a *no* vote on Initiative 2 would retain fluoridation and its attendant benefits, both dental and monetary.

A four-page tabloid containing a great amount of information was designed specifically for the doorbelling activities. The tabloid featured pictures, short statements of fact, and quotes from a variety of community people. The individuals represented a broad range of life-styles and political views, and included the president of the Seattle-King County Dental Society, a member of the League of Women Voters, a dietitian, a dean from the schools of dentistry and medicine of the University of Washington, a PTA representative, a public health water engineer, labor union officials, senior citizens, and the mayoral candidates.

Also, posters were printed and located in prominent view in places such as hospitals, dental offices, and cars; they also were carried by the doorbellers. The Detroit fluoridation committee contributed excellent ideas for the posters, and the Seattle committee readily adopted them.

Nonpaid publicity: This phase of the campaign was aggressively and opportunistically implemented by many members of the committee. One of the cochairmen and one of the publicity committee chairmen, who is the public information officer for the local health department, were able to capitalize on newsworthy elements of the campaign and exploit them to the fullest. The health department and the University of Washington dental school took courageous, outspoken positions on issues raised by the opposition. Timely news conferences were called by the director of the health department to denounce the accusations of the antifluoridationists.

The dean of the dental school released data from a current public school survey that showed the predictable caries decrease in Seattle's schoolchildren. The data were cited extensively in the mass media, and in at least one instance were effectively presented by the dean on a television news show. After a clear delineation of the factual information, both daily newspapers produced forthright editorials and articles supporting the continuation of water fluoridation. Support of the media is essential to the conduct and success of the campaign. This support should be actively developed because it can be very helpful during the last stages of the campaign when editorials are potentially very influential in determining the outcome of an election.

Paid newspaper advertising: Quarter-page advertisements were run in Seattle's two daily newspapers on the Friday before election day and on the day before the election. Two advertisements were run in the *Seattle Shopping News.* One advertisement featured impact statements from local and national representatives of the health and environmental departments, clearly confirming the economy and safety of water fluoridation. In the other advertisement, every physician of the King County Medical Association was listed as being in support of continued fluoridation. The intent of this particular advertisement was to associate the trusted family physician with the safety of water fluoridation. A strong visual emphasis was given to the "Vote no on 2" theme in these advertisements.

Summary

This overview and analysis of the 1973 campaign to retain fluoridation in Seattle is limited to a presentation of the factors most influential in achieving the successful outcome. Naturally, a political landslide victory of this type is the result of many complex factors and should be viewed in the historical context of evolution rather than revolution. For Seattle, it shows that the fluoridation issue has come of age. By the voters' overwhelming endorsement of continued

fluoridation, they have moved this issue from the political to the health realm where indeed it belongs.

It is the authors' opinion that three factors were primarily responsible for this victory:

—Aggressive doorbelling campaign. Sixty-five percent of the precincts in Seattle were canvassed primarily by dental and dental auxiliary students.

—Broad-based community support. The media, labor unions, political caucuses and candidates, public institutions, League of Women Voters, Municipal League, the PTA, Head Start, free clinics, professional organizations, Seattle Model Cities Program, and others supported retainment of fluoridation.

—Lack of a sizable countermovement. No paid radio or television advertisements, minimal distribution of handout flyers and posters, and little evidence of any systematic or organized canvassing of any target group or section of the city by the antifluoridationists were seen.

Communities interested in fluoridation would do well to consider the time and expense required to conduct a successful campaign. Wherever possible, the city councils, legislatures, and state boards of health should be encouraged to enact water fluoridation measures. The ballot is probably the least efficient and most expensive means of implementing water fluoridation. However, when it becomes necessary to bring the issue to the voters, then it is incumbent upon the profluoridation forces to run the campaign in a politically intelligent manner. The need for an astute political approach to the campaign cannot be overemphasized. The profluoridation committee must acknowledge the existing sociopolitical structure and work within that framework to influence the voter.

The desired result of this campaign activity was to win the election. Fluoridation in relation with health education is desirable, but under the time constraints of an election, it must be considered secondary. It is of critical importance to select achievable objectives in the campaign, develop a cadre of manpower resources, formulate a plan, and then execute it aggressively. Fortunately, in the 1973 Seattle campaign, this formula was followed with almost no cause for deviation. With the objectives clearly identified and the plan formulated, the individual volunteers carried out their assignments with dedication, poise, good humor, and outstanding results.

The authors wish to acknowledge the following persons for their support and contributions to the campaign: Abe Bergman, MD; Lawrence Bergner, MD; Alex Bishop; James Collins; Helen Danforth; Claudia Deibert; J. David Erickson, DDS; Kenneth and Martha Fales; Mr. and Mrs. N. G. Gray; Olin Hoffman, DDS; Johnny N. Johnson, DDS; Peggy Kronfield; Cora Leukhart; Don Lopp; Ed Marcuse, MD; Dan E. Middaugh; Rosalie Miller, DDS; Myrtle Mitchell; Eldon H. O'Bryant, DDS; Ken Peters, DDS; John Small; Leo Sreebny, DDS; Nicholas Suhadolnik, DDS; Oscar Verlo; Norma Wells; Scott Wilson; plus many others, too numerous to mention. This paper won a special award in the ADA Preventive Dentistry Awards competition in 1974.

Reprinted from the Journal of the American Dental Association, Vol. 91, Sept. 1975, pp. 583-588.

WINNING A LARGE FLUORIDATION CAMPAIGN
Using Minimal Manpower and Budget

BY
JOEL M. BORISKIN, D.D.S.
Chief, Dental Health Bureau
Alameda County Health Care Services Agency
Oakland, California

The East Bay Municipal Utility District is a 277-square-mile two-county area situated across San Francisco Bay from the city of San Francisco. There are about 1,100,000 water customers of EBMUD and about 500,000 registered voters living within the district. EBMUD encompasses 30 cities, the largest of which are Oakland, Berkeley, Richmond and Walnut Creek. According to California statute, water fluoridation can only be instituted in EBMUD by popular vote, and after two embarrassing fluoridation election defeats in 1960 and 1964, a 1974 effort won by a dramatically narrow 0.5 percent margin. Numerous post-election efforts to stop fluoridation were also defeated. EBMUD has continued to provide fluoridation without interruption since the installation in 1976 of feeder equipment.

The entire pre- and post-election campaign efforts were implemented by a core committee of no more than 10 people at any time. No more than four of those were full-time. The entire campaign budget was about $27,000 (about 5.5 cents per voter) and post-election expenses to insure implementation of the vote totalled less than $10,000. Virtually no door-to-door canvassing was done. Campaign volunteers were few and irregularly available. Nevertheless, the effort was successful, due to important strategic concepts, maximal use of media and funds, and the undying optimism and commitment of the core committee.

Background

In 1921 the California Municipal Utility District Act was passed and incorporated into the *Public Utility Code.* The Act provided for the creation of multi-county utility district areas throughout the State. Each district elects its own board of directors. There are now four such districts in California.

In 1923, EBMUD was created. It provides water and sewage services, maintains extensive recreational facilities at its many water reservoirs and, from its major dam, generates considerable electrical energy, which is sold to local power companies.

Of the 1,100,000 residents living within EBMUD's jurisdiction, about 250,000 are minors. There are about 300,000 metered customers. EBMUD is the only State Municipal Utility District that provides drinking water. The primary source of that water is the Mokelumne River watershed, a 575-square-mile section of the Sierra Nevada mountain range located about 200 miles east of the district.

The water is transported by overland aqueducts nearly 100 miles long to local reservoirs, where it is distributed to six district

90

water treatment plants. There, fluoridation and other treatment processes take place. From the treatment plants, nearly 3,000 miles of piping distribute the water to customers. The natural fluoride content of the pretreated water is in the range of 0.05 parts per million to 0.14 parts per million fluoride ion.

Of the 1,100,000 EBMUD residents, approximately 80 percent live in Alameda County (southern geographic area). The remainder live in Contra Costa County (northern geographic area). The population is as diversified as the geography of the district. From severe pockets of poverty in the inner cities of Oakland and Richmond to the affluence of Piedmont and Orinda, the entire economic, cultural and educational spectrum of America is reflected in the people served by EBMUD.[1]

As of December 31, 1975, there were 6,795 communities and government agencies in the United States with authorization to fluoridate.[2] EBMUD ranks seventh in size among them (there are only seven with populations greater than 1,000,000). This achievement was in the making for more than 25 years, since the very first endeavors to gain fluoridation for EBMUD were in the mid-1950s.

Early requests by local health authorities were rebuffed by the EBMUD Board of Directors on the ground that the board lacked authority to order fluoridation without electorate approval. However, after considerable legal wrangling, the state attorney general ruled in 1954 that the board could order the program.[3]

Confronted with renewed pressure from both pro- and anti-fluoridation forces following the 1954 ruling, the district's board assumed a "hands-off" policy. By 1959, it managed to have the California Municipal Utility District Code amended to require a district-wide majority vote before fluoridation could be instituted. In 1960, only one year after the 1959 amendment passed, the first of three fluoridation elections was held.

Past Elections

Prior to the 1974 victory for EBMUD fluoridation, two fluoridation election defeats occurred—one in June 1960 and one in June 1964. The 1960 vote was a devastating 57 percent "no" to 43 percent "yes". In 1964, the margin improved, but was still a discouraging 53 percent "no" to 47 percent "yes".[4] Thanks to the continued commitment of

proponents in the two losing endeavors, fairly detailed descriptions of methodology and tactics used by them were recorded for future pro-fluoridation efforts. The documents served as a cornerstone of the 1974 campaign strategy formulation.

In 1960 and 1964, local health departments served as the central campaign organizations, with endorsements from civic leaders and major local health groups as backdrops to the effort. Public health nurses and aides were mobilized for door-to-door canvassing, while a speakers' bureau sponsored by the health department jumped at every opportunity to publicly debate anti-fluoridationists.

A district-wide mailing culminated the 1964 campaign shortly before election day. Yet, despite the massive availability and effort of volunteer help in canvassing and mailing, coupled with large financial donations from medical and dental groups, the efforts failed. Why?

In analyzing the election returns and microfilm records of local newspaper articles printed one week before the 1960 and 1964 elections, certain facts became evident:

- Grassroots voters were not reached by campaign efforts, possibly because most of the campaigning was done by health professionals instead of by a cross section of the community. In addition, research into newspapers showed that the campaigns had a relatively low visibility.
- Debate forums, used extensively by fluoridation proponents, rarely proved educational. By emphasizing the debates, pro-fluoridationists legitimized their opposition's stand, perhaps unwittingly.
- In 1964, nearly $25,000 was spent on a single campaign mailing. Such lump expenditures, compared to appropriations for more visible and diversified publicity, may have been an unwise use of campaign money.
- Lead time for organizing the campaign was short. In 1960, proponents had only about six months to organize. In 1964, they had less than a year. This left campaigners unprepared to avert the effects of the anti-fluoridationists' last-minute media blitz.
- The language of pro-fluoridation messages in both the 1960 and 1964 efforts seemed quite technical compared to the more

down-to-earth emotionalism of their opponents' fear-exploiting propaganda.

- Both the 1960 and 1964 elections were consolidated with statewide primary elections rather than with statewide general elections. General elections historically have a greater voter turnout usually helpful to pro-fluoridation causes.
- Ballot proposition wording in the two losing bids was ambiguous and negative in tone.

Gleaning as much as possible from past experience, a new and different election strategy began taking shape. In late 1972, local health departments and dental society leaders began talking about a renewed effort to gain fluoridation for EBMUD.

The 1974 Campaign

Early in 1973, the Comprehensive Health Planning Councils (forerunners of the current Health Systems Agencies) in Alameda and Contra Costa counties simultaneously recognized that dental disease was reaching serious levels in the two-county area, especially in economically disadvantaged areas. spurred by requests from school personnel and health department officials, the two-county Comprehensive Health Planning Councils convened. Representatives from all major professional and health groups were invited. The meeting was chaired by Tom Bates, who was then a young Alameda County Board of Supervisors member committed to attacking the dental disease problem. Bates subsequently was elected assemblyman (D-Alameda County) and continues to support fluoridation.

After hearing testimony from a variety of sources citing the need to reduce dental disease, attendees agreed that water fluoridation was the first and most important step in the war against tooth decay.

The supervisor agreed to assist in the creation of a bi-county committee to implement a fluoridation campaign. Four or five individuals volunteered to help recruit, beginning the committee's organization. Three weeks after the initial meeting, the first meeting of the campaign committee was held. The group was named "People For Fluoridation".

From May 1973, through November 1973, the primary goal of People for Fluoridation was to generate broadly based representation among its membership through an intensive recruit-

ment drive, centered mostly in low-income areas where tooth decay had the highest incidence. It was hoped that the campaign membership's final makeup would include health professionals working side by side with community leaders from low-income areas.

Unfortunately, the recruitment drive was a dismal failure. Getting prospective members to attend more than a few committee meetings was practically impossible. Even after six months of effort, by November the core committee consisted of only one physician, one lay person, two county dental health officers, a public health nurse, two dental society representatives, one community health worker and the county supervisor.

All others who had attended earlier meetings were listed as members, but were not, at that point, actively involved. Although the core committee had some avenues to pursue for further recruitment of volunteers, it was generally felt that without additional support, the Fluoridation '74 effort would have to be put off to the next election.

Explanations for the core committee's failure to generate enthusiasm were varied. First, many committee members found it difficult to invest sufficient time in the recruitment effort. Second, they were recruiting support for fluoridation at a time when the natural food craze was at its peak in the Bay Area, making fluoride a less-than-popular community project. Third, many proponents who went through the disappointment of the prior effort simply had had enough of the issue and were pessimistic toward the renewed effort.

By early December 1973, only one new member was added to the core committee, but this addition proved to be the most helpful and critical. A representative of the local Jaycee chapter and an extremely knowledgeable and dedicated individual, the new member, William H. Tonsall, OD, gave a tremendous uplift to the committee's esprit de corps and contributed significant expertise to the effort.

At that point the core committee became the steering committee. The members' first decision was that although they were deficient in representation from the widely varying elements within the district, they had to turn their energies toward campaign strategy, since election day was only 11 months away.

Developing the Campaign Strategy

Strategy crystallized through the combination of seven sources of input and information:

- Professional input through physicians and dentists on the committee;
- Contribution of ideas by a lay individual who had been involved in three previous fluoridation elections in the area, two of which were successful;
- Input from local elected officials familiar with mass media and political activities in the area;
- Orientation from the Jaycee representative, who kept the effort geared to the broadly-based concept;
- Input from members of two previous unsuccessful efforts in EBMUD;
- In-depth studies, previously mentioned, of the prior fluoridation elections; and
- Counseling from a political campaign manager on use of local mass media.

From the wide spectrum of input emerged a singular fact: the pro-fluoridation effort had to be *political,* handled in a strictly political fashion, similar to any other political issue. It has been shown that health professionals frequently want to handle a fluoridation campaign as an "informational and educational effort."[5] Through investigation, the committee realized that such an orientation could only lead to disappointment at the polls. A more realistic approach was in order. The committee hoped that voter education would be a positive spin-off of the campaign.

Members agreed that, because of the enormity of the task ahead, they had to devise the most efficient and invulnerable method of delivering a simple, convincing message to approximately 350,000 registered voters (the number projected to vote), without allowing the opposition to undermine their campaign endeavors. This required a fully realistic assessment of the committee's capabilities.

Step 1: Getting Fluoridation on the Ballot

The first real test was to convince the EB-MUD Board of Directors to place an issue on the ballot. The board had ultimate authority to decide whether district voters would have a chance to vote on fluoridation. In 1966, this same board had refused a request by pro-fluoridationists for a new vote on the grounds that the group did not appear "capable of conducting a legitimate campaign," and that they did not demonstrate "widespread interest among district residents for a fluoridation election."

The problem was that the board did not set clear guidelines stating what it wished to see as proof of "widespread public interest" in a fluoridation election. To further compound the problem, the board would not be bound to call an election, even if the committee succeeded in acquiring the legally required number of signatures on an initiative petition demanding a vote, because a quirk of California law exempts special districts, such as EB-MUD, from the normal initiative process. Special districts are governed essentially by their own election regulations, which in this case did not include the initiative petition process. Getting the board to place the issue on the ballot, with no guidelines or assurances, was the committee's major hurdle.

In January 1974, members decided to use a multi-faceted approach to substantiate their request for a place on the ballot. The committee wanted to acquire six areas of support for its request. Therefore, it circulated a petition requesting a fluoride vote through every dental office in the district as well as at shopping malls and other business centers. The goal was to collect 50,000 signatures, or about 10 percent of the registered voters. Following circulation of the petition, the committee obtained endorsements from all city councils and county boards of supervisors in the district; conducted a public opinion poll to indicate that a significant majority of residents wanted a fluoride vote; encouraged private citizens to deluge individual district board members with letters encouraging them to call a vote; obtained individual endorsements from all state and federal elected officials who represented the district; and obtained endorsements from all prominent health groups and community leaders urging the board to call a vote.

The committee had no real choice but to use this approach, since EBMUD's board had not indicated what kind of evidence it wished to receive.

EBMUD's board was required by state law to consolidate a fluoridation vote with either a state-wide primary or a state-wide general election. After considerable discussion, committee members decided to request that the fluoride issue be placed on the general election ballot. The rationale stemmed from the fact that anti-fluoridation voters, although almost always a minority of the total registered voter census,[6] are a highly motivated group of voters and generally go to the polls more often than the average pro-fluoridation voters. Perhaps this motivation stems from their imagined fears of the alleged dangers of fluoridation. Or, the higher turnout may simply be explained by the fact that the average anti-fluoridation voter has been shown to be in the older age categories that historically have a better voter turnout.[7]

Regardless, it was evident that the better the overall voter turnout, the better chances were of neutralizing the anti-fluoridation vote. A general election would be more likely to bring out the silent majority of proponents than a primary election. In retrospect, this one decision may have indeed been one of the most critical to the fluoridation campaign's ultimate success.

In mid-January 1974, People For Fluoridation told the EBMUD board of its desire to place a fluoridation measure on the November 1974 general election ballot and requested a deadline to present substantiating evidence supporting its request for a vote. June 11, 1974 was set as the deadline. The January appearance before EBMUD's board was the first public notification by the pro-fluoridation group of its intent. It stimulated a wave of anti-fluoride letters-to-the-editor in local newspapers, signaling the reorganization of the anti-fluoride campaign.

With help from local health departments and $100 in donations from committee members, People For Fluoridation printed petitions and accompanying instructions in an office kit form. On February 7, 1974, the committee had its petition drive kickoff. The well-publicized meeting at a local school auditorium was attended by a grand total of 15 persons. Six were campaign committee members, one was a guest speaker and five were anti-fluoridationists. The terribly discouraging turnout did not deter the committee however. The next day it proceeded to mail nearly 1,000 petition kits to dental offices throughout the district, since the intended distribution of the kits at the kickoff meeting was a complete failure.

Committee members then went to work,

with the help of a few members of local dental auxiliary groups, to periodically call every dental office receiving a petition kit and encourage office staff to actively collect signatures on the petition forms from patients, relatives and friends. The petition kit included petition forms, an instruction sheet, a display placard and fluoridation information pamphlets designed for the office waiting area. The reminder calls from committee volunteers stimulated greater petition activity.

Simultaneously, the other five activities outlined earlier were pursued to substantiate the request for a fluoride vote. First, every member of every city council in the district was contacted, in some cases taking advantage of relationships previously established with members of the dental community.

Concurrently, all local health organizations were solicited for endorsements and support. A public opinion poll was begun by a graduate student of a local college, local legislators were solicited and the public was asked to write letters to individual EBMUD board members requesting a fluoridation election.

This flurry of activity by the small fluoridation committee began to raise eyebrows, and word of its work somehow reached the EBMUD board. Less than enthusiastic about calling a new fluoride vote, the board quickly issued, for the first time, a written set of four criteria that had to be satisfied before it would authorize another fluoridation election.

The very stringent requirements were issued in March, two months after People For Fluoridation announced its intent to the board and only three months before the petition deadline of June 11. Fortunately, as if by some intuitive accident, the four election criteria set by the board exactly coincided with the first four of the six evidence-gathering areas decided upon by the committee in early January.

The board's four criteria of "evidence of public interest in a fluoridation election" were: 1) submission of a petition, containing signatures representing 5 percent of registered voters, requesting an election; 2) written endorsements from city councils and boards of supervisors representing a majority of district residents; 3) a public opinion poll showing that a majority or near majority of residents favored fluoridation or wished to vote on it; and 4) numerous letters from district residents requesting an election.

By March 1974, the date EBMUD issued what it probably thought were impossibly difficult criteria, People For Fluoridation had already been working for two months toward satisfying the very same requirements. To the surprise of the board and the anti-fluoridationists, the committee was well prepared by the June 11 deadline. In addition to satisfying the four given requirements, the committee also presented 37 health organization endorsements. Numerous local politicians from both parties also testified on behalf of People for Fluoridation.

The evidence was overwhelming and left the board no choice but to order a vote. After a public hearing, the board voted unanimously to place the fluoridation issue on the November general election ballot. Proposition C, the fluoridation measure, would appear on the ballot the committee had hoped for.

Step 2: Wording of the Proposition

It has been postulated that the only piece of election literature all voters ever see is the ballot proposition itself.[8] With a fluoridation issue, this becomes quite critical, since the general public's knowledge about the subject is surprisingly limited.[9] The proposition's wording became the most important piece of educational material. It was, therefore, critical to the fluoridation committee that the wording not only be clear in its intent but also informative, explaining fluoridation's purposes and benefits.

EBMUD's legal staff had other ideas about how Proposition C ought to be worded. Under extreme pressure from both sides, it opted for a phrase extracted from a 1959 state statute that would have made the proposition read, "Shall the East Bay Municipal Utility District add fluorine and fluorine compounds to the public water supply of said district?" This is how the proposition had appeared in the two unsuccessful fluoridation votes in the district.

People For Fluoridation vehemently objected to the inaccuracy of the term "fluorine" instead of "fluoride," since fluorine is the elemental gaseous form. Fluorine is not used in water treatment. In addition the term fluoride is a more common word that the general public immediately associates with toothpaste, dental appointments and protection against tooth decay.

The committee also felt that the proposi-

tion should include a statement explaining the purpose of adding fluoride to drinking water and the amount that would be added. The committee's suggested wording was, "Shall the East Bay Municipal Utility District add fluoride compounds to the water supply of said district, at an average concentration of one part fluoride per one million parts of water, as recommended by the California State Department of Health for the prevention of tooth decay?"

After considerable wrangling and numerous heated exchanges with EBMUD staff in negotiations over the proposition form, People For Fluoridation was denied its preferred wording, but was successful in obtaining a change in the wording used in previous referenda.

The final proposition read "Shall the East Bay Municipal Utility District add fluoride compounds to the water supply of said district subject to the regulations of the California State Department of Health?"

Although this was a considerable improvement over past wordings, People For Fluoridation felt it was still incomplete in conveying the purpose of a water fluoridation program to the voter. However, because the board had the ultimate authority in decisions on wording, the committee had no recourse.

In July and August, as prescribed by code, the board publicly announced its intent to place fluoridation on the upcoming ballot. Immediately, anti-fluoridationists began pamphleting, making public presentations, having press conferences and campaigning intensively throughout the district. Seeing the well-organized activity of fluoridation opponents was indeed sobering.

The fluoridation committee's first realization was that with an election coming up in only four months, it faced a well organized, experienced opposition. People For Fluoridation had an empty treasury, completely drained by its endeavors of the previous six months. Knowing that its opponents would get considerable help from the National Health Federation (the California-based national anti-fluoridation group) in addition to their own local capabilities, the fluoridation committee's urgent need for money to conduct a campaign was apparent.

Step 3: Fundraising

An experienced campaign manager, who appeared at one of the committee's earlier meetings, estimated that a minimum of $100,000 would be necessary to conduct a successful campaign, a sum the committee knew was far beyond its ability to raise in only three-and-a-half months. Understanding, though, that the success of the effort hinged on the committee's ability to raise money, People For Fluoridation immediately began to contact a variety of potential sources.

Business, community service organizations, local foundations, professional organizations and every other possible sympathetic group were solicited. The only organizations that responded were local dental society chapters and one dental insurance corporation with a majority of dentists on its board of directors.

It was disappointing to learn that, even though the committee had the widespread support of political, religious, health and community organizations, there was no financial commitment by those groups, who would benefit the most by fluoridation's success.

It goes without saying that the campaign could not have begun without the substantial financial commitment of local dentists. In the opinion of many, local dental professional support is the single most critical element to the success of any fluoridation election effort.[10] Although People For Fluoridation did not expect to have considerable manpower assistance from local dentists, the financial commitment and generosity of the dental profession was sufficient.

Over a three-and-a-half month period, approximately $27,000 was donated to People For Fluoridation from all sources. Of this, $26,000 was contributed by dentists and their organizations. The remaining $1,000 constituted non-dental contributions, such as individual physician donations, lay and business gifts, and small individual gifts of less than $5.

Of the $26,000 contributed by dentists, $10,000 came as a lump sum donation from the Alameda County Dental Society, whose members practice in the heart of EBMUD. $4,000 came from lump sum contributions of three other local dental society chapters. $5,000 came as an "in-kind" contribution from a dental insurance corporation and the remaining $7,000 came from individual, out-of-pocket contributions from individual dentists practicing throughout the district. Some of the single contributions were as high as $250.

The $7,000 bloc of donations deserves some discussion. As experienced fluoride campaigners know, this is a considerable sum to be raised in the form of individual, out-of-pocket donations solicited from a total of 900 dentists practicing in the water district area (an average of $7.78 per dentist). By utilizing the concept of a "money tree," People For Fluoridation was able to single out and appeal to the most motivated and concerned members of the dental profession, who would be most likely to contribute.

The money tree technique works by having one well known and respected dentist identify and contact 10 other dentists who are personal acquaintances. He or she asks the dentists to contribute a fixed sum (in this case, $100) to be sent to him or her. The dentist then asks each of the 10 dentists to contact 10 others whom they know personally. Thus, the money tree grows.

To avoid overlap, each dentist in the tree develops a list of 10 prospects and sends the list to the first dentist for verification before requesting donations. The tree grows until all likely contributors have been reached. The critical factor, of course, in the success of the money tree is that the original or "seed" dentist must have a high degree of popularity and command a great deal of respect from his or her peers.

Dentists must also have considerable working knowledge of their dental communities so they can properly select the first groups of 10 to start the tree.

The advantage of the money tree concept over other solicitation methods is that prospective donors are contacted by a personal acquaintance rather than by a campaigner that they are unfamiliar with.

The $5,000 "in-kind" contribution referred to earlier came from a dental insurance corporation with a large number of dentists on its boards of directors. The money was donated in the form of payment for campaign literature. More than 100,000 pamphlets were distributed during the 10 weeks before election day. The simple, artistic pamphlets gave the campaign considerable visibility and served as a helpful educational tool.

By far, the largest portion of the campaign treasury, more than 50 percent of total campaign finances, came as lump sum contributions from local dental society chapter treasuries. Work by fluoridation committee members and their colleagues to convince chapter boards of directors to commit such sums required careful estimation and tabulation of expected expenses as well as the presentation of a clear and well-organized campaign plan with an itemization of expenditures.

At no time did committee members offer a promise of victory as part of their request. It is a strong testimonial to the commitment of the 900 local dental practitioners to community dental welfare that they would donate $26,000 toward an effort that had failed twice before.

Another non-monetary contribution not listed above was the donation of 3,000 square feet of prime location, ground-floor office space in the heart of a heavily trafficked area in downtown Oakland for use as campaign headquarters. The large floor-to-ceiling windows of the office building gave People For Fluoridation hundreds of square feet of display area for posters and banners, making the headquarters visible to all nearby pedestrian and vehicle traffic.

Step 4: Use of Limited Funds

Regardless of the fact that local dental professionals were exceptionally generous in their contributions, the $27,000 budget amounted to only 5.4 cents per registered voter, one third the amount needed to do even one districtwide mailing at bulk-rate costs. It is an understatement to say that People For Fluoridation was seriously underfunded due to the unwillingness of non-dental organizations to provide financial support.

Circumstances demanded the formulation of a spending strategy that provided maximum impact at minimum cost. Use of mass media, pamphleting and other non-mailing techniques became the order of the day. But even excluding large mailings, finances were still severely limited.

The committee turned again to the expertise of sympathetic local political leaders and the experience of previous fluoridation campaigners. From this emerged a campaign manager who worked for nearly nothing and helped the committee get the most for its mass media dollar. He also contributed his expertise to the overall campaign-spending plan.

Given its funding limitations, the committee agreed on six basic campaign guidelines:

1) Get maximum visibility during the two weeks before the election;

2) Concentrate energies in the low-income areas of the community that would benefit most from the program;
3) Keep campaign messages short and simple;
4) Refuse any public debate forums for television, radio or before large groups;
5) Keep public image 100 percent positive; and
6) Emphasize endorsements of prominent local individuals and organizations with which all segments of the community could identify.

Guideline No. 1

Reliable political studies have shown that most voters do not make up their minds on controversial political issues until the last few days before an election. By beginning a more concentrated media and pamphleting effort only two weeks prior to election day, People For Fluoridation conserved funds, yet gave ample time to reinforce the "yes" vote, thus negating last minute anti-fluoridation propaganda. Without additional funding, the committee decided to concentrate almost all of its expenditures in the last two weeks.

Guideline No. 2

The rationale to concentrate on low-income areas was that those communities were generally less familiar with the fluoridation issue, had the most to gain by fluoridation and were most vulnerable to the anti-fluoridation approach. People For Fluoridation had to reach those areas because it had prior knowledge that anti-fluoridationists would focus on those groups with the text of their voters' pamphlet statement. In addition, it was felt that media messages directed at low-income communities would be picked up by others sympathetic to the effort's purpose.

Guideline No. 3

Simplicity was the byword because the committee felt that a simpler message would be easily repeated. Repetition, the committee hoped, would mean better recall of the issue by voters at the polls. "Yes on C, fluoride prevents tooth decay, naturally!" became the only slogan used on all billboards, radio spots and written materials. Language such as "fluoride is completely safe," "fluoride is proven effective," and other more technical language was reserved only for lengthier written materials.

Guideline No. 4

It was the committee's early experience that agreeing to debate with anti-fluoridationists would give credibility to their message and provide them a legitimized forum to spread their fearmongering and raise doubts about fluoridation's safety. Although People For Fluoridation could technically win a debate because its scientific material was reliable and the opposition's wasn't, frequently, the anti-fluoridationists' expert speakers could turn the committee's victory into theirs through deception and rhetoric.

So the message went out—no debates. In response to public requests for a debate participant from People For Fluoridation, the group simply responded by refusing on the grounds that its presence would undeservedly legitimize the anti-fluoridationists' totally irresponsible position. Additionally, the anti-fluoridationists' namecalling and inflammatory remarks inevitably reduced debates to shouting matches, making them unenjoyable and non-educational for the listener.

This position, of course, disappointed local television stations, which thrived on the controversial aspect of the issue. In response to their prodding and threats, the committee reminded them of its right to equal time if the stations were to air anti-fluoridation positions. People For Fluoridation would agree to provide a separate presentation, either before or preferably after one by an anti-fluoridationist. The anti-fluoridationists' only opportunity to publicly debate People For Fluoridation was on a few call-in radio talk shows. The committee was sure to have its own people call in to such shows and raise doubts about the credibility of the anti-fluoridation guest. It then demanded equal time for a guest of its own.

Guideline No. 5

Maintaining a totally positive public image meant that People For Fluoridation's messages would emphasize the beneficial aspects of fluoridation. It also would refuse to take the defensive position of proving why fluoridation was not harmful. It all but ignored the myriad of anti-fluoride objections, publicly dismissing them as hogwash, and concen-

trated on how much good fluoridation would do in terms of cost savings, better health, and improving the quality of people's lives. It wanted the public's unconscious mental associations with Proposition C to be of positive things such as health, happiness and financial savings.

Guideline No. 6

It has been shown that the general public is not very familiar with the issues surrounding fluoridation.[11] This lack of knowledge breeds indecision, which many times leads voters to look toward community leaders for guidance. With that in mind, in acquiring endorsements, People For Fluoridation examined the population that it wished to reach. Its political and organizational endorsements crossed political, social, ethnic, economic and educational lines. People For Fluoridation acquired local newspaper endorsements and publicized supporters wherever it could.

Once the committee agreed on its six guidelines, members set priorities for action. A logo was designed to give recognition and distinction to the effort. Once the logo and campaign slogan were developed, campaign material was printed. Before it finished, the committee had 120,000 "Yes on C" pamphlets; 5,000 quarter-card billboards (roadside signs stapled to poles); hundreds of large signs for local buses; 2,000 professional outdoor posters; 21 roadside billboards; and hundreds of smaller "Yes on C" handout cards.

As part of the unified effort to gain visibility, People For Fluoridation took out small newspaper advertisements in most East Bay papers every day for two weeks prior to election day. The day before the election, half-page to quarter-page ads in the larger circulation papers were bought.

One of the most cost-effective strategies involved an intensive radio campaign during the two weeks before election day. Radio spots were placed with increasing frequency as election day approached. Stations were carefully selected based on ratings. Pre-recorded spots were tailored to the target radio audiences. Utilizing radio, People For Fluoridation was assured that, for a relatively modest cost, tens of thousands of voters would hear its message at least once before election day.

As a final effort, the committee rented a flatbed truck with a loud-speaker system attached, decorated it with campaign material and drove it throughout the district on the Saturday and Sunday preceding election day, broadcasting the pro-fluoridation message.

During this time, campaign headquarters served as meeting place, storage facility, distribution center and think tank, where the committee had press conferences, strategy meetings and finally its victory party on election night. Although the committee intended to use the headquarters as home base for a door-to-door effort, volunteers to walk precincts never materialized. Those few volunteers that did participate found that people in the district were very hesitant about opening their doors to strangers, no matter how well identified.

All this effort required strict coordination, which was accomplished by meeting on a weekly basis. At every meeting, each member of the small committee would be given an assignment to be completed by the next weekly meeting. Individual assignments were enormous. Toward the end of the campaign, some members were spending more than 50 hours per week on the fluoridation effort.

As a final last-ditch approach, committee members and a few volunteers got on the phone during the last week, urging voters to cast a "yes" vote on Proposition C. This was an extremely effective technique, though time consuming. Precincts telephoned by the committee showed a significantly higher "yes" vote than did neighboring precincts, where no phoning was done.

Election Results

The vote on Proposition C was so close that People For Fluoridation did not know it had won until after 2 a.m. the day following the election. Of 543,927 registered voters, only 294,974 voted on the fluoridation measure. The total vote count on Proposition C was 149,035 (50.52 percent) "yes" to 145,939 (49.48 percent) "no," a margin of 3,096 votes, 1.02 percent.

Most "yes" votes came from younger, higher income, more educated citizens. Most "no" votes were cast by elderly, less educated citizens as is typical during many fluoridation elections.[12] What was significantly atypical, accounting for a substantial number of "yes" votes, was the 51 percent "yes" vote from the city of Oakland, largest of the EB-MUD cities.

Twenty-five percent of the total votes cast on the measure came from Oakland, a city that with its numerous low-income and high-density areas, had in the past been decisively anti-fluoridation. In the 1960 election, Oakland turned a 36 percent "yes" vote. In 1964 it cast 41 percent "yes" votes. The 1974 vote was up 10 percent from the previous election, and up 15 percent from the 1960 vote. The committee concentrated heavily in Oakland and other low-income areas as part of overall campaign strategy, and it clearly paid off.

Election Follow-Up

Although the victory celebration was indeed rewarding, the feeling of complacency was not to last long. Almost immediately after their election defeat, anti-fluoridationists began a concerted and organized effort to impede the program's implementation. Through threats of legal action, numerous personal appearances before EBMUD's board, a strong letter-writing campaign and other methods, they hoped to intimidate the board into delaying construction of fluoridation facilities.

Realizing that its hard work could be jeopardized if the implementation phase was left entirely to the board (which had been less than sympathetic to fluoridation activity), the weary committee regrouped to develop a post-election strategy.

Only four of the original members were willing to persevere, but the victory brought new willingness to become involved from other community leaders, some from outside the dental profession. The new group decided to form a public health liaison committee to EBMUD, which would meet on a regular basis with EBMUD engineering staff for updates on progress toward completion of the fluoridation facilities.

Committee members included representatives from all three district health departments, dental and medical societies, health consumer groups and various political and community organizations. EBMUD was quite willing to meet and report regularly to the liaison committee, and it was mutually agreed that a three-month implementation interval would be appropriate.

The formation of the liaison committee was extremely helpful in a number of ways:
• It kept continuous pressure on EBMUD to keep completion of the fluoridation facil-

ity as a high priority project;
- It kept the community informed on progress toward completion of the facility;
- It combated anti-fluoridationist attempts to delay implementation of the measure;
- It helped the committee to understand construction details; and
- It allowed representatives of the group to have input into the design, construction and operation of the program.

The total project cost for construction and materials was about $750,000 and took 21 months to complete. The district originally estimated that it would take 18 months to complete, but certain unforeseen delays in completing paperwork, including an environmental report, slowed progress. The design and operation of the system is superb, and fluoride ion concentration rarely shows a greater fluctuation than 0.05 parts per million in any given month. The district takes hundreds of water fluoride samplings per month in various locations throughout the water system.

Before, during and after construction of the fluoridation facilities, anti-fluoridationists continued to use every possible means to combat the program.

In December 1975, they filed a lawsuit against EBMUD, charging that the election was illegal and that fluoridation was causing serious health problems. The lawsuit, although totally spurious, forced the committee to raise money once again to file a friend of the court brief on behalf of the district to be sure that the election would be fully defended. Fortunately, the dental profession again gave financial assistance. In March 1976, the case was thrown out of court.

Again, in mid-1977, anti-fluoridationists began circulating a petition to get fluoridation back on the ballot. Their target election dates were June 1978 or November 1978. Fluoride opponents had done their homework, collecting a considerable number of signatures on a petition requesting a new vote. Again, the committee went to work, getting reiterations of previous endorsements, commissioning another public opinion poll showing that most EBMUD residents favored fluoride and even circulating another pro-fluoride petition. In June 1978, the EBMUD board voted 4-3 to deny the anti-fluoridationists' request for a new vote based on the information People For Fluoridation provided.

To this date, anti-fluoridationists continue their attempts to undo fluoridation, but repeated defeats have dampened their spirits. Pro-fluoridationists look forward to the day when opponents will finally resign themselves to the fact that fluoridation for EBMUD is here to stay. Nevertheless, the importance of remaining diligent after the election was clearly proven, especially in the very narrow defeat of anti-fluoridationists in their bid for a vote last June. A total of $10,000 was spent following the election to preserve the fluoridation victory.

Summary

In November 1974, EBMUD voted by a narrow margin to adopt a water fluoridation program. Continued post-election efforts by anti-fluoridationists to stop fluoridation failed. The program remains in effect today.

A realistic and committed attitude toward the success of the effort and continued diligence following the vote were critical to the final outcome.

References

1. *Fact Sheet.* East Bay Municipal Utility District. pp. 1-6, 1973.
2. *Fluoridation Census—1975.* U.S. Department of Health, Education and Welfare Center for Disease Control, p. 11, 1977.
3. *Opinion of Edmund G. Brown, Attorney General and Wiley Manual, Assistant Attorney General.* State of California, Office of the Attorney General. No. 53/237. 1954.

4. *Fact Sheet on Fluoridation.* East Bay Municipal Utility District. p. 1. 1974.
5. Plaut, Thomas F.: "Practical Politics and Public Health." *Harvard Public Health Alumni Bulletin.* 17:2. 1960.
6. "Current Opinions of Fluoridation." National Opinion Research Center. PPB-42, p. 1. 1972.
7. Gamson, William A.: "Public Information in a Fluoridation Referendum." *Health Education Journal.* 1961.

100

8. Wallace, C.J., Legett, B.J., and Retz, P.A.: "The Influence of Mass Media on the Public's Attitude Toward Fluoridation of Drinking Water in New Orleans." *Journal of Public Health Dentistry*. pp. 40-46 Winter. 1975.

9. Scism, T.E.: "Fluoridation in Local Politics: Study of the Failure of a Proposed Ordinance in One American City." *American Journal of Public Health*. 62:1340-1345. 1972.

10. Mencher, L.F.: "Fluoridation: Analysis of a Successful Community Effort-Challenge to State and Local Dental Societies." ADA 12th National Dental Health Conference. 1961.

11. Scism, T.E.: op. cit.

12. Shaw, C.T.: "Characteristics of Supporters and Rejectors of a Fluoridation Referendum and a Guide for Other Community Programs." *JADA*. 78:39-341. 1969.

Reprinted from the *California Dental Association Journal*, pp. 53-63, June, 1979.

POSTSCRIPT 1980

On June 3, 1980, EBMUD voters approved "Measure T" to continue fluoridation by a vote of 173,606 to 142,819. Since fluoridation had been in effect for four years, a "yes" vote represented a continuation of the status quo. The ballot wording was also more favorable than in the 1974 election. It said: "Shall East Bay Municipal Utility District continue to add fluoride compounds to the water of said District subject to the regulations of the State Dept. of Health?"

The antifluoridationists were much better organized, much better funded and much more active than they were in 1974. But so were we. Alameda Contra Costa Citizens to Save Fluoridation, our proponent group managed to raise approximately $65,000— about 11¢ per registered voter. We achieved a much broader degree of political support; and our "no debate" policy was almost 100% successful in throttling access to the media for antifluoridation propaganda.

Campaign Activities

Our approach was strictly "political." We sought help from every major political official in the area and received endorsements from most of them. Such "outside" endorsements not only increased the credibility of our campaign; they also opened up effective channels of communication to voters. Messages favoring Measure T accompanied or were included in campaign literature distrib-

uted by political parties, individual candidates for office and proponents of other ballot propositions.

Some of our messages were targeted to specific voting districts on the basis of their past records. For example, if a high percentage of voters in a precinct had favored a particular candidate for office, that candidate's endorsement and photograph on a message would be used to gain support for Measure T.

We hired an astute campaign manager to coordinate volunteer efforts, but he also guided our last-minute efforts which included the targeted mailings. In some neighborhoods, adult volunteers rang doorbells to distribute literature. In others, boy scouts and boys' club members did the job. One dental school professor excused his students from class to go door-to-door for fluoridation.

We also telephoned voters. Although telephoning is less effective than talking face-to-face, it is non-threatening and can reach more people in a shorter period of time. We made thousands of phone calls from our campaign headquarters during the final two weeks of the campaign and think that this effort had a tremendous impact.

On Mother's Day we had a "run" for fluoridation at a location central to the district. More than 350 runners participated. T-shirts prepared for the event said, "Smile America, Mother's Day Run for Fluoridation" on the front and "Fluoride is Working, Vote Yes on

T June 3rd" on the back. Although the event required a tremendous amount of work, it was great fun and well worth the effort. It focused public attention on the issue and helped to enlarge our list of people to call upon for volunteer activity.

Emotional Commitment

Almost every person on our committee worked 100-hour weeks toward the end of our campaign. Since our margin of victory in 1974 was only ½ of 1%, we assumed this time that every vote was important. Our opponents did extensive canvassing and wrote a powerful ballot argument for the voter's pamphlet (illustrated below). But we out-canvassed them, outphoned them, outspent them and outmaneuvered them.

Winning a fluoridation campaign is hard work. The best way to understand why this is so is to understand the feelings of your opponents. If you thought that every time you took a drink of water, took a shower, boiled vegetables, watered your pansies or washed your car, you were exposed to a deadly poison, you too might dedicate yourself to removing this "noxious chemical" from your environment. To win a fluoridation election, its proponents must achieve the same level of commitment.

JOEL M. BORISKIN, D.D.S.

ARGUMENT AGAINST MEASURE T

NO on Measure "T" will:
- REMOVE A SERIOUS ENVIRONMENTAL POLLUTANT
- PREVENT DEATHS AND ILLNESSES FROM CHRONIC FLUORIDE POISONING
- RESTORE YOUR RIGHT TO DECIDE WHAT MEDICINE GOES INTO YOUR BODY

FLUORIDATION IS HARMFUL:
- Fluoridation causes over 10,000 CANCER DEATHS yearly.—Dr. Dean Burk, Chief Chemist, Emeritus, National Cancer Institute
- Fluoridated water DAMAGES HUMAN ENZYME SYSTEMS resulting in impaired health.—Dr. John Yiamouyiannis, Science Director, NHF
- Fluoridated water causes GENETIC DAMAGE.—Dr. Aly Mohammed, Chairman, Biology Department, University of Missouri
- Adverse reactions to fluoride include dental fluorosis, skin eruptions, gastric distress, headache and weakness.—Physicians' Desk Reference
- Fluoridation leads to CHRONIC POISONING and sometimes death.— George Waldbott, MD, Allergist, Author
- "I entered an injunction against fluoridation after lengthy hearings. The trial brought into my court experts on the subject. The evidence is convincing that fluoridated water is extremely deleterious to the human body. There was no convincing evidence to the contrary."—Pennsylvania Supreme Court Justice John Flaherty, 11/16/78
- "Ralph Nader has been worried for years about the inadequacy of follow-up tests on TOTAL FLUORIDE INTAKE."—Jack Anderson

- Fluoride is classified a "CHEMICAL CONTAMINANT" in drinking water.—Environmental Protection Agency
- Fluoride is POISONOUS as arsenic and cyanide.—California Pharmacy Law #4160
- Death and illnesses resulted from ACCIDENTAL FLUORIDE OVERSPILL into Annapolis Maryland's water supply.—Tribune, 11/28/ 79, 12/4/79

STOP FLUORIDATION BECAUSE:

- People ingest less than 1% of water used. Over 99% of the fluoride becomes a cumulative, nonbiodegradable, ENVIRONMENTAL POLLUTANT.
- Fluoride is NOT an "essential nutrient"; therefore, "deficiency" is impossible.—National Academy of Sciences, FDA (3/16/79)
- 12 Nobel scientists and 16 major European countries reject fluoridation.
- "If you fluoridate drinking water, YOU CAN'T CONTROL THE DOSE. No prudent doctor would hand you a potent drug and say, 'Take as much as you like.'"—Max Schlachter, MD, Oakland

VOTE **NO** ON "T"

STOP FLUORIDATION

s/Dr. Alexis T. Bell, Professor,
Department of Chemical Engineering and
Assistant Dean, College of Chemistry,
University of California, Berkeley

s/John R. Lee, M.D., Family Practice,
Lecturer on Nutrition, Medical Writer

s/Dr. John B. Neilands, Professor,
Department of Biochemistry,
University of California, Berkeley,
Environmental Activist

Editors' Note

John R. Lee, M.D., one of the signers of the voter's pamphlet, travels to various parts of the United States to testify against fluoridation. His most effective testimony is the claim that he has personally observed instances of fluoride allergy in patients he has treated.

Close scrutiny of the ballot argument, however, should raise considerable doubt about his credibility as a scientific observer. The list of "adverse reactions to fluoride" in the Physicians' Desk Reference refers to fluoride tablets when taken in excessive dosage. This has nothing to do with drinking fluoridated water at 1 ppm. The statements that fluoride is "poisonous," an "environmental pollutant" and a "chemical contaminant" are also based upon information taken out of context. The correct position of the Environmental Protection Agency is stated in this book. The correct position of the National Academy of Sciences is stated also.

DON'T LET THE POISONMONGERS SCARE YOU!
by Stephen Barrett, M.D.

In hundreds of American communities citizens have voted against healthier teeth.

Why?

They were confused—by poisonmongers.

These alarmists in our society are using confusion and a scare vocabulary as weapons against fluoridation. They are cheating all of us, but especially our children.

The benefits of fluoridation are supported by 20,000 scientific studies which prove the poisonmongers wrong.

What do the poisonmongers say?

Instead of telling you that fluoride is found naturally in all water, they call it a "pollutant." Instead of telling you that fluoride is a nutrient essential to life, they call it a "poison." Instead of the big truth, that fluoridation has never harmed anyone, they tell the big lie and say it causes hundreds of ailments.

In proper concentration, fluoride prevents two out of three cavities. But instead of telling you what does happen, the poisonmongers tell you what could happen—*in their imagination.* They say, "Wait and see," without telling you that scientists have studied fluoridation for more than 70 years.

As far back as 1892 a British physician suggested that high tooth decay rates in London might be due to lack of fluoride in the diet. In 1908, a Colorado dentist named Frederick McKay reported that something in the drinking water of certain communities helped lessen tooth decay.

That "something," Dr. McKay learned in 1931, was fluoride.

Spurred on by this discovery, U.S. Public Health Service dental scientists found that a concentration of one part fluoride to one million parts of water would strengthen teeth while they were forming. Many communities had this concentration naturally in their water supply. By 1945 engineers could adjust the concentration of those which had too little.

Dr. Barrett, a practicing psychiatrist, is editor of *The Health Robbers—How To Protect Your Money And Your Life* and co-author of the college textbook *Consumer Health— A Guide To Intelligent Decisions.* As chairman of the board of directors of the Lehigh Valley Committee Against Health Fraud, Inc., since 1970, he has become the nation's most vigorous opponent of health fraud and quackery. He is a scientific advisor to the American Council on Science and Health and has been a member of the committee on quackery of the Pennsylvania Medical Society and the committee on health fraud of the Pennsylvania Health Council.

In that year, studies of controlled fluoridation began. As the evidence built up, thousands of communities acted to obtain its benefits. Today, more than 105 million Americans drink fluoridated water.

But 70 million other American receive public water supplies which are not fluoridated—thanks largely to the efforts of poisonmongers. Any community which considers fluoridation will be flooded with scare propaganda.

Antifluoridation activity in America is orchestrated primarily by a health food industry organization called the National Health Federation (NHF). Though its name may sound impressive, NHF supports the gamut of quackery and looks with disfavor on such proven health measures as smallpox and polio vaccination and the pasteurization of milk. Twelve of its leaders have been in legal difficulty and five have received prison sentences for questionable "health" activities.

In 1974, NHF hired as its "Science Director" a biochemist named John Yiamouyiannis, Ph.D., in order to "break the back" of fluoridation promotion. Within a few months he began issuing reports which claim that fluoridation causes cancer. The reports are based upon actual government statistics—*which he misinterprets.* When scientists at the National Cancer Institute compared cancer rates in fluoridated and non-fluoridated cities, they found *no* link between fluoridation and cancer. Many other

104

prominent scientists and scientific organizations have reached the same conclusion.

Curiously, the National Health Federation itself once funded a scientific study of fluoridation. In 1972, it paid $16,000 to the Center for Science in the Public Interest, a group led by former associates of Ralph Nader. While it was underway, NHF proudly announced that the study would "put the fluoride controversy in proper perspective." When the study came out favorable to fluoridation, however, NHF suddenly became silent about it.

Fluoridation prevents two out of three cavities. It has never harmed anyone. It is endorsed by Consumers Union, the American Dental Association, the American Medical Association, the U.S. Public Health Service and almost every other major health organization in this country.

If you live in a fluoridated community, consider yourself lucky. If you do not, *don't let the poison-mongers scare you.*

Fluoridation is a modern health miracle.

Three free copies of this report may be obtained by sending a stamped self-addressed 4½ × 9 envelope to LVCAHF, P.O. Box 1602, Allentown, Pa. 18105. Additional copies may be purchased for $5.00 per hundred.

FIGHTING HEALTHY TEETH
By Mary Bernhardt and Bob Sprague

On May 27, 1975, 213,573 people in Los Angeles exercised their democratic privilege—and voted against healthier teeth! Since 1973, more than 270 Nebraska communities have done the same. In cities from coast to coast, citizens have voted to deprive themselves, their children, and their neighbors' children of the proven health benefits of fluoridation.

Of course, none of these negative voters meant to inflict cavities upon anyone. They were confused—influenced by alarmists who claim that adding fluoride to a city's water supply will "poison" people.

These alarmists are the "poison-mongers." Antagonistic to scientific research, they are commonly known as "antis" (short for "antifluoridationists"). The sad fact is that people can easily be frightened by things which they do not understand and can easily be confused by contradictory arguments.

There should be no mystery about what fluoridation is. Fluoride is a mineral which occurs naturally in most water supplies. Fluoridation is the adjustment of the natural fluoride concentration to about one part of fluoride to one million parts of water. More than 20,000 scientific studies attest to fluoridation's safety and effectiveness in preventing tooth decay.

Since it began, fluoridation has encountered opposition from scattered groups and individuals. Several well-funded national multi-issue organizations have managed to disseminate large amounts of scare propaganda throughout the country. Among them are the Rodale Press, the John Birch Society and the National Health Federation.

The antis' basic technique is the big lie. It consists of claiming that fluoridation causes cancer, heart disease, kidney disease and other serious ailments which people fear. The fact that there is no supporting evidence for such claims does not matter.

A variation of the big lie is the laundry list. List enough "evils," and even if proponents can reply to some of them, they will never be able to cover the entire list.

A key factor in any anti campaign is the use of printed matter.

The aim of anti "documents" is to create the illusion of scientific controversy. Often they quote statements which are out of date or out of context. Quotes from obscure or hard-to-locate journals are particularly effective. Another favored tactic is to misquote a profluoridation scientist, knowing that even if the scientist himself protests, his reply will not reach all of the people who saw the original misquote.

Half-truths are commonly used. For example, saying that fluoride is a rat poison ignores the fact that poison is a matter of dose. Large amounts of many substances—even pure water—can poison people. But the trace amount of fluoride contained in fluoridated water will not harm anyone.

"Experts" are commonly quoted. It is possible to find someone with scientific credentials who is against just about anything. Most "experts" who speak out against fluoridation, however, are not experts on the subject. Curiously, when anti experts change their minds in favor of fluoridation, they sometimes find that the antis keep on quoting their earlier positions.

Innuendo is a technique that has broad appeal because it can be used in a seemingly unemotional pitch.

Some antis admit that fluoridation has been found safe "so far" but claim that its long-range effects have "not yet" been fully explored. No doubt, some antis will continue to use this argument for a few hundred more years.

The bogus reward is a fascinating technique. Some antis offer large rewards to anyone who will prove that fluoridation is safe.

A $100,000 reward offer has survived for a long time—but a close look will show why. The offer does not state who would judge the evidence, but of course the judges would be appointed by the antis themselves.

Since the scientific community is so solidly in favor of fluoridation, antis try to discredit it entirely by use of the conspiracy gambit. Favorite "conspirators" are the U.S. Public Health Services, the American Dental Association, the American Medical Association, the Communist Party and the aluminum industry. Apparently, in the minds of the anti, these groups could all be working together to "poison" the American people!

Scare words will add zip to any anti campaign. Not only the more obvious ones like "cancer" and "heart disease", but also more specialized ones like "mongoloid births" and "sickle cell anemia."

Ecology words are currently in vogue. Fluoride is called "artificial" and "a pollutant" which is "against nature." Faced with the fact that fluoridation merely copies a natural phenomenon, the antis reply that "natural" fluoride differs from "artificial" fluoride—a fact as yet undiscovered by scientists.

The antis' most persuasive argument, both to legislators and to the

106

public, is to call for a public vote. The antis are dealing from a stacked deck. It is not difficult to confuse voters by flooding their community with scare propaganda. The average citizen does not have the educational background to sort out claim and counterclaim or to judge which "authorities" to believe.

As a public health measure, fluoridation is unusual in several ways. It is a copy of a naturally occurring phenomenon. It is supported by libraries full of articles which document its safety and effectiveness—more so than any other public health measure. But most significant, it is the only health measure which is often put to public vote.

Don't let the poisonmongers scare you. Fluoridation is a modern health "miracle."

Excerpted from: **The Health Robbers** Copyright ® by the Lehigh Valley Committee Against Health Fraud, Inc. Published by George F. Stickley Co., 210 W. Washington Square, Philadelphia, PA 19106.

Scientific Breakthrough Announced:

FLUORIDATION PREVENTS CANCER!!!

Boston (AP) A team of respected scientists from Boston University has discovered that fluoridation of water can prevent cancer. Using government statistics, cancer death rates in Boston from 1950 to 1975 were compared with those of nearby Medford. The results indicate conclusively that water fluoridation is preventing at least 35,000 deaths from cancer each year in the United States.

Did you think it might be true?
If you did, then you were fooled.
Here are the real facts.

REAL FACT #1
Water fluoridation is a safe, effective and economical way to prevent tooth decay.

REAL FACT #2
Fluoridation is endorsed by every major health professional society and governmental health agency in the United States.

REAL FACT #3
The National Health Federation (NHF) is an organization which promotes questionable "health" products and ideas. Twelve of its leaders have been in legal difficulty and five have received prison sentences for questionable health activities.

REAL FACT #4
On June 1, 1974, NHF announced that fighting fluoridation would be its #2 priority and that Dr. John Yiamouyiannis had been hired to "break the back of fluoridation."

REAL FACT #5
Since that time, Dr. Yiamouyiannis has issued reports and traveled throughout the country claiming that fluoridation causes cancer. His claim is based on government statistics which he misinterprets.

REAL FACT #6
Anyone can issue reports and make headlines if he tries hard enough.

Don't base your feelings about fluoridation on rumors!
Ask a trained professional whom you trust.

This message prepared by
The Lehigh Valley Committee Against Health Fraud, Inc.
P.O. Box 1602. Allentown. PA 18105

SOMETHING TO THINK ABOUT
by Charles H. Patton, D.D.S, President, American Dental Association

Ask The Person Who Knows About Fluoridation

Once upon a time, there lived in a small village, an old woman who couldn't make up her mind. She put off decisions, hoping they would somehow settle themselves. Since they rarely did, her life became a series of untidy crises.

Then, one day, she had an idea. "I know what I'll do," she said, "I'll have other people make up my mind for me. That way I won't have the trouble of deciding, but the decision will still be made."

Delighted with this notion, she sat right down to list all the current decisions to be made. Her list looked like this:

What kind of roast should I have Sunday?

What should I do about the leak in the roof?

Why are my rose bushes dying?

"Now then," she asked herself, "who should make up my mind for me?" Picking up her pencil, she wrote the name of the village druggist next to the first question, the shoemaker's next to the second, and the milkman's next to the last.

"Thank goodness," she sighed, "that's done. Now my troubles are over."

As a matter of fact, they had just begun. Though the druggist, shoemaker, and milkman were all trained in their own areas, they had no expert knowledge about the questions she was asking. Consequently, the old woman ended up with a tough roast, a leaky roof, and dead rose buses.

This may sound like just a foolish fairy tale, but it has application in modern-day America. On a health issue of overriding importance, many of us are deciding exactly as the old woman did. We are asking the right questions, but of the wrong people. The issue to which I refer is fluoridation of community water supplies.

The fluoridation story began over 20 years ago. It was noted that people who lived in certain areas of the nation experienced fewer cavities than did people elsewhere.

A great number of careful studies were begun. As a result, it was determined that the lower decay rate in these certain areas could be ascribed to the natural presence of fluoride in the water.

Further investigation showed that when fluoride is naturally present, or added, the decay rate is reduced by as much as 65 percent. This is accomplished without ill effects of any kind. Finally, it was shown that the necessary equipment for fluoridating can be installed and operated at an approximate annual cost of 10 cents per person. Lifetime benefits from fluoridation, thus, cost no more than the fee for filling one cavity.

This was a public health bargain of remarkable significance. As the results became clear, every recognized health organization in the nation endorsed the process. The nation's scientists expected that communities across the country would swiftly install the process. Their expectation has not been realized. For reasons a sociologist could best explain, fluoridation has attracted opposition.

For example, the anti-fluoridationists scream that fluoride is poison. America's scientists patiently explain that many substances in common use by human beings are beneficial when used in *proper* amounts though harmful when used improperly. Improper use of aspirin is the cause of many accidental poisonings each year. Yet properly controlled, it remains one of our most useful drugs.

The anti-fluoridationists scream that fluorides have a harmful effect on the kidneys of adults. America's scientists pointed out that at the proposed amounts of ingestion, elimination, principally in the urine, is virtually complete.

Understandably, many of our fellow citizens have become confused, and in their confusion have settled for the status quo by rejecting fluoridation. But the confusion is unnecessary. The fallacy which causes the confusion is the same one indulged in by the old woman. The people are asking the right questions, but of the wrong people.

Fluoridation is a scientific process leading to better public health. When a question arises about fluoridation, it is only common sense to ask the men trained in the art and science of health care.

Ask your family physician or write the American Medical Association. Ask your family dentist or write the American Dental Association. Ask the U.S. Public Health Service. Ask the U.S. Department of Health, Education, and Welfare. Ask the American-Association for the Advancement of Science.

In the final analysis, the nation's standard of dental health depends upon the actions of the citizenry. If that action is to be beneficial, it must be enlightened. It will be enlightened if you "ask the man who knows," and evaluate his answers in the light of his training, his experience, and his sworn obligation to protect your health.

Reprinted from *Today's Health*, Oct. 1961, p. 15.

OFFICIAL POLICY OF THE AMERICAN MEDICAL ASSOCIATION:
FLUORIDATION OF PUBLIC WATER SUPPLIES

Revised December 1, 1974

The position of the American Medical Association on the matter of fluoridation of public water supplies is frequently sought by the public and by people in the health professions. The following material is intended to supply, briefly and concisely, this information.

On December 1, 1974, the House of Delegates of the American Medical Association adopted the following policy statement with respect to fluoridation of community water supplies:

Few health measures have been accorded greater clinical and laboratory research, epidemiological study, massive clinical trial of total community populations, and public attention, both favorable and adverse, than the fluoridation of public water supplies.

In 1957, the American Medical Association (AMA) issued a position statement relative to fluorides and public water supplies (based on what was then known through trial and study). *It is timely to update this statement as there now exist extensive additional experimental, clinical, laboratory, and epidemiological data confirming the safety and efficacy of this important essential nutrient.*

In evaluating these data, the AMA has directed major interest at several aspects of fluoridation: its clinical effectiveness in public water supplies, factors of safety, range of effectiveness, as well as determination of levels of toxicity or other undesirable effects. The mechanics and control of the addition or removal of fluorides from water supplies have been reviewed. A complete understanding of the range of safety and effectiveness as it relates to the population as a whole, all ages and states of health, has been recognized to be of primary importance.

The recommended optimum concentration of fluoride in the water supply (0.7 to 1.2 ppm according to locality) should be consumed throughout life. This conclusion is based on epidemiological studies conducted in areas where fluoride occurs naturally in the water, and in areas where it has been added at the recommended level by mechanical means.

Numerous controlled fluoridation programs, some in operation since 1945, have been evaluated as successful in reducing or preventing dental caries.

Only when relatively large amounts of fluoride (8 to 20 mg/day) are ingested over periods of 10 to 20 years are any generalized adverse effects encountered. No adverse effects have been reported when water containing optimum levels of fluoride has been drunk during periods of 10 to 20 years. Fluoride-induced mottling of tooth enamel has been reported only when fluoride concentration in the water exceeded 1.4 to 1.6 ppm.

Research has established that people consuming water containing the optimum level of fluoride experience no adverse effects on their kidneys, thyroid glands, reproductive functions, growth, development, blood, urine, or hearing. No cases of allergic reactions have been linked with consumption of water fluoridated at the recommended levels.

Research has also provided evidence that suitable amounts of fluoride may be helpful in preventing or alleviating bone diseases such as osteoporosis, especially among older people.

Equipment has been developed, reliable analytical procedures are available, and appropriate safeguards have been established to assure that fluorides can be added safely to public water supplies at the optimum level.

It is in keeping with this perspective that the AMA has reviewed the problem critically and in its entirety, taking cognizance of what has been done, as well as carefully weighing the comments of those opposed to fluoridation, together with their scientific evidence, in order to maintain an objective attitude concerning this important health measure.

No alternative techniques for the prophylactic application of fluorides can at present replace the fluoridation of drinking water as an effective and practical public health measure. Where water fluoridation at optimum levels cannot be used, however, other ways of supplying the proper amount of fluoride

110

should be encouraged.

On the basis of this careful analysis of information, the AMA considers the fluoridation of public water supplies at the recommended rate to be a desirable and safe health measure for total populations and urges all communities to adopt the necessary measures.

This statement on fluoridation was adopted by the
AMA House of Delegates, Dec. 1, 1974.

FLUORIDATION OF WATER SUPPLY
MG Edwin H. Smith, Jr., DC, USA

It is a professional truism that prevention is preferable to treatment for any disease. The simple expedient of fluoridating communal water supplies offers effective prevention of the most common disease in our nation—dental decay, which affects over 95% of our population. Water fluoridation, the least expensive dental public health measure for the control of caries, demonstrates its greatest efficacy for children, who may realize a new dental decay reduction of 60% to 70%.

Adults also receive considerable benefit, though not to the same dramatic extent. At this time when the capabilities of health care providers are strained to the utmost to meet the demands placed on them, and more and more of the population view health care as the right of every citizen, it is absolutely essential that every proven public health measure be implemented.

Value Established Beyond Question

Extensive research, conducted over a period of 35 years, has established beyond question the benefits of 1.0 or 1.5 ppm of fluoride in communal drinking water in reducing tooth decay. These same studies have also proven unequivocally the safety of fluoridation for those who drink the treated water. To quote Dr. Luther Terry, former US Surgeon General: "Experience reveals that fluoridated water prevents up to two thirds of the tooth decay that children would or-

dinarily suffer. Furthermore, it is medically safe for people of all ages—and its benefits last for a lifetime."

Unbelievably, with the results of this research and expert opinion available to all, less than 50% of the nation's water supplies are fluoridated!

Why the Delay in Implementation?

Given the proved effectiveness and safety of fluoridation and the need for prevention, the question may be asked, "Why has this dental public health measure been so slowly implemented within our communities?" Part of the answer seems to lie in the fact that implementation of fluoridation has been dependent on political action and has had to be approved by referendum, by elected officials, or some combination of these (and other) factors. *As a result, fluoridation may well be the only public health measure that has had to wait for the vote of the citizen.*

The situation is further complicated by the objections of a small but vocal minority to whom the concept of adding fluorides to the communal water supply is an unacceptable approach to the control of dental caries. This viewpoint overlooks the fact that in the course of water treatment to make it esthetic, potable, and palatable, many chemicals other than fluorides may be employed, such as acids, sodium hydroxide, carbonates, flocculents, and various disinfectants. There are also chemicals that occur naturally and

are permitted to be present in significantly greater concentrations than the 0.7 to 1.2 ppm recommended for fluoridation, such as chlorides up to 250 ppm, nitrates up to 45 ppm, and sulfates up to 250 ppm. Fluoridation opponents have made no strenuous criticism of the use or presence of these chemicals in drinking water.

Delay is Costly

The lack of unanimous agreement on this subject of fluoridation is unfortunate—and costly.

The difference in the amount of dentistry required by those people drinking fluoridated water and those drinking non-fluoridated water is eye-opening. When stated in dollars, the cost is overwhelming. In 1964, it was estimated that the cost of dentistry required by citizens of the United States because their drinking water was not fluoridated was in excess of $700,000,000 annually. Because of inflation, today's cost would be at least twice that amount.

The facts are clear—fluoridation is safe, economical, and effective. It is our obligation as professionals to ensure that the citizens of our country realize the benefits of this remarkable public health contribution. To do less would be to abrogate our professional responsibilities and to deny improved dental health to our entire citizenry.

Additional Readings

Englander HR, de Palma R, Kesel RG: The Aurora-Rockford, Ill, study: I. Effects of water having naturally occurring fluoride on dental health of young adults. *J Am Dent Assoc* 65:614-621, 1962.

Russell AL, Elyave E: Domestic water and dental caries: VII. A study of the fluoride-dental caries relationship in an adult population. *Public Health Rep* 66:1389-1401, 1951.

Murry J: Fluoridation studies and dental caries: A review. *Br Dent J* 129:467-470, 1970.

Crooks EL Jr, et al: A 20-year study of the effectiveness of fluoride in the Richmond water supply. *Va Dent J* 49:24-26, 1972.

Arnold FA: Fluorine in drinking water: Its effect on dental caries. *J Am Dent Assoc* 23:247-255, 1944.

Hilleboe HE, et al: Newburgh-Kingston caries-fluorine study: Final report. *J Am Dent Assoc* 52:290-325, 1956.

Over Ninety-Five Million on Fluoridated Water Supplies, PPB-38. Division of Dental Health, Public Health Service, April 1972.

Water Quality and Treatment, ed 3, American Water Works Association, Inc. New York, McGraw-Hill Book Co, 1971, p 45.

Economic Benefits From Public Health Services, publication 1178. Public Health Service, April 1964.

Ewell KR, Easlick AK: *Classification and Appraisal of Objections to Fluoridation.* Ann Arbor, University of Michigan Press, 1960.

DEPARTMENT OF HEALTH, EDUCATION, AND WELFARE
WASHINGTON, D.C. 20201

SURGEON GENERAL
OF THE
PUBLIC HEALTH SERVICE

Statement on Fluoridation

Increased attention to the prevention of disease and to health maintenance can reduce much of the human suffering and expense that results from ill health. Fluoridation of a community's water supply is an excellent example of a disease prevention effort that can improve the health status of our Nation's citizens and reduce health care costs for children. Fluoridation is the most effective, least costly public health measure for preventing tooth decay --one of the most prevalent health problems, yet only three of every five persons who could be provided the benefits of fluoridation now receive them.

More than 30 years of research and community experience have demonstrated the benefits and safety of fluoridation. Tooth decay, the leading chronic disease in children, can be reduced by as much as two-thirds in children who drink fluoridated water from birth. Many of these children can be completely free of dental decay. Lifetime benefits can be derived from drinking fluoridated water and the cost of children's dental care can be cut in half. Extensive scientific research has uncovered no valid evidence that any health problem is caused or aggravated by drinking optimally fluoridated water.

The Public Health Service strongly endorses the fluoridation of community water supplies at recommended concentrations, and stresses that making fluoridated drinking water available to its residents is the single most important step a community can take to improve dental health. I urge health officials and concerned citizens in communities with fluoride-deficient water supplies to act now to see that this deficit is corrected and to ensure the benefits of fluoridation for their community.

Julius B. Richmond, M.D.
Surgeon General

October 1978

NATIONAL AND INTERNATIONAL ORGANIZATIONS THAT HAVE ENDORSED FLUORIDATION

American Academy of Dental Medicine
American Academy of Pediatrics
American Association for the Advancement of Science
American Association of Dental Schools
American Association of Industrial Dentists
American Association of Public Health Dentists
American College of Dentists
American Commission on Community Health Services
American Dental Association
American Dental Hygienists Association
AFL-CIO
American Heart Association
American Hospital Association
American Institute of Nutrition
American Legion
American Medical Association
American Nurses Association
American Osteopathic Association
American Pharmaceutical Association
American Public Health Association
American Public Welfare Association
American School Health Association
American Society of Dentistry for Children
American Veterinary Medical Association
American Water Works Association
Association of Public Health Veterinarians
Association of State and Territorial Dental Directors
Association of State and Territorial Health Officers
British Medical Association
Canadian Dental Association

Canadian Medical Association
Canadian Public Health Association
College of American Pathologists
Commission on Chronic Illness
Consumer Federation of America
Consumers Union
Federation Dentaire Internationale
Federation of American Societies for Experimental Biology
Great Britain Ministry of Health
Health Insurance Association of America
Health League of Canada
Inter-Association Committee on Health
International Association of Dental Research
International Dental Federation
Mayo Clinic
National Commission on Community Health Services
National Congress of Parents and Teachers
National Education Association
National Health Council
National Institute of Municipal Law Officers
National Nutrition Consortium
National Research Council
Office of Civil Defense
Pan American Health Organization
Royal College of Physicians (London)
Society of Toxicology
U.S. Department of Agriculture
U.S. Department of Defense
U.S. Department of Health, Education, and Welfare
U.S. Environmental Protection Agency
U.S. Jaycees
World Health Organization

 # Environmental Information

FLUORIDATION OF DRINKING WATER

Questions have been raised recently about possible cancer-causing compounds found in drinking water produced by the reaction of chlorine and certain organic substances present in water supplies. Concern has arisen that the fluoride added to public drinking water supplies to reduce tooth decay is also producing possible cancer-causing compounds.

The possibility that the chlorine used to disinfect water may be forming cancer-producing compounds is now being evaluated. However, there is absolutely no scientific evidence linking the <u>fluoridation</u> of public water supplies to cancer.

FLUORIDE AND FLUORINE

The reason for this is that fluoride has a cancer-causing potential only in its elemental form. In that state, it is even more reactive than chlorine and in all probability would form fluorinated organic compounds when combined with organic matter in drinking water. But elemental fluorine is <u>not</u> used for water fluoridation, and it is very unlikely that it ever will be.

Instead, the most commonly used fluorides in the fluoridation of water are sodium fluoride, sodium silicofluoride, and fluosilicic acid. In the fluoridation process, all of these compounds break up into minute particles and become inert--that is, they are unable to form fluorinated organic compounds, and thus have no cancer-causing potential.

Both the American Cancer Society and the National Cancer Institute support these findings.

The American Cancer Society states: "No valid scientific evidence known to the Society supports a causative relationship of a compound of the fluoridation process to cancer; all of these compounds break up into minute particles (ions), and become chemically inert--that is, they are unable to form fluorinated organic compounds, and thus have no cancer-causing potential."

And according to the National Cancer Institute: "Water fluoridation applied for the purpose of dental caries prophylaxis poses no hazard relative to cancer causation."

April 1975

U.S. ENVIRONMENTAL PROTECTION AGENCY, WASHINGTON, D.C. 20460

HOW DOES YOUR STATE STAND ON FLUORIDATION?

The first number in each State refers to the percentage of its population using natural or adjusted fluoridation. The second number shows the State's position in a ranking of all States according to percentages. Statistics as of December 31, 1975.

116

Conn. : 79.4 #4
Del. : 39.5 #33
Md. : 68.1 #7
Mass. : 21.6 #44
N.H. : 13.3 #47
N.J. : 21.4 #45
R.I. : 66.3 #9
Vt. : 37.0 #35
D.C. : 98.4 #1
P.R. : 81.4

Me. 40.6 #31

Vt.
N.H.
Mass.
R.I.
Conn.
N.Y. 66.1 #10
N.J.
Del.
Pa. 46.2 #25
Md.
W. Va. 50.7 #23
Va. 51.2 #20
N.C. 45.4 #27
S.C. 52.8 #18
Ohio 41.4 #30
Ky. 51.0 #21
Tenn. 66.9 #8
Ga. 41.4 #29
Fla. 35.8 #36
Mich. 76.1 #5
Ind. 61.2 #16
Ala. 31.5 #38
Wis. 62.2 #13
Ill. 86.2 #2
Miss. 24.7 #41
Iowa 61.9 #14
Mo. 42.0 #28
Ark. 38.3 #34
La. 23.2 #42
Minn. 71.5 #6
N. Dak. 50.8 #22
S. Dak. 61.5 #15
Nebr. 45.8 #26
Kan. 51.5 #19
Okla. 63.3 #12
Texas 58.7 #17
Mont. 26.7 #40
Wyo. 21.3 #46
Colo. 83.8 #3
N. Mex. 63.8 #11
Idaho 33.5 #37
Utah 2.4 #51
Ariz. 31.2 #39
Wash. 39.8 #32
Oreg. 10.7 #48
Nev. 3.0 #50
Cal. 22 #43
Hawaii 6.4 #49
Alaska 42.2 #24

FIFTY LARGEST CITIES IN RANK ORDER FROM CENSUS OF 1970*

Rank	City	Population (1,000)	Fluoridation Status	Date Instituted
1.	New York, NY	7,895	Adjusted	1965
2.	Chicago, IL	3,367	Adjusted	1956
3.	Los Angeles, CA	2,814		
4.	Philadelphia, PA	1,949	Adjusted	1954
5.	Detroit, MI	1,511	Adjusted	1967
6.	Houston, TX	1,233	Natural (part)	
7.	Baltimore, MD	906	Adjusted	1952
8.	Dallas, TX	844	Adjusted	1966
9.	Washington, DC	757	Adjusted	1952
10.	Cleveland, OH	751	Adjusted	1956
11.	Indianapolis, IN	745	Adjusted	1951
12.	Milwaukee, WI	717	Adjusted	1953
13.	San Francisco, CA	716	Adjusted	1952
14.	San Diego, CA	697	Discon't 1954	1952
15.	San Antonio, TX	654		
16.	Boston, MA	641	Adjusted	1978
17.	Memphis, TN	624	Adjusted	1970
18.	St. Louis, MO	622	Adjusted	1955
19.	New Orleans, LA	593	Adjusted	1974
20.	Phoenix, AZ	582		
21.	Columbus, OH	540	Adjusted	1973
22.	Seattle, WA	531	Adjusted	1969
23.	Jacksonville, FL	529	Natural	
24.	Pittsburgh, PA	520	Adjusted	1952
25.	Denver, CO	515	Adjusted	1954
26.	Kansas City, MO	507	Discon't 1964	1962
27.	Atlanta, GA	497	Adjusted	1969
28.	Buffalo, NY	463	Adjusted	1955
29.	Cincinnati, OH	453	Adjusted	1979
30.	Nashville-Davidson, TN	448	Adjusted	1953
31.	San Jose, CA	446	Adjusted	1965
32.	Minneapolis, MN	434	Adjusted	1957
33.	Fort Worth, TX	393	Adjusted	1965
34.	Toledo, OH	384	Adjusted	1955
35.	Portland, OR	383		
36.	Newark, NJ			
37.	Oklahoma City, OK	366	Adjusted	1954
38.	Oakland, CA	362	Adjusted	1976
39.	Louisville, KY	361	Adjusted	1951
40.	Long Beach, CA	359	Adjusted	1971
41.	Omaha, NE	347	Adjusted	1969
42.	Tulsa, OK	332	Adjusted	1953
43.	Miami, FL	335	Adjusted	1952
44.	Honolulu, HI	325		
45.	El Paso, TX	322	Natural	
46.	St. Paul, MN	310	Adjusted	1952
47.	Norfolk, VA	308	Adjusted	1952
48.	Birmingham, AL	301		
49.	Rochester, NY	296	Adjusted	1952
50.	Tampa, FL	278		

*From Statistical Abstract of the United States, 1971, Table 20, pp. 21-23

ADVERTISING MATS

The ads on the next seven pages were created for the American Dental Association by the New York advertising agency, Ogilvy & Mather, Inc. The ads can be used to inform your community and generate voter support. Designed for newspaper insertion, they can also be printed as flyers for distribution in community mailings, handouts at professional offices, PTA meetings, city council meetings, shopping centers, etc.

The first five ads are primarily for educational purposes. For maximum impact, it is suggested that they be used in the order presented in this book. The last two ads are recommended to generate voter support during the period immediately preceding a referendum. They can be simultaneously printed in newspapers and distributed as flyers and posters throughout the community—including, if legally permissible, at local election polls. The "Vote for Fluoridation" advertisement can be personalized by inserting the referendum date in the space allotted within the headline by using the matching type provided on the following page.

Additional campaign materials can be obtained from the ADA Council on Dental Health, 211 East Chicago Avenue, Chicago, IL 60611.

We could reduce our children's cavities up to 65% Cost: just pennies a year. How? Fluoridated water.

In Chicago, the cavity rate dropped sharply after they fluoridated their water supply. The same thing happened in many other cities across the country.

It could happen in our town. Our children could grow up with healthier teeth and bones...and about 65% less cavities. All we have to do is vote for fluoridation.

Every Major Health Organization Recommends Fluoridation

Every qualified health organization in America urges fluoridation. That includes the American Dental Association, the American Medical Association, the Public Health Service and the World Health Organization. The PTA and AFL-CIO support it, too. Going without fluoridation is like doing without vitamins or pasteurized milk.

Fluoride Is A Nutrient, Like Calcium

Fluoride is not, strictly speaking, a drug. It's a nutrient like calcium, thiamine, niacin, riboflavin, Vitamin D—and all the other nutrients we need for good health. There is some fluoride in all water. Unfortunately, our water doesn't have quite enough to protect dental health. But if we had just one part of fluoride per million parts of water, we'd all be better off for it. Especially our children. They'd grow up with the healthy teeth and bones nature meant them to have.

Fluoride Cuts Cavities By Up To 65%

Fluoride builds teeth and bones as milk does. Just a small amount of fluoride every day can prevent up to 65% of

tooth decay. And children raised on fluoridated water can keep their teeth for a lifetime. This has been proven again

and again, ever since Grand Rapids, Michigan, and Newburgh, New York, fluoridated more than 30 years ago.

Fluoride Is Safe

More than 100,000,000 people now drink fluoridated water. Some of the big cities that have fluoridated water are: Cleveland, Dallas, Minneapolis, Chicago, Detroit, New York City, Miami, San Francisco, Philadelphia.

In over 30 years, not one harmful side effect has been proven. Many vitamins don't

have as "safe" a safety record!

Isn't Fluoride Toothpaste Enough?

A toothpaste with fluoride in it is an effective way to protect the surface of the teeth. By all means, use it. But fluoridated water builds a lifetime of protection into teeth. As a result, fluoridated water is about three times more effective—and it benefits every child. It's the only way to make sure all children—both rich and poor—have better dental health.

All This For Just Pennies A Year

The equipment that our town would need to fluoridate is not expensive. It would cost each of us only a few cents a year. Just think! For so little, we can go a long way toward wiping out tooth decay in our town.

Our Kids Deserve A Break

More than 100 million people throughout the U.S. now enjoy better dental health because their water has fluoride in it. This includes virtually entire states like Connecticut, Illinois and Maryland. Why not us?

Why should our kids grow up with more cavities than kids from Detroit, Memphis, Atlanta, New York City or Cleveland? Our children deserve a break! Let's see that they get it.

Let's fluoridate! It's about time we gave our kids a break.

For only pennies a year we could almost wipe out tooth decay in this town.

In Chicago, the cavity rate dropped sharply after they fluoridated their water supply. The same thing happened in many other cities across the country.

It could happen in this town. Our children could grow up with healthier teeth and bones...and about 65% less tooth decay. All we have to do is vote for fluoridation.

Every Major Health Organization Recommends Fluoridation

Every qualified health organization in America urges fluoridation. That includes the American Dental Association, the American Medical Association, the Public Health Service and the World Health Organization. The PTA and AFL-CIO support it, too. Going without fluoridation is like doing without vitamins or pasteurized milk.

Fluoride Is A Nutrient, Like Calcium

Fluoride is not, strictly speaking, a drug. It's a nutrient like calcium, thiamine, niacin, riboflavin, Vitamin D—and all the other nutrients we need for good health. There is some fluoride in all water. Unfortunately, our water doesn't have quite enough to protect dental health. But if we had just one part of fluoride per million parts of water, we'd all be better off for it. Especially our children. They'd grow up with the healthy teeth and bones nature meant them to have.

Fluoride Cuts Cavities By Up To 65%

Fluoride builds teeth and bones as milk does. Just a small amount of fluoride every day can prevent up to 65% of tooth decay. And children raised on fluoridated water can keep their teeth for a lifetime. This has been proven again and again, ever since Grand Rapids, Michigan, and New-burgh, New York, fluoridated more than 30 years ago.

Fluoride Is Safe

More than 100,000,000 people now drink fluoridated water. Some of the big cities that have fluoridated water are: Cleveland, Dallas, Minneapolis, Chicago, Detroit, New York City, Miami, San Francisco, Philadelphia.

In over 30 years, not one harmful side effect has been proven. Many vitamins don't have as "safe" a safety record!

Isn't Fluoride Toothpaste Enough?

A toothpaste with fluoride in it is an effective way to protect the surface of the teeth. By all means, use it. But fluoridated water builds a lifetime of protection into teeth. As a result, fluoridated water is about three times more effective—and it benefits every child. It's the only way to make sure all children—both rich and poor—have better dental health.

All This For Just Pennies A Year

The equipment that our town would need to fluoridate is not expensive. It would cost each of us only a few cents a year. Just think! For so little, we can go a long way toward wiping out tooth decay in our town.

Our Kids Deserve A Break

More than 100 million people throughout the U.S. now enjoy better dental health because their water has fluoride in it. This includes virtually entire states like Connecticut, Illinois and Maryland. Why not us?

Why should our kids grow up with more cavities than kids from Detroit, Memphis, Atlanta, New York City or Cleveland? Our children deserve a break! Let's see that they get it.

Let's fluoridate! It's about time we gave our kids a break.

The poorest kids in Chicago could grow up with better teeth than the richest kid in our town. We can change all that.

A child growing up in Chicago will grow up with healthier teeth because the water there is fluoridated. So is the water in most of the United States.

In our town, it's not. This means that all our children, rich and poor alike, could grow up with bad teeth—teeth with up to three times as many cavities as they would otherwise have.

We think this is a crying shame. We think it's time we caught up with the rest of this country—and fluoridated our water, too.

Every Major Health Organization Recommends Fluoridation

Every qualified health organization in America urges fluoridation. That includes the American Dental Association, the American Medical Association, the Public Health Service and the World Health Organization. The PTA and AFL-CIO support it, too. Going without fluoridation is like doing without vitamins or pasteurized milk.

Fluoride Is A Nutrient, Like Calcium

Fluoride is not, strictly speaking, a drug. It's a nutrient like calcium, thiamine, niacin, riboflavin, Vitamin D—and all the other nutrients we need for good health. There is some fluoride in all water. Unfortunately, our water doesn't have quite enough to protect dental health. But if we had just one part of fluoride per million parts of water, we'd all be better off for it. Especially our children. They'd grow up with the healthy teeth and bones nature meant them to have.

Fluoride Cuts Cavities By Up To 65%

Fluoride builds teeth and bones as milk does. Just a small amount of fluoride every day can prevent up to 65% of tooth decay. And children raised on fluoridated water can

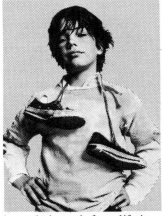

keep their teeth for a lifetime. This has been proven again and again, ever since Grand Rapids, Michigan, and Newburgh, New York, fluoridated more than 30 years ago.

Fluoride Is Safe

More than 100,000,000 people now drink fluoridated water. Some of the big cities that have fluoridated water are: Cleveland, Dallas, Minneapolis, Chicago, Detroit, New York City, Miami, San Francisco, Philadelphia.

In over 30 years, not one harmful side effect has been proven. Many vitamins don't have as "safe" a safety record!

Isn't Fluoride Toothpaste Enough?

A toothpaste with fluoride in it is an effective way to protect the surface of the teeth. By all means, use it. But fluoridated water builds a lifetime of protection into teeth. As a result, fluoridated water is about three times more effective—and it benefits every child. It's the only way to make sure all children—both rich and poor—have better dental health.

All This For Just Pennies A Year

The equipment that our town would need to fluoridate is not expensive. It would cost each of us only a few cents a year. Just think! For so little, we can go a long way toward wiping out tooth decay in our town.

Our Kids Deserve A Break

More than 100 million people throughout the U.S. now enjoy better dental health because their water has fluoride in it. This includes virtually entire states like Connecticut, Illinois and Maryland. Why not us?

Why should our kids grow up with more cavities than kids from Detroit, Memphis, Atlanta, New York City or Cleveland? Our children deserve a break! Let's see that they get it.

Let's fluoridate! It's about time we gave our kids a break.

If you think it's about time we caught up with the rest of America, sign and mail this coupon.

Parents for Fluoridation, Box XXX, Town, State, Zip
Second address line, for more address, address, address

I agree. It's time our kids enjoyed better dental health through a fluoridated water supply.

Let's give our kids the break they deserve. Let's fluoridate!

Name _____

Address _____

City _____ State _____ Zip _____

The American Medical Association, the American Dental Association and the Public Health Service agree. Our kids will suffer until we fluoridate our water.

Unlike most children in other U.S. cities, our children will grow up with bad teeth—teeth with up to three times more cavities than they should get. Why? Because we have not fluoridated the water in our town.

We think this is a crying shame. We think it's time we caught up with the rest of this country—and fluoridated our water, too.

Every Major Health Organization Recommends Fluoridation

Every qualified health organization in America urges fluoridation. That includes the American Dental Association, the American Medical Association, the Public Health Service and the World Health Organization. The PTA and AFL-CIO support it, too. Going without fluoridation is like doing without vitamins or pasteurized milk.

Fluoride Is A Nutrient, Like Calcium

Fluoride is not, strictly speaking, a drug. It's a nutrient like calcium, thiamine, niacin, riboflavin, Vitamin D—and all the other nutrients we need for good health. There is some fluoride in all water. Unfortunately, our water doesn't have quite enough to protect dental health. But if we had just one part of fluoride per million parts of water, we'd all be better off for it. Especially our children. They'd grow up with the healthy teeth and bones nature meant them to have.

Fluoride Cuts Cavities By Up To 65%

Fluoride builds teeth and bones as milk does. Just a small amount of fluoride every day can prevent up to 65% of tooth decay. And children raised on fluoridated water can keep their teeth for a lifetime. This has been proven again

and again, ever since Grand Rapids, Michigan, and Newburgh, New York, fluoridated more than 30 years ago.

Fluoride Is Safe

More than 100,000,000 people now drink fluoridated water. Some of the big cities that have fluoridated water are: Cleveland, Dallas, Minneapolis, Chicago, Detroit, New York City, Miami, San Francisco, Philadelphia.

In over 30 years, not one harmful side effect has been proven. Many vitamins don't have as "safe" a safety record!

Isn't Fluoride Toothpaste Enough?

A toothpaste with fluoride in it is an effective way to protect the surface of the teeth. By all means, use it. But fluoridated water builds a lifetime of protection into teeth. As a result, fluoridated water is about three times more effective—and it benefits every child. It's the only way to make sure all children—both rich and poor—have better dental health.

All This For Just Pennies A Year

The equipment that our town would need to fluoridate is not expensive. It would cost each of us only a few cents a year. Just think! For so little, we can go a long way toward wiping out tooth decay in our town.

Our Kids Deserve A Break

More than 100 million people throughout the U.S. now enjoy better dental health because their water has fluoride in it. This includes virtually entire states like Connecticut, Illinois and Maryland. Why not us?

Why should our kids grow up with more cavities than kids from Detroit, Memphis, Atlanta, New York City or Cleveland? Our children deserve a break! Let's see that they get it.

Let's fluoridate! It's about time we gave our kids a break.

We won't let our children drink milk that isn't pasteurized. How come we let them grow up with water that isn't fluoridated?

Because the water in our town is not fluoridated, our children, rich and poor alike, could grow up with bad teeth—teeth with up to three times as many cavities as they otherwise would have.

We think this is a crying shame. We think it's time we caught up with the rest of this country—and fluoridated our water, too.

Every Major Health Organization Recommends Fluoridation

Every qualified health organization in America urges fluoridation. That includes the American Dental Association, the American Medical Association, the Public Health Service and the World Health Organization. The PTA and AFL-CIO support it, too. Going without fluoridation is like doing without vitamins or pasteurized milk.

Fluoride Is A Nutrient, Like Calcium

Fluoride is not, strictly speaking, a drug. It's a nutrient like calcium, thiamine, niacin, riboflavin, Vitamin D—and all the other nutrients we need for good health. There is some fluoride in all water. Unfortunately, our water doesn't have quite enough to protect dental health. But if we had just one part of fluoride per million parts of water, we'd all be better off for it. Especially our children. They'd grow up with the healthy teeth and bones nature meant them to have.

Fluoride Cuts Cavities By Up To 65%

Fluoride builds teeth and bones as milk does. Just a small amount of fluoride every day can prevent up to 65% of

tooth decay. And children raised on fluoridated water can keep their teeth for a lifetime. This has been proven again

and again, ever since Grand Rapids, Michigan, and Newburgh, New York, fluoridated more than 30 years ago.

Fluoride Is Safe

More than 100,000,000 people now drink fluoridated water. Some of the big cities that have fluoridated water are: Cleveland, Dallas, Minneapolis, Chicago, Detroit, New York City, Miami, San Francisco, Philadelphia.

In over 30 years, not one harmful side effect has been proven. Many vitamins don't

have as "safe" a safety record!

Isn't Fluoride Toothpaste Enough?

A toothpaste with fluoride in it is an effective way to protect the surface of the teeth. By all means, use it. But fluoridated water builds a lifetime of protection into teeth. As a result, fluoridated water is about three times more effective—and it benefits every child. It's the only way to make sure all children—both rich and poor—have better dental health.

All This For Just Pennies A Year

The equipment that our town would need to fluoridate is not expensive. It would cost each of us only a few cents a year. Just think! For so little, we can go a long way toward wiping out tooth decay in our town.

Our Kids Deserve A Break

More than 100 million people throughout the U.S. now enjoy better dental health because their water has fluoride in it. This includes virtually entire states like Connecticut, Illinois and Maryland. Why not us?

Why should our kids grow up with more cavities than kids from Detroit, Memphis, Atlanta, New York City or Cleveland? Our children deserve a break! Let's see that they get it.

Let's fluoridate! It's about time we gave our kids a break.

The last time we voted on fluoridation, we lost. And our children have been paying for it ever since.

We're about to vote on fluoridation again! This time, please get a few facts straight:

What Is Fluoride?

Fluoride is not, strictly speaking, a drug. It's a nutrient like the calcium, iron, riboflavin and vitamin D which you need in your diet every day. Without it, teeth are much more likely to decay. Especially children's teeth.

There is some fluoride in all water. Ours just doesn't happen to have enough to protect dental health.

Who Says We Need It?

Fluoridation is one of the few things that every qualified health organization supports. That includes the American Dental Association, the American Medical Association, the Public Health Service and the World Health Organization. The PTA and AFL-CIO are in favor of it.

What Will It Do For Us?

Fluoride will help our children have healthier teeth and bones .... and about 65% less tooth decay. Amazingly little can do amazingly much. The following are only a few of the cities that have fluoridated their water for many years with just one part of fluoride per million parts of water: Chicago, Philadelphia, New York City, Detroit, Atlanta, Miami, San Francisco, Dallas, Cleveland, Minneapolis.

What Makes Us So Sure Fluoride Is Safe?

Experience does.

Some cities have been fluo-ridating their water more than 30 years. And in other cities many generations have bene-fited from the fluoride natural-ly present in the water supply. More than 100,000,000

Americans drink fluoridated water every day. Yet — with all these people, and all that time — not one harmful side effect has ever been proven. Many vitamins do not have that "safe" a safety record!

All This For Just Pennies A Year.

The equipment that our town would need to fluoridate is not expensive. It would cost each of us only a few cents a year. Just think! For so little, we can go a long way toward wiping out tooth decay in this town!

Why All The Controversy?

Every public health measure has always stirred up controversy. People were against polio vaccine. And pasteurization. Yet if they stopped pasteurizing milk, you'd be up in arms! Making our children do without the fluoride they need is just as bad.

Look, we've been bombarded with a lot of statements about fluoride — some warped, some confusing, some outright lies. If you have any doubts, consult your dentist or your physician.

And remember: Our children need fluoride. Let's catch up with the rest of America.

Let's fluoridate! It's about time we gave our kids a break.

Vote for fluoridation

Our children have gone without it long enough.

The children in our town get up to three times more cavities than they should get—simply because we don't fluoridate our water.

We think this is a crying shame. We think it's time we caught up with the rest of the country!

Every Major Health Organization Recommends Fluoridation

Every qualified health organization in America urges fluoridation. That includes the American Dental Association, the American Medical Association, the Public Health Service and the World Health Organization. The PTA and AFL-CIO support it, too. Going without fluoridation is like doing without vitamins or pasteurized milk.

Fluoride Is A Nutrient, Like Calcium

Fluoride is not, strictly speaking, a drug. It's a nutrient like calcium, thiamine, niacin, riboflavin, Vitamin D—and all the other nutrients we need for good health. There is some fluoride in all water. Unfortunately, our water doesn't have quite enough to protect dental health. But if we had just one part of fluoride per million parts of water, we'd all be better off for it. Especially our children. They'd grow up with the healthy teeth and bones nature meant them to have.

Fluoride Cuts Cavities By Up To 65%

Fluoride builds teeth and bones as milk does. Just a small amount of fluoride every day can prevent up to 65% of tooth decay. And children raised on fluoridated water can keep their teeth for a lifetime.

This has been proven again and again, ever since Grand Rapids, Michigan, and Newburgh, New York, fluoridated more than 30 years ago.

Fluoride Is Safe

More than 100,000,000 people now drink fluoridated water. Some of the big cities that have fluoridated water are: Cleveland, Dallas, Minneapolis, Chicago, Detroit, New York City, Miami, San Francisco, Philadelphia.

In over 30 years, not one harmful side effect has been proven. Many vitamins don't have as "safe" a safety record!

Isn't Fluoride Toothpaste Enough?

A toothpaste with fluoride in it is an effective way to protect the surface of the teeth. By all means, use it. But fluoridated water builds a lifetime of protection into teeth. As a result, fluoridated water is about three times more effective—and it benefits every child. It's the only way to make sure all children—both rich and poor—have better dental health.

All This For Just Pennies A Year

The equipment that our town would need to fluoridate is not expensive. It would cost each of us only a few cents a year. Just think! For so little, we can go a long way toward wiping out tooth decay in our town.

Our Kids Deserve A Break

More than 100 million people throughout the U.S. now enjoy better dental health because their water has fluoride in it. This includes virtually entire states like Connecticut, Illinois and Maryland. Why not us?

Why should our kids grow up with more cavities than kids from Detroit, Memphis, Atlanta, New York City or Cleveland? Our children deserve a break! Let's see that they get it.

Let's fluoridate! It's about time we gave our kids a break.

January	1981	82	83
February	0	0	0
March	1	1	1
April	2	2	2
May	3	3	3
June	4	4	4
July	5	5	5
August	6	6	6
September	7	7	7
October	8	8	8
November	9	9	9
December	,		

ASK YOUR DOCTOR!

FLUORIDATION — QUESTIONS & ANSWERS

Q.   What is fluoridation?

A.   **Fluoride occurs naturally in most public water supplies. Fluoridation is an adjustment of fluoride concentration to approximately one part of fluoride to one million parts of water.**

Q.   What does fluoridation do?

A.   **In proper concentration, fluoride helps developing teeth become stronger and resistant to decay.   Studies comparing fluoridated with non-fluoridated communites show that people in non-fluoridated areas have three times as many cavities.**

Q.   How many people now drink fluoridated water?

A.   **About 100 million Americans.**

Q.   Is it safe?

A.   **Yes.**

Q.   Who recommends it?

A.   **Fluoridation is endorsed by all major health organizations, the U.S. Public Health Service and all state departments of health. Allentown City Council was guided in its decision by recommendations of the Lehigh County Dental Society, the Lehigh County Medical Society and the Bi-City Board of Health.**

Q.   How much does it cost?

A.   **Less than 15¢ per person per year.**

Q.   Will I notice anything when it starts?

A.   **No. Fluoride, in proper concentration, has no taste or odor.**

Q.   Why do some people oppose fluoridation?

A.   **People are often afraid of things which they do not fully understand. Unfortunately, the people of Allentown have been exposed to a great deal of misinformation spread by anti-fluoridation leaders.**

Q.   Is Fluoridation "undemocratic"?

A.   **No. People who oppose fluoridation and people who favor it both actually want the same thing — — better health. Fluoridation will bring better health.**

A Public Service Message From Your

LEHIGH COUNTY MEDICAL SOCIETY

THE _____ COUNTY DENTAL SOCIETY SAYS THAT FLUORIDATION IS GOOD FOR YOU!

- **PREVENTS CAVITIES**
- **SAVES MONEY**
- **HARMS NO-ONE**

IS YOUR DENTIST ON THIS LIST?

Anthony Abdalla, D.D.S.
Samuel Albright, D.D.S.
William Baringer, D.D.S.
Thomas Bastian, D.D.S.
J. Carl Behler, Sr. D.D.S.
J. Carl Behler, Jr. D.D.S.
Robert Beideman, D.D.S.
Allen C. Brader, D.D.S.
Richard Branca, D.D.S.
Fred Bratton, D.D.S.
Seymour Brown, D.D.S.
William Bryan, D.D.S.
William Burfeind, D.D.S.
Ronald K. Burke, D.D.S.
John Canzano, D.D.S.
Robert Chisdak, D.D.S.
Frank Cianfrani, D.D.S.
Nevin Cope, D.D.S.
W. Richard Covert, D.D.S.
Alan Crawford, D.D.S.
Joseph Csanadi, D.D.S.
Thomas Davis, D.D.S.
Ronald C. Dileo, D.D.S.
Howard M. Duffield, D.D.S.
Victor Ehrens, D.D.S.
William Evans, D.D.S.
Robert Fexa, D.D.S.
Brooke D. Fulford, D.D.S.
Robert Galione, D.D.S.
Elton Gilbert, D.D.S.
Barry Glassman, D.D.S.
Karl Glassman, D.D.S.
Joseph Goldstone, D.D.S.
George Gromel, D.D.S.
Karl Groner, D.D.S.
H. William Gross, D.D.S.
Jerome Grossinger, D.D.S.

Joseph Hacker, D.D.S.
Warren Hamscher, D.D.S.
Martin Held, D.D.S.
Albert Hellman, D.D.S.
James Henninger, D.D.S.
Dixon Herwig, D.D.S.
Newton Hess, D.D.S.
Simon Horkowitz, D.D.S.
Alfred L. Jenkins, D.D.S.
Thomas Jenkins, D.D.S.
Harold Jones, D.D.S.
Edward Judt, D.D.S.
Jerome P. Kaplan, D.D.S.
George Kirch—
...
...
...er, D.D.S.
...a Lychak, D.D.S.
Thomas McKee, D.D.S.
Donald C. McLean, D.D.S.
Robert Minogue, D.D.S.
Rodney Minner, D.D.S.
Evan C. Moll, D.D.S.
Edward Ormanoski, D.D.S.
David Packman, D.D.S.
Wistar Paist, D.D.S.
Morton Parmet, D.D.S.
Sidney Parmet, D.D.S.
R.F. Peters, Jr. D.D.S.

Louis Pizzolatto D.D.S.
Charles Potter, D.D.S.
Sheva Rapoport, D.D.S.
Richard Reimer, D.D.S.
Walter Risley, D.D.S.
John L. Salines, D.D.S.
Leonard Salines, D.D.S.
S.J. Salivonchik, D.D.S.
Franklin Soul, D.D.S.
William K. Schaffer, D.D.S.
William H. Schaeffer, Jr., D.D.S.
Stuart Schwartz, D.D.S.
Howard S. Selden, D.D.S.
George Shoenberger, D.D.S.
M. Lee Seinfeld, D.D.S.
Walter Sellers, D.D.S.
Nevin Shaffer, D.D.S.
Robert Siegfried, D.D.S.
H. Silfies, Jr. D.D.S.
Daniel Siegal, D.D.S.
Merwin Smith, D.D.S.
Joseph Smith, D.D.S.
Robert Smith, D.D.S.
John Solan, D.D.S.
Francis Solga, D.D.S.
Robert Stockdale, D.D.S.
Michael Stroock, D.D.S.
Philip Tighe, D.D.S.
Dominic Vettese, D.D.S.
John Waddell, D.D.S.
Howard T. Weaver, Jr. D.D.S.
Roland Warntz, D.D.S.
Bruce Wechtler, D.D.S.
Benjamin Weinberger, D.D.S.
Edward Weiner, D.D.S.
Louis Yerkes, D.D.S.
John Ziegler, D.D.S.

> By using the word "doctor" instead of dentist, this can be adapted for use by a local medical society or by several professional societies combined.

A public service from _____ County Dental Society.

RECOMMENDED PUBLICATIONS

The Tooth Robbers: A Pro-Fluoridation Handbook
 $8.50 each; 6-25, $6.75 each; 26-50, $6.05 each; 51-99, $5.35 each; 100 or more, $5.05 each.

The Health Robbers—How To Protect Your Money And Your Life
 A comprehensive exposé of quackery edited by Stephen Barrett, M.D. Contains chapters on fluoridation and the National Health Federation. $12.95 each; bulk prices on request.

> Order from the George F. Stickley Co., 210 West Washington Square, Philadelphia, PA 19106.

The Poisonmongers	45¢ each; 10 for $3.00; 100 for $18.00
The Unhealthy Alliance	60¢ each; 10 for $4.00; 100 for $24.00
Don't Let The Poisonmongers Scare You!	
Fighting Healthy Teeth	100 for $ 5.00
Fluoridation Prevents Cancer!!!	500 for $20.00
Ask the Person Who Knows	

> Order from the Lehigh Valley Committee Against Health Fraud, Inc., P.O. Box 1602, Allentown, PA 18105.

Why Your Dentist Recommends Fluoridation (#G2)
 Flyer describing fluoridation's benefits and costs.
 100 for $2.15; 500 for $10.20; 1,000 for $19.95; 10,000 for $172.00.

Fluoride Helps Prevent Tooth Decay (#G9)
 Flyer describing fluoridation alternatives.
 100 for $2.15; 500 for $10.20; 1,000 for $19.35; 10,000 for $172.00.

Fluoridation for Your Community and Your State (#G19)
 44-page booklet about campaigning for fluoridation.
 $1.50 each; 10 for $9.00.

Fluoridation Facts (#G21)
 Superb 24-page booklet of questions and answers.
 25 for $7.75; 100 for $29.40; 500 for $139.35; 1,000 for $263.15.

What About Fluorides? (#G55)
 Small flyer
 100 for $2.25; 500 for $10.50; 1,000 for $20.00.

Fluoridation: A White Paper (#DHB-108)
 13-minute, 16mm movie

$85.00 for purchase
(Available for free loan from Modern Talking Picture Service,
5000 Park Street, North, St. Petersburg, FL 33709.)
Order from the American Dental Association,
211 East Chicago Avenue, Chicago, IL 60611

Fluoridation of Water Supplies—Questions and Answers
An extremely well-written discussion published by the British Medical Association. $2.00 each airmail postpaid.

*Order from the British Dental Association,
64 Wimpole Street, London, W1M 8AL, England*

A Two-Part Report On Fluoridation

Reprint of the fluoridation articles from the July and August, 1978, issues of Consumer Reports. $.50 each; 10 for $4.50; 100 for $40.00; 1,000 for $300.00.
Order from CU Reprints, Consumers Union,
Orangeburg, NY 10962.

---

did you know?

WE ARE <u>FOR</u> WATER FLUORIDATION FOR OUR COMMUNITY BECAUSE WE <u>KNOW</u> IT IS A SAFE, EFFECTIVE AND ECONOMICAL WAY TO REDUCE DENTAL DISEASE IN YOUNG AND OLD.

OUR WATER IS FLUORIDE-DEFICIENT, AND <u>WE</u> ARE PAYING THE CONSEQUENCES. WE URGE YOU TO SIGN BELOW.

SIGNED

NOTES